DYNAMIC PROGRAMMING

MATHEMATICS IN SCIENCE AND ENGINEERING

A SERIES OF MONOGRAPHS AND TEXTBOOKS

Edited by Richard Bellman

University of Southern California

MATHEMATICS IN SCIENCE AND ENGINEERING

In preparation

DYNAMIC PROGRAMMING
Sequential Scientific Management

A. Kaufmann

Institute of Grenoble
Compagnie Bull-General Electric
Grenoble, France

R. Cruon

Interservices Operations
Research Center
Paris, France

Translated by Henry C. Sneyd

1967

ACADEMIC PRESS   NEW YORK · LONDON

Originally published in the French language by Dunod, Paris in 1965
under the title "La Programmation Dynamique : Gestion Scientifique Séquentielle."

ACADEMIC PRESS INC.
111 Fifth Avenue, New York, New York 10003

United Kingdom Edition published by
ACADEMIC PRESS INC. (LONDON) LTD.
Berkeley Square House, London W.1

LIBRARY OF CONGRESS CATALOG CARD NUMBER: 66-29730

PRINTED IN THE UNITED STATES OF AMERICA

112759

FOREWORD TO THE FRENCH EDITION

The realization at the present time is that mathematics is not only essential to the physicist in developing his theories about the micro-universe, but also to the economist engaged in planning on a national scale; not only to the engineer whose specialized work is in mechanics or chemical kinetics, but also to the industrialist who wishes to turn existing conditions to the best account; not only to the mathematician himself, but also to the epidemiologist studying the dissemination of diseases or of ideas; this discovery and its application in practice have produced some strange partnerships and may be said to have produced a real revolution.

Not only are there analogies in the systems, but even in the details of mathematics and other sciences. A chemical reaction resembles the effect of advertising by competitors on possible customers; the potential is similar to the demand expressed by the volume of traffic between different points in a traffic network.

Dynamic programming is a striking feature of this revolution. While the calculus of variations is a theory which has long been known to the mathematician and the physicist, albeit not much used by them, the intuition of the industrialist caused him to make use of it still earlier, even if he was incapable of giving his ideas the theoretical form which would have made them of value to others. This is why contemporary specialists in management are so keenly interested in programming.

It may well be asked why it should now be necessary to generalize a method which has always been used by men of action. It is partly because the world of today, together with its system of action and production, has suddenly become so complex that problems can no longer be dealt with by an intuitive approach, and also because very exact calculations are now required if the future is to be predicted and controlled. Here is a whole field of study and of new problems for the mathematician.

HERBERT P. GALLIHER

PREFACE TO THE FRENCH EDITION

The work of great importance carried out by the research groups under the direction of R. Bellman in the United States and L.S. Pontryagin in the U.S.S.R. has revealed the value of dynamic programming as a method of optimization for the sequential phenomena encountered in economic studies or in advanced technological programs such as those associated with space flights.

The sequential character of many economic problems—and in this book we deal mainly with those of the microeconomy—is very obvious. Whether they deal with the management of production and stocking, the operation of equipment, prospecting for mines, investments, not to mention macroeconomic problems such as national planning, their sequential character requires a special approach. This must not only enable us to carry out the work of optimization, but should also throw light on the problem by introducing exact concepts. A criterion of decision, policies or strategies, the influence of information on the quality of the decision should all be defined as precisely as possible.

In this work we deal with sequential problems which are discrete in time. The dynamic programs which are considered are defined for a deterministic universe (Chapters 1 and 2) or one with probabilities (Chapters 3 to 5); both categories are of equal importance in the practice of operations research or of scientific management. Their separate study will involve some repetition, but at the same time will help the reader to become familiar with the technique of dynamic programming. In the case of uncertainty, the concept of Markovian chains is of basic importance, and at the appropriate stage we have given the necessary information about this theory, limiting our explanation to the case, which is of most practical value, where there is a finite number of states. In addition to the models of "Markovian decision chains" studied by R. Howard, we have introduced dynamic programs with "a decomposed form," a special case of great practical value.

The question of convergence with an infinite horizon is treated with some thoroughness, and the influence of an introduced rate, in particular, is studied in detail.

In the final chapter we give some generalizations for the models which have been studied earlier, limiting our consideration to programs which are time discrete, both with a certain and uncertain future. In a second volume,* it is our intention to deal with programs with continuous time, and in particular, programs with adaptations.

The present work has been undertaken with the same aim as our earlier book "Waiting Line Phenomena"† which appeared in 1961. The large amount of encouragement which we have received since then has confirmed our decision to publish more works of this kind—still too few in French—at once sufficiently advanced to be of use to the specialist, but with special care devoted to their instructional aspect so that they may be of value to the student or to the engineer who has no previous knowledge of the subject. For this purpose, we have given many examples to explain the theoretical developments, and we have also, wherever it could be useful, had recourse to the concept of graphs, so valuable in many branches of applied mathematics.

Professor Herbert P. Galliher of the Department of Industrial Engineering at the University of Michigan has kindly agreed to write a foreword for this book. We owe much to the work of Professor Galliher, whose qualities as a scientist as well as his kindness have been made known to many French research workers.

We wish also to thank MM. René Descamps, Jacques Ferrier, and Jacques Melese, as well as our friends and colleagues in the group of studies on Dynamic Administration instituted by the French Association of Information and Operations Research with whom we have had many fruitful discussions. We are equally grateful to M. Claude Bruter who has read the manuscript and has suggested several improvements.

A. KAUFMANN
R. CRUON

---

* To be published by Dunod, Paris.
† Published in French by Dunod, Paris under the title "Les phénomènes d'attente." No English language edition available.

CONTENTS

Chapter 1. Discrete Dynamic Programs with a Certain Future and a Limited Horizon

Chapter 2. Discrete Dynamic Programs with a Certain Future and an Unlimited Horizon

Chapter 3. Discrete Dynamic Programs with a Random Future and Limited Horizon

LIST OF PRINCIPAL SYMBOLS

$\exists a$ There is an a.

$\forall a$ For every a.

$\emptyset$ Empty set.

$\in \mathbf{A}$ Belongs to set $\mathbf{A}$.

$\subset$ Operative for nonstrict inclusion.

$\cap$ The intersection of two sets.

$\cup$ Operative for the union of two sets.

$\prec$ Relation of a strict order.

$a_n(x_{n-1}, y_n)$ Value of the pair (x_{n-1}, y_n) or present value of stage (n, D).

$[\mathscr{B}]$ Boolean matrix associated with a graph.

$b_n(y_n, x_n)$ Value associated with the pair (x_{n-1}, y_n) or present value of the stage (n, H).

$\mathbf{C}_k$ Equivalence class in the set of vertices of a graph.

$[\mathscr{C}(z)]$ Matrix defined by (32.3).

$[\mathscr{D}]$ Decision matrix defined by (37.5) and (37.6).

d_{ij} Element of the above decision matrix in a dynamic program with Markovian chain in a decomposed form.

$[\mathscr{E}_M]$ Unit matrix of order M.

E_i State of a Markovian chain.

$f(x)$ Value of an optimal policy over an infinite period when the initial state is x.

$f^*(z)$ Generatrix function of the sequence, or function $f(n)$.

$f_n(x, r)$ Actual value with coefficient r of an optimal policy for n periods.

$f_{0,N}(x_0, x_N)$ Value of an optimal policy (optimal value) from x_0 to x_N. In the stationary case, $f_{0,N} = f_N$.

$f_{0,n}(x_0, x_n)$ Value of an optimal subpolicy (optimal value) from x_0 to x_n.

$f_{0,n}(\cdot, x_n)$ Value of an optimal subpolicy from $n = 0$ to x_n.

$f_{n,N}(x_n, \cdot)$ Value of an optimal subpolicy from x_n to $n = N$. In the stationary case, $f_{n,N} = f_{N-n}$, $\forall n$. In Section 12, we state $f(x) = f_n(x, \cdot)$.

$f_{n,N}(x_n, x_N)$ Value of an optimal subpolicy from x_n to x_N. In the stationary case, $f_{n,N} = f_{N-n}$, $\forall n$.

$g_{n,N}(y_n)$ Expected value of an optimal strategy from y_n to $n = N$ (special notation for H.D. dynamic programs).

$H_n(x \mid y_n)$ Cumulative probability function of the state variable x_n at time n, knowing y_n (decomposed form).

$H_n(x \mid x_{n-1}, y_n)$ Cumulative probability function of the state variable x_n at time n, when x_{n-1} and y_n are known. In the stationary case, $H_n = H$, $\forall n$.

INF   Operative for lower bound of.

$\mathbf{K}$ Set of the decision vectors.

$\{k\}$ Decision vector (Markovian finite chain).

M Number of states in a Markovian chain.

MAX	Operative sign for maximum.
MIN	Operative sign for minimum.
N	Number of periods with a limited horizon.
n	Integer marking a time or a period.
$O(X_i)$	Ordinal function of a graph.
OPT	Operative sign, depending on the problem considered, for either maximum or minimum.
$[P(n)]$	Vector of the probabilities of state at time n in a Markovian chain.
$p_i(n)$	Probability of state E_i at time n in a Markovian chain.
p_{ij}	Probability of transition from state i to state j in a Markovian chain.
$p_{ij}^{(k)}$	Probability of transition from state i to state j when decision k is taken (programs with finite Markovian chain).
$q(i, k)$	Present expected value when the state at the beginning of the period is i and the decision is k (programs with finite Markovian chain).
$\{q\}$	Vector of the present values (programs with finite Markovian chain).
$q_n(x_{n-1}, y_n)$	Present expected value for the period n when x_{n-1} and y_n are known. In the stationary case, we state $q_n = q$, $\forall n$.
$[\mathscr{R}^{(k)}]$	Matrix of the present values corresponding to the permanent strategy $\{k\}$ and of which the elements are $r_{ij}^{(k)}$.
r	Coefficient of discounting per period $r = 1/(1 + i)$, where i is the introduced rate over a period.
$r_{ij}^{(k)}$	Present value for a period when the state at the beginning of the period is i, the decision taken is k, and the state at the end of the period is j (programs with finite Markovian chain).
$s(r)$	Total value with an introduced rate of a policy over an infinite number of periods.
$s(\varpi)$	Value of the policy ϖ.
$\{s_n(r)\}$	Vector of present values over n periods for a given strategy.
SUP	Operative sign for upper bound of.
T	Set of transitory states in a Markovian chain.
$[\mathscr{T}]$	Transition matrix in a Markovian chain.
$[\mathscr{T}^{(k)}]$	Transition matrix corresponding to the permanent strategy k and of which the elements are $p_{ij}^{(k)}$.
$[\mathscr{T}^*(z)]$	z transform of $[\mathscr{T}]^n$.
$u_n(y_{n-1}, x_n, y_n)$	Value of the trinomial (y_{n-1}, x_n, y_n) or present value of period n (special notation for H.D. dynamic programs).
$v_n(x_{n-1}, x_n)$	Value associated with the change of state from x_{n-1} to x_n (present value). In the stationary case, $v_n = v$, $\forall n$.
$v_n(x_{n-1}, y_n, x_n)$	Value of the trinomial (x_{n-1}, y_n, x_n) or present value of period n (program in the face of a random future).
v_{ij}	Value of the arc (X_i, X_j) in a graph.
X	Set of the vertices of a graph, or union of the set of possible states at all the times in a stationary program.
$\mathbf{X}_n$	Set of the vertices of a graph for which the ordinal function has the same value.
$\mathbf{X}_n(x_0, x_N)$	Set of the possible states at time n when the initial state is x_0 and the final state is x_N.
$\mathbf{X}_n(x_0, \cdot)$	Set of possible states at time n when the initial state is x_0 and the final state is not defined.
$\mathbf{X}_{0,n}(x_0)$	Set of possible states at time n when the initial state is x_0 (Chapter 3).

X_i	Vertex of a graph.
x_n	State variable (or state vector) at time n.
$\tilde{x}_n$	Special value of the variable x_n.
$x_{n-1}'^*(x)$	First decision of a subpolicy which is optimal for n periods.
Y	Union of the sets of possible decisions for every period in a stationary program.
$y(x)$	Decision function.
y_n	Decision variable at period n.
$[\mathfrak{Z}]$	Dynamic matrix defined by (29.7).
z_{ij}	Elements of the dynamic matrix $[Z]$.
ΓX_i	Set of the vertices x_j such that there is an arc (X_i, X_j).
Γ^{-1}	Inverse correspondence of Γ.
$\Gamma_{\mathbf{A}}$	Correspondence defined by $\Gamma_{\mathbf{A}} X_i = (\Gamma X_i) \cap \mathbf{A}$, with $X_i \in \mathbf{A} \subset \mathbf{X}$.
$\Gamma_n x_{n-1}$	Set of possible states at time n when the state at time $(n-1)$ is x_{n-1}. In the stationary case, $\Gamma_n = \Gamma \forall n$.
Γ_n^{-1}	Inverse correspondence of Γ_n.
$\Gamma^{(n)}x$	$\Gamma^{(n)}x = \Gamma(\Gamma^{(n-1)}x)$, with $\Gamma^{(1)} = \Gamma$.
$\Delta_n x_{n-1}$	Set of possible decisions at period n when the state at time $n-1$ is x_{n-1}. In the stationary case, $\Delta_n = \Delta$, $\forall n$.
$\Delta_n(y_{n-1}, x_n)$	Set of possible decisions at period n when y_{n-1} and x_n are known (special notation for H.D. programs).
$\{\delta\}$	Vector column of relative values.
$\varphi(x)$	Average optimal value per period over an infinite number of periods.
$\varphi_n(x)$	Average value per period of an optimal subpolicy over n periods.
Π	Set of policies or of strategies.
$[\Pi]$	Matrix defined by (32.17).
$\varpi_{0,N}(x_0, x_N)$	Policy from x_0 to x_N.
$\varpi_{0,N}^*(x_0, x_N)$	Optimal policy from x_0 to x_N.
$\varpi_{0,N}(x_0, \cdot)$	Policy from x_0 to $n = N$.
$\varpi_{0,n}(\cdot, x_n)$	Subpolicy from $n = 0$ to x_n.
$\varpi_{ij}(x_i, \cdot)$	Subpolicy from x_i to $n = j$.
$\varpi_{0,N}(x_0)$	Strategy from x_0 to $n = N$.
$\varpi_{ij}(x_i, x_j)$	Subpolicy from x_i to x_j.
$[\varpi]$	State vectors with permanent control in an uni-reducible Markovian chain.
$\{\sigma\}$	Vector of the average values per period over an infinite number of periods for a given strategy.
σ_N	Average value per period calculated over N periods.
$\Omega_N(x_{n-1}, y_n)$	Set of possible states at time n when x_{n-1} and y_n are known. In the stationary case, $\Omega_n = \Omega$, $\forall n$.

DYNAMIC PROGRAMMING

CHAPTER I

DISCRETE DYNAMIC PROGRAMS WITH A CERTAIN FUTURE AND A LIMITED HORIZON

1. General Introduction

The search for the optimal trajectory of a moving object which must remain in contact with a surface is already an old problem which has been illuminated by the works of Bernoulli, Lagrange, Hamilton, and numerous modern mathematicians. This problem occurs in the "calculation of variations," and its interest is by no means only a historical one, for the engineer and the economist are increasingly faced with questions of optimization which are, mathematically, of the same nature.

Let us consider a system in which, at each instant t, the state is defined by a point $x(t)$ in a space with n dimensions. This system can be controlled by means of a vector $y(t)$ in such a manner that the data of the function $y(t)$ enable us to calculate $x(t)$ as the solution, for example, of a differential equation. But $y(t)$ must satisfy certain constraints, such that

$$f_k(x, y) = 0,$$

where the f_k terms are given functionals. Finally we have a functional of x and y,

$$F(x, y),$$

which may represent equally an energy or the value of a preference.

The problem lies in finding on the surface S defined by the constraints a trajectory $x(t)$ which optimizes F (renders it maximal or minimal, depending on the case) between the instants $t = 0$ and $t = T$ where $x(0)$ and $x(T)$ are given.

When we study the methods used to resolve a problem of this kind, we discover that they can be reduced to the principle which Bellman has termed "the principle of optimality." If we consider an optimal trajectory between the points A and B (Fig. 1.1), we find that under certain conditions, in particular if we have chosen a suitable area for the evolution of the system, each portion MN of this path is itself optimal among the possible paths from M to N. This property, which is known as the principle of optimality (or at least as one form of the principle), must naturally be proved, so that it can be called the theorem of optimality before being applied to a given class of problems.

The proof, which is almost self-evident, depends on the following observation: if a better trajectory from M to N existed it is along this that the optimal path A to B would pass. In addition, if this principle is to be true, it means that the contribution to the functional F of the part MN of the trajectory must depend only on M and N, and not on the portions AM and NB of the trajectory.

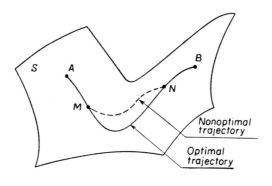

FIG. 1.1

The problems which have to be considered are often of a more compli-cated form than those described above. In particular, the state variables may be uncertain, in other words, certain changes of state may be subject not only to control, but also to probability. But in each of these problems, however complex it may be, the principle of optimality must be employed over a suitable space. Its use does not mean that the calculations will necessarily be simple, and frequently it will be impossible to obtain a solution, either because a suitable space for applying it has not been chosen, or because we do not know the algorithm which will enable us to find the optimal trajectory by calculations of an acceptable length.

In this volume our main attention will be devoted to problems of economic management, and only to those cases where time varies in a discrete manner. Our aim is to find, among the possible states of each system, an optimal trajectory for a certain function of value by choosing suitable control variables. But, to employ a terminology more akin to that of economics, we shall replace the word "trajectory" by the word "policy" in deterministic systems and by that of "strategy" in stochastic problems. The surface containing the trajectories will become the "constraints," the state variables will retain their name, and the control variables will be called "decision variables." Indeed, from the standpoint of mathematics, the same theory, if suitably adapted, is equally valid for physics or for economics.

We can obtain an immediate idea of the way in which the principle of optimality will be used in problems of management with a deterministic future if we study Figs. 1.2 and 1.3.

The problem is to find a route or policy of minimal value between the points A_0 and A_6 on this oriented graph. By applying the principle of optimality it is quickly apparent that there are two optimal routes $(A_0, A_1, B_2, A_3, C_4, A_5, A_6)$ and $(A_0, B_1, B_2, A_3, C_4, A_5, A_6)$ with the minimal value 27.

The reasoning which enables us to find them is easy. Starting from A_0, we find that there is only one optimal route to A_1 and one to B_1. At A_1 we write 4 and at B_1 8. We now look for the optimal routes from A_0 to A_2, B_2, and C_2, but in accordance with the principle of optimality, we need only consider the routes from A_1 and B_1 which have already been given a number; hence we shall write 11 at A_2, 9 at B_2, and 13 beside C_2. In looking for the optimal routes from A_0 to A_3, B_3, and C_3 we need only consider A_2, B_2, and C_2 which have already been numbered, and so on. It must be understood that this is a very elementary example, and later on we shall make a more general study of this type of discrete problem with a limited future.

In other problems of management, probability enters. It will then be necessary to take a criterion which is appropriate to the type of system we are considering. Often this will be the "expected total value." We shall again use the principle of optimality, returning from the future towards the past to find the set of optimal decisions, which will be known as the optimal strategy. In problems with an unlimited future the word "policy" will give place to that of "strategy" in order to show that we now have to describe all the decisions which we *might* have to take as a result of probability.

Figure 1.4 shows a very elementary example of a stochastic system into which stages of decision (D) and of probability (H) enter alternately. In stage H it is necessary to bring back to the points where this stage begins the expected value of the arcs and vertices which have already been marked, while taking into account the probabilities associated with them. The maximal strategy is shown in Fig. 1.5, and later on we shall explain in greater detail the method used to obtain it.

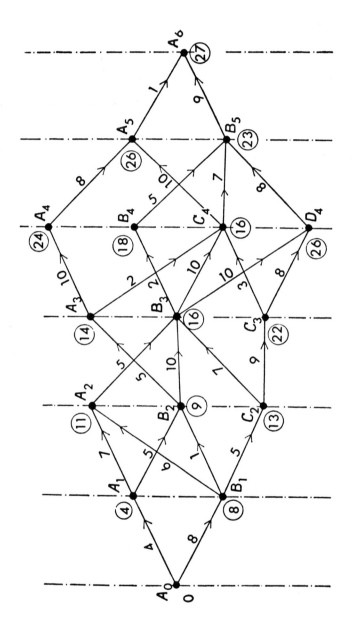

Fig. 1.2

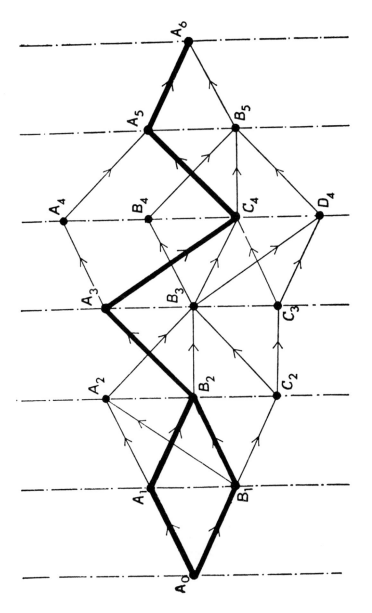

Fig. 1.3

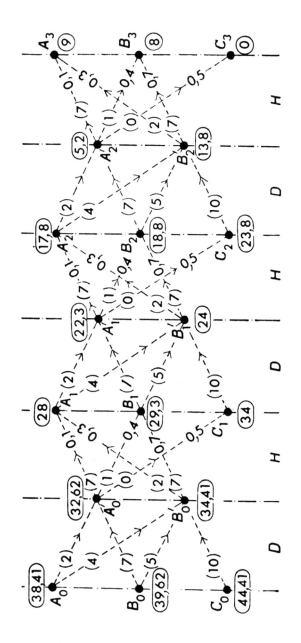

FIG. 1.4

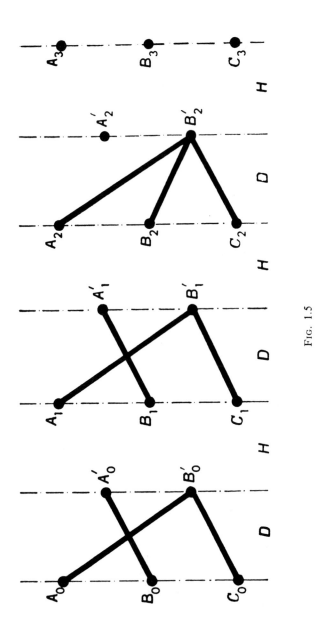

Fig. 1.5

2. A Numerical Example

We shall begin by considering a simple example so that the reader may grasp the essential features of dynamic programs with a certain future.

TABLE 2.1

Period n :	1	2	3	4	5	6
Demand d_n :	8	5	3	2	7	4
Purchase price p_n :	11	18	13	17	20	10

In order to carry out its production schedule, a firm of manufacturers must stock up every two months with a certain basic material. The purchase price p_n and the demand d_n , $n = 1, 2,..., 6$, are given for the next 6 two-monthly periods (Table 2.1). Owing to limited storage space, the stock must never exceed a certain value S. The initial stock is 2 and the final stock must be nil. The problem is to ascertain the quantities to be bought at the beginning of each period in such a way that the total cost will be minimal.

Let us call

x_0 the stock at time n (end of period n before the purchase a_{n+1}),
a_n the quantity bought at the beginning of period n,
y_n the stock at the beginning of period n, after purchase a_n .

We have

$$y_n - x_{n-1} = a_n , \qquad n = 1, 2,..., 6; \qquad (2.1)$$

$$y_n - x_n = d_n , \qquad n = 1, 2,..., 6. \qquad (2.2)$$

Figure 2.1 shows a solution which is clearly not the best one.

The state of the system at n can be described by the value of either x_n or y_n for, as d_n is known in advance, the relation (2.2) makes the choice between these variables a matter of indifference. We shall make an arbitrary choice of x_n for the state variable.

At each period n we must make a decision which can be described by the value of either a_n , y_n , or x_n in accordance with (2.1), and shall

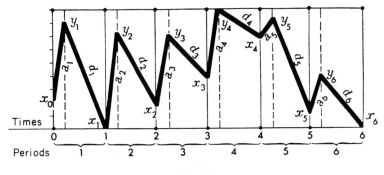

FIG. 2.1

arbitrarily select x_n, which will therefore be both the state variable and the decision variable.[1]

The data of the problem impose the following constraints:

$$0 \leqslant x_n \leqslant S, \tag{2.3}$$

$$0 \leqslant y_n \leqslant S, \tag{2.4}$$

$$x_{n-1} \leqslant y_n, \tag{2.5}$$

$$y_n - x_n = d_n, \tag{2.6}$$

where all these relations are valid for $n = 1, 2, ..., 6$.

Let us use (2.6) to eliminate y_n from inequalities (2.3) to (2.5).

$$0 \leqslant x_n \leqslant S, \tag{2.7}$$

$$0 \leqslant x_n + d_n \leqslant S, \tag{2.8}$$

$$x_n \leqslant x_{n+1} + d_{n+1}. \tag{2.9}$$

The three inequalities (2.7), (2.8), and (2.9) are equivalent to a dual inequality for $n = 1, 2, ..., 5$, since x_6 is given,

$$\max(0, x_{n-1} - d_n) \leqslant x_n \leqslant \min(S - d_n, x_{n+1} + d_{n+1}). \tag{2.10}$$

We see that the interval defined for x_n depends on x_{n-1} and x_{n+1}; hence the state variable of the period following the one which has been

---

[1] The present example is also treated in A. Kaufmann's work [42], but with a different notation.

considered will enter as a parameter, and in Section 5 it will be shown
how, in certain cases, this fact can considerably complicate the process
of optimization.

Finally, let us use (2.1) and (2.2) to express a_n as a function of x_n :

$$a_n = x_n + d_n - x_{n-1}, \qquad n = 1, 2,..., 6. \tag{2.11}$$

Now, assuming that $S = 9$ in order to make a numerical calculation
possible, let us look for the optimal policy, that is to say, for the sequence

$$\varpi^* = (x_1{}^*, x_2{}^*,..., x_6{}^*), \tag{2.12}$$

which minimizes the total expenditure.

We shall begin the optimization arbitrarily with period 6, though we
could, as will be shown later, also begin with period 1.

PERIOD 6

Knowing that $x_6 = 0$, let us find the interval over which x_5 can vary.
From (2.10), for $n = 5$,

$$\max(0, x_4 - d_5) \leqslant x_5 \leqslant \min(S - d_5, x_6 + d_6); \tag{2.13}$$

let

$$\max(0, x_4 - 7) \leqslant x_5 \leqslant \min(9 - 7, 0 + 4), \tag{2.14}$$

or also

$$\max(0, x_4 - 7) \leqslant x_5 \leqslant 2. \tag{2.15}$$

The expenditure for period 6, that is, between times 5 and 6 and when
the state variable passes from the value x_5 to that of $x_6 = 0$, will be

$$v_6(x_5, x_6) = v_6(x_5, 0) = p_6 a_6$$
$$= p_6(x_6 + d_6 - x_5)$$
$$= 10(0 + 4 - x_5)$$
$$= 40 - 10x_5 . \tag{2.16}$$

If we wished to minimize $v_6(x_5, 0)$ we should give x_5 the largest
possible value, namely 2, in accordance with (2.15). This would amount
to buying such quantities during the preceding periods that the stock
would be as large as possible at time 5 and only the minimum would have

to be purchased during period 6. But to do so would clearly not be a good policy, since we have not yet taken into account the varying price of the material for the different periods. Hence we are not at present able to say anything about x_5, and will now see what we can conclude about periods 5 and 6 combined.

PERIODS 6 AND 5

Let us discover the interval of variation for x_4. In accordance with (2.10), for $n = 4$,

$$\max(0, x_3 - d_4) \leqslant x_4 \leqslant \min(S - d_4, x_5 + d_5); \qquad (2.17)$$

let

$$\max(0, x_3 - 2) \leqslant x_4 \leqslant \min(7, x_5 + 7), \qquad (2.18)$$

or again,

$$\max(0, x_3 - 2) \leqslant x_4 \leqslant 7. \qquad (2.19)$$

This means that in (2.15) we have $x_4 - 7 \leqslant 0$, whence

$$0 \leqslant x_5 \leqslant 2. \qquad (2.20)$$

The expenditure for periods 5 and 6 combined, in other words, between times 4 and 6, will be

$$
\begin{aligned}
s_{4,6}(x_4, x_6) &= s_{4,6}(x_4, 0) \\
&= p_5 a_5 + v_6(x_5, 0) \\
&= p_5(x_5 + d_5 - x_4) + 40 - 10x_5 \\
&= 20(x_5 + 7 - x_4) + 40 - 10x_5 \\
&= 180 - 20x_4 + 10x_5. \qquad (2.21)
\end{aligned}
$$

We can state about x_4 what we said earlier about x_5. But if we assume that the decisions for periods 1 to 4 have led to a certain value for x_4 which we will call $\tilde{x}_4$, the best value $x_5{}^*$ for x_5 will be the one which minimizes $s_{4,6}(\tilde{x}_4, 0)$. It is very important to observe that $x_5{}^*$ can only depend on $\tilde{x}_4$ (though this is not, in fact, the case here), and that it is never dependent on the decisions, whether good or bad, which have resulted in $\tilde{x}_4$. Hence, whatever the previous decisions have been, the minimal expenditure for periods 6 and 5 combined will be

$$f_{4,6}(x_4, 0) = \operatorname*{MIN}_{0 \leqslant x_5 \leqslant 2} [180 - 20x_4 + 10x_5]. \qquad (2.22)$$

Let us observe that the second subject of $f_{4,6}$ represents the value of x_6, and obviously the minimal expenditure would be different if we had taken a value other than 0 for x_6.

If we consider the expression inside the brackets of (2.22) we find that it is a monotone increasing function of x_5 ; hence the minimum will be obtained when x_5 is equal to its lower bound, namely

$$x_5{}^* = 0 \qquad (2.23)$$

and

$$f_{4,6}(x_4, 0) = 180 - 20x_4 . \qquad (2.24)$$

Figure 2.2 gives the results obtained for periods 6 and 5 combined.

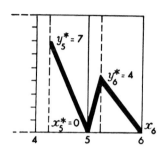

FIG. 2.2

PERIODS 6, 5, AND 4

In accordance with (2.10), for $n = 3$,

$$\max(0, x_2 - d_3) \leqslant x_3 \leqslant \min(S - d_3, x_4 + d_4); \qquad (2.25)$$

let

$$\max(0, x_2 - 3) \leqslant x_3 \leqslant \min(6, x_4 + 2). \qquad (2.26)$$

Let us now assume that, starting from time 4, we take the optimal decision $x_5{}^* = 0$. For any decision in period 4, that is, for any value of x_4 , the expenditure for the three combined periods will be

$$\begin{aligned}
s_{3,6}(x_3, x_6) &= s_{3,6}(x_3, 0) \\
&= p_4 a_4 + f_{4,6}(x_4, 0) \\
&= p_4(x_4 + d_4 - x_3) + 180 - 20x_4 \\
&= 17(x_4 + 2 - x_3) + 180 - 20x_4 \\
&= 214 - 17x_3 - 3x_4 . \qquad (2.27)
\end{aligned}$$

Hence, in accordance with (2.19), the minimal expenditure for the three combined periods will be

$$f_{3,6}(x_3, 0) = \min_{\max(0, x_3 - 2) \leqslant x_4 \leqslant 7} [214 - 17x_3 - 3x_4]. \qquad (2.28)$$

The expression inside the brackets is a monotonically decreasing function of x_4 and we shall therefore take

$$x_4{}^* = 7; \qquad (2.29)$$

whence

$$f_{3,6}(x_3, 0) = 193 - 17x_3 . \qquad (2.30)$$

Also, on account of (2.29), (2.26) now becomes

$$\max(0, x_2 - 3) \leqslant x_3 \leqslant 6. \qquad (2.31)$$

Figure 2.3 shows the results for periods 6, 5, and 4 combined.

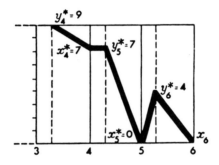

FIG. 2.3

PERIODS 6, 5, 4, AND 3

In accordance with (2.10), for $n = 2$,

$$\max(0, x_1 - d_2) \leqslant x_2 \leqslant \min(S - d_2, x_3 + d_3); \qquad (2.32)$$

let

$$\max(0, x_1 - 5) \leqslant x_2 \leqslant \min(4, x_3 + 3). \qquad (2.33)$$

If the decisions made for periods 6, 5, and 4 are optimal, the expenditure for periods 6 to 3 will be

$$\begin{aligned}
s_{2,6}(x_2, x_6) &= s_{2,6}(x_2, 0) \\
&= p_3 a_3 + f_{3,6}(x_3, 0) \\
&= p_3(x_3 + d_3 - x_2) + 193 - 17x_3 \\
&= 13(x_3 + 3 - x_2) + 193 - 17x_3 \\
&= 232 - 13x_2 - 4x_3 . \qquad (2.34)
\end{aligned}$$

Hence, in accordance with (2.31), the minimal expenditure for these four periods will be

$$f_{2,6}(x_2, 0) = \min_{\max(0, x_2-3) \leqslant x_3 \leqslant 6} [232 - 13x_2 - 4x_3]. \tag{2.35}$$

As the expression within the brackets is a monotone decreasing function of x_3, we take

$$x_3^* = 6; \tag{2.36}$$

whence

$$f_{2,6}(x_2, 0) = 208 - 13x_2. \tag{2.37}$$

Also, in accordance with (2.36), (2.33) becomes

$$\max(0, x_1 - 5) \leqslant x_2 \leqslant 4. \tag{2.38}$$

The results for the 4 periods are shown in Fig. 2.4.

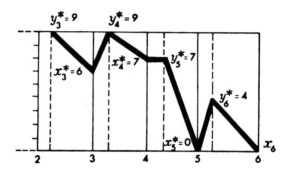

FIG. 2.4

PERIODS 6 TO 2

In accordance with (2.10), for $n = 1$,

$$\max(0, x_0 - d_1) \leqslant x_1 \leqslant \min(S - d_1, x_2 + d_2), \tag{2.39}$$

and since $x_0 = 2$ and $d_1 = 8$, let

$$0 \leqslant x_1 \leqslant \min(1, x_2 + 5); \tag{2.40}$$

and lastly,

$$0 \leqslant x_1 \leqslant 1. \tag{2.41}$$

The result is that (2.38) becomes

$$0 \leqslant x_2 \leqslant 4. \tag{2.42}$$

If, during periods 6 to 3, the decisions taken are optimal, the cost for the set of periods 6 to 2 will be

$$
\begin{aligned}
s_{1,6}(x_1, x_6) &= s_{1,6}(x_1, 0) \\
&= p_2 a_2 + f_{2,6}(x_2, 0) \\
&= p_2(x_2 + d_2 - x_1) + 208 - 13x_2 \\
&= 18(x_2 + 5 - x_1) + 208 - 13x_2 \\
&= 298 - 18x_1 + 5x_2 .
\end{aligned}
\tag{2.43}
$$

From (2.42), the minimal expenditure for the five periods will therefore be

$$
f_{1,6}(x_1, 0) = \underset{0 \leqslant x_2 \leqslant 4}{\text{MIN}} [298 - 18x_1 + 5x_2];
\tag{2.44}
$$

whence

$$
x_2^* = 0
\tag{2.45}
$$

and

$$
f_{1,6}(x_1, 0) = 298 - 18x_1 .
\tag{2.46}
$$

The results obtained are shown in Fig. 2.5.

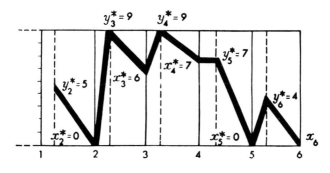

FIG. 2.5

SET OF THE SIX PERIODS

If the decisions taken during periods 6 to 2 are optimal, the cost for the six periods will be

$$
\begin{aligned}
s_{0,6}(x_0, x_6) &= s_{0,6}(2, 0) \\
&= p_1 a_1 + f_{1,6}(x_1, 0) \\
&= p_1(x_1 + d_1 - x_0) + 298 - 18x_1 \\
&= 11(x_1 + 8 - 2) + 298 - 18x_1 \\
&= 364 - 7x_1 .
\end{aligned}
\tag{2.47}
$$

Hence, in accordance with (2.41), the minimal cost for the set of six periods will be

$$f_{0,6}(x_0, 0) = f_{0,6}(2, 0)$$

$$= \underset{0 \leqslant x_1 \leqslant 1}{\text{MIN}} \, [364 - 7x_1], \qquad (2.48)$$

whence

$$x_1{}^* = 1 \qquad (2.49)$$

and

$$f_{0,6}(2, 0) = 357. \qquad (2.50)$$

To conclude, the optimal policy (Fig. 2.6) is

$$\varpi^* = (1, 0, 6, 7, 0). \qquad (2.51)$$

The corresponding quantities to be purchased are

$$a_1{}^* = 7, \quad a_2{}^* = 4, \quad a_3{}^* = 9, \quad a_4{}^* = 3, \quad a_5{}^* = 0, \quad a_6{}^* = 4, \qquad (2.52)$$

and the total minimal cost is 357.

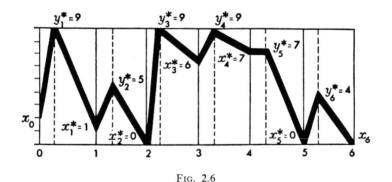

FIG. 2.6

3. Mathematical Model of a Discrete Dynamic Program with a Certain Future

In the last example we considered a system in which the state at each time n $(n = 0, 1,..., N)$ is defined by a state variable x_n. In a more general way, it is possible to consider a system in which the state is defined by several variables[2] forming a vector x_n. This vector must

---

[2] Hence x_n will represent a vector in a space with p dimensions, including the case where $p = 1$, that is, where x_n is a scalar.

express the state in a manner which eliminates the need to decide between two different evolutions of the system between the periods 1 and n from the time that they lead to the same x_n . We shall have occasion to return to this very important point, and in every case will retain the term *state variable* for x_n , with the proviso that it can also be a vector or a scalar.

At each period n, defined as the pair of times $(n - 1, n)$, a decision has to be taken about the value of x_n , but in general the domain of variation of x_n is limited by the constraints which are dependent on the value of x_{n-1} .

Thus, in the previous example where x_n was a scalar, we should have had

$$\max[0, x_{n-1} - d_n] \leqslant x_n \leqslant S - d_n .$$

For the moment we will set aside the constraint,

$$x_n \leqslant x_{n+1} + d_{n+1} ,$$

into which x_{n+1} enters.

Hence we shall assume, in a general way, that the constraints of the problem define, for each value of n and of x_n , a set of possible values for x_{n+1} which we shall call $\Gamma_{n+1}x_n$. It follows that

$$x_{n+1} \in \Gamma_{n+1}x_n , \tag{3.1}$$

an expression which shows that x_{n+1} is an element of the set $\Gamma_{n+1}x_n$.

In our example, $\Gamma_{n+1}x_n$ was the set of values greater than 0 and $x_n - d_{n+1}$, but smaller than $S - d_{n+1}$.

Reciprocally, if x_{n+1} is given, x_n must belong to a certain set,

$$x_n \in \Gamma_{n+1}^{-1}x_{n+1} , \tag{3.2}$$

where $\Gamma_{n+1}^{-1} x_{n+1}$ is the set of values x_n such that $x_{n+1} \in \Gamma_{n+1}x_n$. In mathematical parlance Γ_{n+1} is a correspondence (usually with more than one meaning) of the set of values of x_n with the set of values of x_{n+1} , and Γ_{n+1}^{-1} is the inverse correspondence of Γ_{n+1} (whence the sign employed).

In the example already given, (3.2) was expressed

$$x_n \leqslant x_{n+1} + d_{n+1} .$$

The constraints into which x_n enters can then be expressed in the condensed form,

$$x_n \in \Gamma_n x_{n-1} \cap \Gamma_{n+1}^{-1}x_{n+1} , \tag{3.3}$$

which shows that x_n must belong to the sets $\Gamma_n x_{n-1}$ and $\Gamma_{n+1}^{-1} x_{n+1}$ at the same time.

Hence x_n belongs to the intersection of these sets.

If we start from an initial given state, the domain of possible evolutions $\mathbf{X}_n(x_0, \cdot)$ of the system will be progressively defined by the correspondences Γ_n :

$$x_1 \in \Gamma_1 x_0 \quad \mathbf{X}_1(x_0, \cdot) = \Gamma_1 x_0 \, ,$$

$$x_2 \in \Gamma_2 x_1 \quad \mathbf{X}_2(x_0, \cdot) = \Gamma_2 \mathbf{X}_1 = \bigcup_{x_1 \in \mathbf{X}_1} \Gamma_2 x_1 \, ,$$

$$x_3 \in \Gamma_3 x_2 \quad \mathbf{X}_3(x_0, \cdot) = \Gamma_3 \mathbf{X}_2 = \bigcup_{x_2 \in \mathbf{X}_2} \Gamma_3 x_2 \, ,$$

$$\vdots$$

$$x_n \in \Gamma_n x_{n-1} \quad \mathbf{X}_n(x_0, \cdot) = \Gamma_n \mathbf{X}_{n-1} = \bigcup_{x_{n-1} \in \mathbf{X}_{n-1}} \Gamma_n x_{n-1} \, .$$

(3.4)

If, in addition, we are required to arrive, after N periods, at a certain state x_N, the set of possible values which are given above must be restricted by the successive correspondences $\Gamma_n^{-1} x_n$ for $n = N, N-1, N-2$. The sets $\mathbf{X}_n(x_0, x_N)$ thus obtained satisfy the relation deduced from (3.3).

$$\mathbf{X}_n = \Gamma_n \mathbf{X}_{n-1} \cap \Gamma_{n+1}^{-1} \mathbf{X}_{n+1} \, , \qquad n = 1, 2, ..., N-1, \tag{3.5}$$

where $\mathbf{X}_0$ and $\mathbf{X}_N$ are reduced to a single element,

$$\mathbf{X}_0 = \{x_0\} \quad \text{and} \quad \mathbf{X}_N = \{x_N\}. \tag{3.6}$$

The term "policy from x_0 to x_N" will be applied to any sequence

$$\varpi_{0,N}(x_0, x_N) = (x_0, x_1, x_2, \ldots, x_N), \tag{3.7}$$

such that (3.3) is satisfied for $n = 1, 2, ..., N-1$. The problem which will then confront us will be to find the optimal policies ϖ^* when tested by a criterion which is defined as follows:

With each pair (x_{n-1}, x_n) there is associated a given value $v_n(x_{n-1}, x_n)$ called "the immediate value" of period n; in other words, if at time $(n-1)$ the system is in state x_{n-1}, the value of the decision x_n is $v_n(x_{n-1}, x_n)$. A total value s is associated with every policy ϖ and is defined by:

$$s(\varpi) = \sum_{n=1}^{N} v_n(x_{n-1}, x_n). \tag{3.8}$$

The criterion which we take is to minimize (or maximize, depending on the concrete meaning of v_n) the value of the policy.

In the first example we had

$$v_n(x_{n-1}, x_n) = p_n a_n = p_n(x_n - x_{n-1} + d_n)$$

and the optimal policy was the one which gave the minimal value.

Let Π represent the set of policies, and let us assume that we wish to maximize the value of the policy. Hence the optimal policy or policies ϖ^* will be defined by

$$s(\varpi^*) = \operatorname*{MAX}_{\varpi \in \Pi} s(\varpi). \tag{3.9}$$

More frequently we shall state

$$s(\varpi^*) = \operatorname*{OPT}_{\varpi \in \Pi} s(\varpi),$$

the sign OPT indicating either MAX or MIN, depending on the problem.

The optimal value of $s(\varpi)$ defined by (3.9) will be called $f_{0,N}(x_0, x_N)$; and for $0 \leqslant i \leqslant j \leqslant N$, we shall use the term "subpolicy from x_i to x_j" for any sequence

$$\varpi_{ij}(x_i, x_j) = \{x_i, x_{i+1}, ..., x_n, ..., x_j\} \tag{3.10}$$

such that (3.3) is satisfied for $n = i + 1, i + 2, ..., j - 1$.

A subpolicy from x_i to x_j will be called optimal if its value

$$s_{i,j}(\varpi_{i,j}) = \sum_{n=i+1}^{j} v_n(x_{n-1}, x_n) \tag{3.11}$$

is maximal (or minimal) among all the subpolicies from x_i to x_j.

Let us consider an optimal policy

$$\varpi^* = (x_0, ..., x_i^*, ..., x_j^*, ..., x_N); \tag{3.12}$$

the subpolicy formed by the portion $\{x_i^*, ..., x_j^*\}$ of ϖ^* is optimal, for if it were not, there would be a subpolicy between these points with a greater (or smaller) value and it would be possible to improve ϖ^* by replacing the portion chosen by this new subpolicy. Hence we can enunciate:

THEOREM OF OPTIMALITY 3.1.   *Every subpolicy $\varpi_{ij}(x_i, x_j)$ taken from an optimal policy $\varpi_{0,N}^*(x_0, x_N)$ is itself optimal from x_i to x_j .*

COROLLARY.   *Among the set of policies containing a given subpolicy $\varpi_{0,k}(x_0, x_k)$, whether optimal or not, the best is the one obtained by completing this given subpolicy by an optimal subpolicy*

$$\varpi_{k,N}^*(x_k, x_N).$$

This theorem, which Bellman has called "the principle of optimality,"[3] is the basis of the method used in dynamic programming, for it enables us to consider a succession of periods 1, 2, 3,..., N and to form an optimal policy by progressive stages. To do so, we can start either at the first or the last period, or indeed at any period we choose.

Let us assume, for example, that we start from period 1. For every possible decision

$$x_1 \in \mathbf{X}_1(x_0, \cdot) = \Gamma_1 x_0,$$

we know the value $v_1(x_0, x_1)$. Next, for each

$$x_2 \in \mathbf{X}_2(x_0, \cdot) = \Gamma_2 \mathbf{X}_1,$$

we look for the set of subpolicies from x_0 to x_2 ; these subpolicies

$$\varpi_{0,2}(x_0, x_2) = \{x_0, x_1, x_2\}$$

are defined by the chosen value x_1 which must be such that

$$x_1 \in \Gamma_1 x_0 \cap \Gamma_2^{-1} x_2 = \mathbf{X}_1(x_0, x_2).$$

The value of any subpolicy $\varpi_{0,2}(x_0, x_2)$ is

$$s_{0,2}(\varpi_{0,2}) = v_1(x_0, x_1) + v_2(x_1, x_2), \tag{3.13}$$

and we obtain the optimal subpolicies from x_0 to x_2 by finding the optimum of $s_{0,2}$ defined by

$$f_{0,2}(x_0, x_2) = \underset{x_1 \in \mathbf{X}_1(x_0, x_2)}{\mathrm{OPT}} [v_1(x_0, x_1) + v_2(x_1, x_2)]. \tag{3.14}$$

Next we consider the set of periods 1, 2, and 3. For every

$$x_3 \in \mathbf{X}_3(x_0, \cdot) = \Gamma_3 \mathbf{X}_2(x_0, \cdot),$$

we find

$$\mathbf{X}_2(x_0, x_3) = \mathbf{X}_2(x_0, \cdot) \cap \Gamma_3^{-1} x_3 ;$$

in accordance with the theorem of optimality, the part $\{x_0, x_1, x_2\}$ of an optimal subpolicy from x_0 to x_3 is optimal from x_0 to x_2. To find the optimal subpolicies from x_0 to x_3 we need only consider those which are optimal from x_0 to x_2. The optimal value from x_0 to x_3 will then be

$$f_{0,3}(x_0, x_3) = \underset{x_2 \in \mathbf{X}_2(x_0, x_3)}{\mathrm{OPT}} [f_{0,2}(x_0, x_2) + v_3(x_2, x_3)], \tag{3.15}$$

---

[3] Enunciated as follows in Bellman's work [10]: "A policy is optimal if, at a given period, whatever the previous decisions may have been, the remaining decisions to be taken form an optimal policy when the result of the preceding ones is taken into account."

and the optimal subpolicies between these points will be those which pass through the maximum values of x_2.

In general terms, after finding $f_{0,n-1}(x_0 , x_{n-1})$ for every $x_{n-1} \in \mathbf{X}_{n-1}(x_0 , \cdot)$,

$$\mathbf{X}_n(x_0 , \cdot) = \Gamma_n \mathbf{X}_{n-1}(x_0 , \cdot). \tag{3.16}$$

For every $x_n \in \mathbf{X}_n(x_0 , \cdot)$, we next find

$$\mathbf{X}_{n-1}(x_0 , x_n) = \mathbf{X}_{n-1}(x_0 , \cdot) \cap \Gamma_n^{-1} x_n . \tag{3.17}$$

Finally, we calculate the optimal value from x_0 to x_n :

$$f_{0,n}(x_0 , x_n) = \underset{x_{n-1} \in \mathbf{X}_{n-1}(x_0, x_n)}{\text{OPT}} [f_{0,n-1}(x_0 , x_{n-1}) + v_n(x_{n-1} , x_n)]. \tag{3.18}$$

If x_{n-1}^* is a value of x_{n-1} which optimizes the second member, every subpolicy from x_0 to x_n obtained by combining x_n with an optimal subpolicy from x_0 to x_{n-1}^* is itself optimal from x_0 to x_n :

$$\varpi_{0,n}^*(x_0 , x_n) = \{\varpi_{0,n-1}^*(x_0 , x_{n-1}^*), x_n\}. \tag{3.19}$$

In this way we obtain the optimal subpolicies from x_0 to every x_n . When we reach $n = N$ we have solved the problem of finding the optimal policy or policies, not only for the value x_N chosen at the beginning, but also for all the values $x_N \in \mathbf{X}_N(x_0 , \cdot)$, in the same way that we have found all the optimal subpolicies in doing so.

In certain problems the value of x_N is not imposed, and we then choose the one for which the optimal policy from x_0 to x_N has the greatest value. In such a case it is important to carry out the optimization as we have done for increasing values of n. Inversely, x_N might have a fixed value while x_0 varies, and optimization would then have to begin at $n = N$ and progress by decreasing values of n. The method is the same, only $f_{0,n}(x_0 , x_n)$ and $\varpi_{0,n}^*(x_0 , x_n)$ are respectively replaced by $f_{n,N}(x_n , x_N)$ and $\varpi_{n,N}^*(x_n , x_N)$.

We shall consider this type of problem at greater length in Section 8.

Observations

(1)   The number of decisions to be taken at period n is not necessarily equal to the number of components of the vector x_n . The constraints (3.3) can, in fact, impose a given value on certain of them, or speaking in a more general form, impose one or more relations between the values of the different components. It might be thought that this would allow us to eliminate one or more components, thereby reducing the size of x_n , but in practice this is not always possible owing to the condition that x_n must completely represent the state of the system at time n. We shall realize this from an example.

Let us assume that x_n has two components $x_n^{(1)}$ and $x_n^{(2)}$ and that $\Gamma_n x_{n-1}$ is defined by

$$x_n^{(1)} \leqslant x_{n-1}^{(1)} + x_{n-1}^{(2)} ,$$

$$x_n^{(2)} \leqslant x_{n-1}^{(1)} + x_{n-1}^{(2)} ,$$

$$x_n^{(1)} + \alpha x_n^{(2)} = \beta x_{n-1}^{(1)} + \gamma x_{n-1}^{(2)} .$$

It will be useful for the numerical calculations to put this system in the form

$$\alpha x_n^{(2)} \geqslant (\beta - 1)x_{n-1}^{(1)} + (\gamma - 1)x_{n-1}^{(2)} ,$$

$$x_n^{(2)} \leqslant x_{n-1}^{(1)} + x_{n-1}^{(2)} ,$$

$$x_n^{(1)} = \beta x_{n-1}^{(1)} + \gamma x_{n-1}^{(2)} - \alpha x_n^{(2)}.$$

The quantity $y_n = x_n^{(2)}$ is the only one which we can choose, taking account of the two inequalities, and from it we deduce the value $x_n^{(1)}$. But if we tried to eliminate all the $x_n^{(1)}$ terms we should introduce the values of $x_{n-2}^{(2)}$, $x_{n-3}^{(2)}$, etc., into the constraints. The quantity $x_n^{(1)}$ has only the function of a counting link between the different periods, but its presence in the state variable is nonetheless a necessary one.

In a general manner, the constraints (3.1) can be represented in the form

$$\begin{cases} y_{n+1} \in \Delta_{n+1} x_n \\ x_{n+1} = \Omega_{n+1}(x_n , y_{n+1}), \end{cases} \tag{3.20}$$

where y_n is a vector with fewer components than the state vector x_n and where Ω_{n+1} is a univocal correspondence. The decision variable will be called y_n, and this more general notation will again be used in Section 7.

(2)   Concept of the upper bound and of the maximum: Let us recall that the upper bound of a numerical set $\mathbf{X}$ is the smallest quantity b such that $x \in \mathbf{X} \Rightarrow x \leqslant b$, where b is a maximum of $\mathbf{X}$ only if $b \in \mathbf{X}$, which is always the case if $\mathbf{X}$ has a finite number of elements.

When using the relation (3.9) we have implicitly assumed that $s(\varpi)$ has a maximum, a condition which obviously exists only if it is uniformly bounded in set $\mathbf{\Pi}$, as always happens in practical cases. However, the condition only assures the existence of an upper bound, which may not actually be reached.

To take a simple example, the function $y = x$ has no maximum in an interval open to the right: in other words, the equation

$$f(x) = \operatorname*{MAX}_{y < x} y .$$

is without a solution, whereas the equation

$$f(x) = \sup_{y < x} y,$$

where the sign SUP indicates upper bound of, obviously has as its solution the function $f(x) = x$.

If the set $\{s(\varpi)\}$ has an upper bound s^* but no maximum, there cannot be an optimal policy. But, for any arbitrarily small number ϵ, we can define policies $\varpi(\epsilon)$ which are quasioptimal (close to ϵ), that is to say, such that $s^* - s(\varpi)$ is smaller[4] than ϵ.

Naturally the same observations apply when the minimum is being sought.

4. Interpretation by the Theory of Graphs. Multistage Graphs

The reader who is familiar with the theory of graphs will have recognized structures in Section 3 known as "transport networks."[5]

Let us recall that the term *graph* is given to a set **X** and a correspondence (usually with more than one meaning) Γ of **X** with **X**. In the dynamic program in Section 3, **X** there is the combination of every $\mathbf{X}_n(x_0, x_N)$ for $n = 0, 1, 2,..., N$, and the correspondence Γ is defined by

$$\Gamma \tilde{x}_{n-1} = \Gamma_n \tilde{x}_{n-1} \cap \mathbf{X}_n(x_0, x_N), \qquad (4.1)$$

where $\tilde{x}_{n-1}$ is the special value of x_{n-1}, such that

$$\tilde{x}_{n-1} \in \mathbf{X}_{n-1}(x_0, x_N).$$

We will assume, so as to be able to draw the graph, that the state variable x_n has only one dimension and that the sets $\mathbf{X}_n$ of possible values are denumerable, though of course our definitions are by no means limited to this case. We can now use points to represent the elements of **X**, that is to say, the values $\tilde{x}_n$ of x_n ; the relation $\tilde{x}_n \in \Gamma_n \tilde{x}_{n-1}$ is shown by an arc joining $\tilde{x}_{n-1}$ and $\tilde{x}_n$ and oriented by an arrow from the former to the latter. (Fig. 4.1.)

A "route," by definition, is a sequence of arcs such that the terminal extremity of one coincides with the initial extremity of the next, a concept analogous to that of "subpolicies" or policies, as defined earlier.

---

[4] See R. Fortet [32] for a more thorough discussion of this question.
[5] For example, see C. Berge, *Théorie des graphes*, Dunod (1958), Chapters 7 and 8.

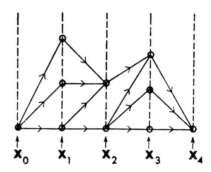

FIG. 4.1.   Graph of a dynamic program for 4 periods.

A "transport network" is formed by a graph and a set of values, such that:

(a) The graph has a single vertex[6] x_0 such that $\Gamma^{-1} x_0 = \varnothing$, where $\varnothing$ is the empty set, and a single vertex x_N such that $\Gamma x_N = \varnothing$.

(b) Each arc has a value.

It is clear that any dynamic program, as defined in Section 3, corresponds to a transport network without a circuit[7] where the value of an arc $(\tilde{x}_{n-1}, \tilde{x}_n)$ is $v_n(\tilde{x}_{n-1}, \tilde{x}_n)$. But it is a special case of a transport network, for the vertices form $N + 1$ sets $\mathbf{X}_n$, such that an arc leaving a vertex $\tilde{x}_n$ belonging to $\mathbf{X}_n$ must go to a vertex $\tilde{x}_{n+1}$ belonging to $\mathbf{X}_{n+1}$.

In accordance with the definitions given at the end of this section, we shall call a network of this kind a "sequential transport network."

It is of importance to observe how this particular structure simplifies the use of Ford's algorithm[8] for finding the minimal or maximal route between two given vertices.

This algorithm is represented by the organigram of Fig. 4.2 and can be applied not only to transport networks without a circuit, but also to any finite graph without a circuit.[9]

We shall take X_i, $i = 1, 2,..., M$, for the vertices of graph $G = (\mathbf{X}, \Gamma)$ which we are considering, and v_{ij} for the value of the arc (X_i, X_j). If $X_j \in \Gamma X_i$, we shall state that $v_{ij} = +\infty$, including $i = j$. Basically, the algorithm consists of giving to each vertex X_i a *tension* λ_i, taken at first

---

[6] A vertex of a graph $(\mathbf{X}, \Gamma)$ is an element of the set $\mathbf{X}$ and is shown on the graph by a point.

[7] A circuit is a route in which the initial and terminal extremities coincide.

[8] L. R. Ford, *Network Flow Theory*, RAND Corp. (1956), p. 923.

[9] As enunciated by Ford, this algorithm is valid for any finite graph in which the arcs have positive values.

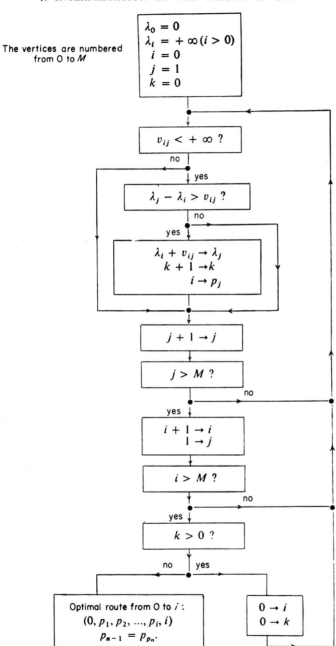

The vertices are numbered from O to M

$$\lambda_0 = 0$$
$$\lambda_i = +\infty \, (i > 0)$$
$$i = 0$$
$$j = 1$$
$$k = 0$$

$$v_{ij} < +\infty \, ?$$

no

yes

$$\lambda_j - \lambda_i > v_{ij} \, ?$$

no

yes

$$\lambda_i + v_{ij} \rightarrow \lambda_j$$
$$k + 1 \rightarrow k$$
$$i \rightarrow p_j$$

$$j + 1 \rightarrow j$$

$$j > M \, ?$$

no

yes

$$i + 1 \rightarrow i$$
$$1 \rightarrow j$$

$$i > M \, ?$$

no

yes

$$k > 0 \, ?$$

no   yes

Optimal route from O to i :
$$(0, p_1, p_2, ..., p_i, i)$$
$$p_{n-1} = p_{p_n}.$$

$$0 \rightarrow i$$
$$0 \rightarrow k$$

FIG. 4.2.   Organigram of Ford's algorithm for finding the routes of minimal value in a finite graph without a circuit.

as $+\infty$ for $i = 1, 2,..., M$. To X_0 will be assigned a tension $\lambda_0 = 0$, and at the end of the calculations the tension λ_i must be equal to the minimal value of a route from X_0 to X_i.

Leaving X_0, we successively consider all the arcs, and whenever we encounter one such that

$$\lambda_j - \lambda_i > v_{ij},$$

we replace λ_j by $\lambda_i + v_{ij}$ and take note that the last arc of the route (among those examined) from X_0 to X_j leaves X_i, which we interpret by giving the value i to an *indicator* p_j.

When it is no longer possible to diminish any λ_j (which we decide by examining the value k indicating the number of diminutions of the λ values in the course of a repetition), we have obtained for every X_i the minimal value of a route from X_0 to X_i. The optimal route[10] passes through the vertices with index $0, p_1, p_2,..., p_i, i$ where $p_{n-1} = p_{p_n}$. The same diagram can be used to find the maximal routes on condition that we first change the sign of all the v_{ij} terms corresponding to the arcs.

Let us now consider a dynamic program with a finite number of periods, and such that the number of possible values for the state variable is also finite for each of the periods. Ford's algorithm can be applied to this problem, but if a suitable procedure is adopted, the diagram can be considerably simplified.

Let us number the vertices of the graph for the dynamic program from 0 to M in the order of increasing periods; the values of the state variable at time 1 will be numbered 1 to α_1, those for time 2, $\alpha_1 + 1$ to α_2, and so on until $\alpha_N = M$.

If we now apply Ford's algorithm, we find that among the arcs leaving vertex i with $\alpha_{n-1} + 1 \leqslant i \leqslant \alpha_n$ (vertices at time n), the only vertices j which can be terminal extremities of an arc (i, j) are those for which $\alpha_n + 1 \leqslant j \leqslant \alpha_{n+1}$ (vertices at time $n + 1$). Hence there is no need to examine the other values of j, and, in addition, when all the arcs leaving the vertices of time n have been examined, the λ_j terms corresponding to the vertices at time $n + 1$ have acquired their definitive value. This result is due to the fact that each route passes in order through a single vertex for each of the times. It is sufficient, therefore, to examine each arc only once. Figure 4.3 shows the organigram simplified in accordance with these two observations, and Fig. 4.4 shows the same algorithm for a case of maximization.

---

[10] The diagram of Fig. 4.2 only provides one optimal route, but it would be easy to modify it so as to obtain the routes with the same value, if there are any.

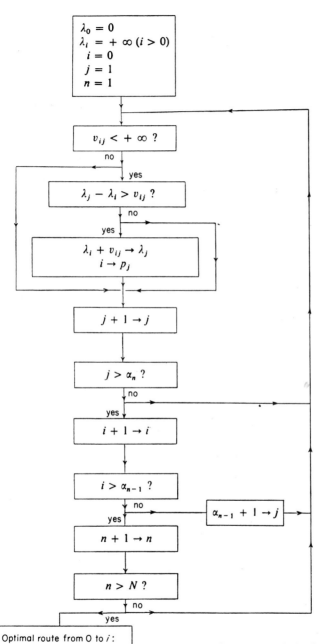

FIG. 4.3. Organigram derived from Ford's algorithm for solving a finite dynamic program in a case of minimization.

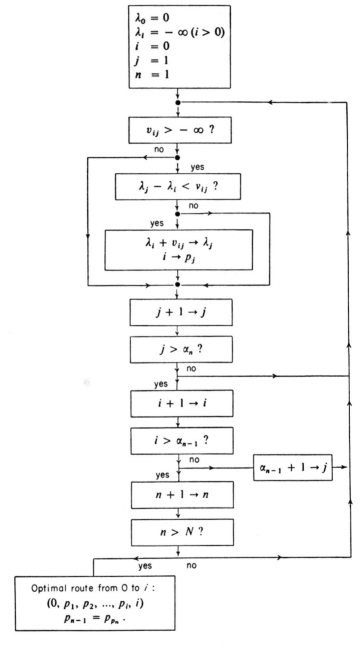

FIG. 4.4.   Organigram derived from Ford's algorithm for solving a finite dynamic program in a case of maximization.

The comparison of this algorithm with the procedure explained at the end of Section 3 shows that the method is the same in both cases; the only difference lies in the order in which we examine the arcs joining a vertex i at time n to a vertex j at time $(n + 1)$. As an exercise, we suggest that the reader should modify the diagram of (4.3) in such a way that all the arcs corresponding to $j = \alpha_{n-1} + 1$ are examined, then all those for which $j = \alpha_{n-1} + 2$, and so on, in accordance with the method used in Section 3. In any case, when all the arcs ending at the vertices of period $(n + 1)$ have been considered, the quantities λ_j represent the optimal value of a route or subpolicy from x_0 to the corresponding vertex and are the same as those called f in Section 3.

Example. To clarify what we have explained above, we will take a simple example and consider a selling organization with four representatives whose distribution in four geographical areas must be arranged to the best advantage. If we use u_n for the number of salesmen sent to area n $(n = 1,..., 4)$, we have

$$\sum_{n=1}^{4} u_n = 4. \tag{4.2}$$

TABLE 4.1

u_n \\ n	1	2	3	4
0	0	0	0	0
1	45	41	25	33
2	78	65	50	48
3	102	80	73	56
4	123	88	90	60

We assume that the profit $v_n(u_n)$ obtained by the u_n representatives in each of the n regions is known (Table 4.1) and we wish to discover the distribution which will maximize the total profit:

$$\sum_{n=1}^{4} v_n .$$

Since the values of $v_n(u_n)$ are given (Table 4.1), the answer to the problem could be found by enumerating all the possible solutions. As a generalization, where we have M representatives to distribute among N areas, we can represent a particular distribution by taking M numbers from 1 to N for the areas to which the different salesmen are assigned; then (since we are not concerned as to which of the salemen are sent to a given region) the number of possible solutions will be equal to the number of M combinations, of N distinct objects, in other words, C_{M+N-1}^M. If $M = N = 4$, there are $C_7^4 = 35$ possible solutions. This problem is combinatorial and at first sight does not seem to be of a sequential kind. Nevertheless, we shall discover that dynamic programming provides a particularly advantageous method of enumeration in this case.

We shall consider in succession 1, then 2,..., areas, and as the number of salesmen to be distributed among the first n areas cannot be decided in advance, it will be treated as a parameter.

$$x_n = \sum_{i=1}^{n} u_i , \qquad n = 1, 2, 3, 4, \tag{4.3}$$

with $x_0 = 0$. If we assign x_{n-1} salesmen to the first $(n-1)$ areas, we have

$$x_n \in \Gamma_n x_{n-1} = \{x_{n-1}, x_{n-1} + 1,..., 4\}. \tag{4.4}$$

If we choose a value of x_n which satisfies this constraint, the value of this decision will be

$$v_n(x_{n-1}, x_n) = v_n(x_n - x_{n-1}) = v_n(u_n), \tag{4.5}$$

where $v_n(u_n)$ is given in Table 4.1.

The conditions of the model in Section 3 are therefore satisfied: we have a system in which the state at time n (or in this case, stage n, to avoid the notion of time), that is, after the distribution among the first n areas, is completely defined by the state variable in the sense that:

(a) The possible values of x_n only depend on x_{n-1} and not on x_{n-2}, x_{n-3}, etc.

(b) The value of the decision x_n only depends on x_n and x_{n-1}.

The graph of the dynamic program is shown in Fig. 4.5 and has been obtained by first applying the constraints (4.3) beginning with $x_0 = 0$, then by using the inverse constraints, commencing with $x_4 = 4$, in accordance with the method explained in Section 3. The arcs with broken lines complete the graph for the case where the imposed value of x_4 is respectively 0, 1, 2, and 3.

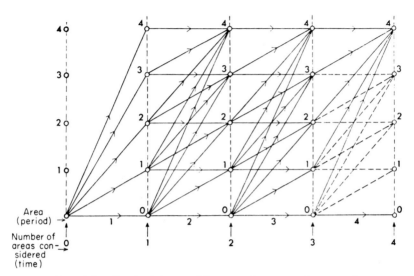

FIG. 4.5. Graph of the possible routes from $x_0 = 0$ to $x_4 = 4$.

First Period. From $x_0 = 0$ to any vertex x_i, there is only one arc or subpolicy, the value of which is

$$f_{0,1}(0, x_1) = v_1(x_0, x_1) = v_1(x_1 - x_0) = v_1(x_1), \qquad (4.6)$$

where the function $v_1(x_1)$ is given in column $n = 1$ in Table 4.1.

Second Period. From x_0 to x_2 there are usually several possible routes; the best is the one which maximizes the expression

$$f_{0,2}(0, x_2) = \underset{0 \leqslant x_1 \leqslant x_2}{\text{MAX}} [f_{0,1}(0, x_1) + v_2(x_2 - x_1)]. \qquad (4.7)$$

Table 4.2 shows the best subpolicies for each value of x_2, expressed either as a function of x_n (column 2) or as a function of u_n (column 3), as well as their value (column 4).

Third Period. We now have

$$f_{0,3}(0, x_3) = \underset{0 \leqslant x_2 \leqslant x_3}{\text{MAX}} [f_{0,2}(0, x_2) + v_3(x_3 - x_2)], \qquad (4.8)$$

and the optimal subpolicies from x_0 to x_3 will be obtained by using arc (x_2^*, x_3) to complete the optimal subpolicies from x_0 to x_2^*, where the latter is the value which optimizes the expression between brackets in (4.8). The results are shown in Table 4.3.

TABLE 4.2

	Optimal policies		
x_2	(x_1^*, x_2^*)	(u_1^*, u_2^*)	$f_{0,2}(0, x_2)$
(1)	(2)	(3)	(4)
0	(0, 0)	(0, 0)	0
1	(1, 1)	(1, 0)	45
2	(1, 2)	(1, 1)	86
3	(2, 3)	(2, 1)	119
4	(2, 4) (3, 4)	(2, 2) (3, 1)	143

TABLE 4.3

	Optimal policies		
x_3	(x_1^*, x_2^*, x_3^*)	(u_1^*, u_2^*, u_3^*)	$f_{0,3}(0, x_3)$
(1)	(2)	(3)	(4)
0	(0, 0, 0)	(0, 0, 0)	0
1	(1, 1, 1)	(1, 0, 0)	45
2	(1, 2, 2)	(1, 1, 0)	86
3	(2, 3, 3)	(2, 1, 0)	119
4	(2, 3, 4)	(2, 1, 1)	144

Fourth Period. As the total number of salesmen is 4, $x_4 = 4$; but it will be observed that the expression

$$f_{0,4}(0, x_4) = \underset{0 \leqslant x_3 \leqslant x_4}{\text{MAX}} [f_{0,3}(0, x_3) + v_4(x_4 - x_3)] \tag{4.9}$$

also gives the solution for $x_4 = 0, 1, 2,$ or 3 (see Table 4.4). All we need do is complete the first four lines of this table, which only requires the examination of 10 extra solutions, to solve the problem of distributing N representatives ($N \leqslant 4$) in 1, 2, or 3 regions. To solve the complete problem, where $1 \leqslant N \leqslant 4$ and $0 \leqslant M \leqslant 4$, we have had to examine $35 + 10 = 45$ solutions, whereas a less rational method of enumeration might have forced us to examine up to

$$\sum_{n=1}^{4} \sum_{m=0}^{4} C_{m+n-1}^{m} = 125$$

possible solutions. For higher values of M and N the advantage of our method would be progressively greater.

TABLE 4.4

	Optimal policies		
x_4	$(x_1^*, x_2^*, x_3^*, x_4^*)$	$(u_1^*, u_2^*, u_3^*, u_4^*)$	$f_{0,4}(0, x_4)$
(1)	(2)	(3)	(4)
0	(0, 0, 0, 0)	(0, 0, 0, 0)	0
1	(1, 1, 1, 1)	(1, 0, 0, 0)	45
2	(1, 2, 2, 2)	(1, 1, 0, 0)	86
3	(2, 3, 3, 3)	(2, 1, 0, 0)	119
	(1, 2, 2, 3)	(1, 1, 0, 1)	
4	(2, 3, 3, 4)	(2, 1, 0, 1)	152

Figure 4.6 shows the graph of the optimal subpolicies from x_0 to x_n given in column 2 of Tables 4.2–4.4. The numbers in parenthesis are the maximal values, the λ_j terms which would have been obtained as a result of optimization by applying the diagram of Fig. 4.4.

ORDINAL FUNCTION OF A FINITE GRAPH WITHOUT A CIRCUIT

In order to give a thorough and precise definition of the important concept of the sequential graph, on which the ideas of the present chapter are based, we remind the reader what we mean by the heading of this section.

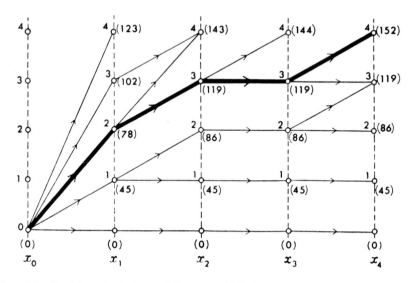

FIG. 4.6.   Partial graph of the possible routes which shows all the optimal subpolicies.

Let us consider a finite graph without circuit $G = (\mathbf{X}, \Gamma)$, and let us define the subsets of vertices, such that[11]

$$\mathbf{X}_0 = \{X_r \mid \Gamma^{-1}X_r = \varnothing\},$$
$$\mathbf{X}_1 = \{X_r \mid \Gamma^{-1}X_r \subset \mathbf{X}_0\},$$
$$\mathbf{X}_2 = \{X_r \mid \Gamma^{-1}X_r \subset (\mathbf{X}_0 \cup \mathbf{X}_1)\}.$$
$$\vdots \tag{4.10}$$
$$\mathbf{X}_N = \left\{X_r \,\middle|\, \Gamma^{-1}X_r \subset \left(\bigcup_{n=0}^{N-1} \mathbf{X}_n\right)\right\},$$

where N is the smallest integer such that

$$\Gamma\mathbf{X}_N = \varnothing. \tag{4.11}$$

We can easily show that the subsets $\mathbf{X}_n$, $n = 0, 1, 2,..., N$, form a partition[12] of $\mathbf{X}$ and are totally and strictly ordered by the relation

$$\mathbf{X}_n < \mathbf{X}_{n'} \quad \Leftrightarrow \quad n < n'. \tag{4.12}$$

[11] Some authors (in particular C. Berge, *op. cit.*) prefer to define the ordinal function of a graph by replacing Γ^{-1} by Γ in (4.10) and Γ by Γ^{-1} in (4.11), thereby inverting the order (4.12).

[12] That is to say,

$$\forall n, n'; \quad n \neq n': \mathbf{X}_n \cap \mathbf{X}_{n'} = \varnothing, \quad \bigcup_{n=0}^{N} \mathbf{X}_n = \mathbf{X}, \quad \mathbf{X}_n \neq \varnothing.$$

The function $O(X_r)$, defined by

$$X_r \in \mathbf{X}_n \quad \Rightarrow \quad O(X_r) = n, \qquad (4.13)$$

is called the ordinal function of the graph.

As an example, Fig. 4.8 shows the ordinal function of the graph of Fig. 4.7.

Various methods are used to find the ordinal function of a finite graph *without a circuit*, and we shall give the one we consider the simplest,[13] referring to Fig. 4.7 in our explanation.

TABLE 4.5

	A	B	C	D	E	F	G	H	I	J	K	V_0	V_1	V_2	V_3
A									1	1		2	0	×	×
B	1		1	1		1						4	3	2	0
C											1	1	1	0	×
D	1							1				2	1	0	×
E												0	×	×	×
F	1											1	1	0	×
G		1			1							2	2	2	0
H											1	1	1	0	×
I												0	×	×	×
J												0	×	×	×
K				1				1				2	0	×	×
Value of the ordinal function												0	1	2	3
Vertices												E I J	A K	C D F H	B G

Let us examine the boolean matrix of the graph, that is, the matrix with elements b_{ij}, $i, j = 1, 2, \ldots, M$, where $M = |\,\mathbf{X}\,|$, such that

$$b_{ij} = 1 \quad \text{if} \quad X_j \in \Gamma X_i$$
$$= 0 \quad \text{if} \quad X_j \notin \Gamma X_i. \qquad (4.14)$$

[13] This method was conveyed to us by M. Demoucron of the Cie. des Machines Bull-General Electric.

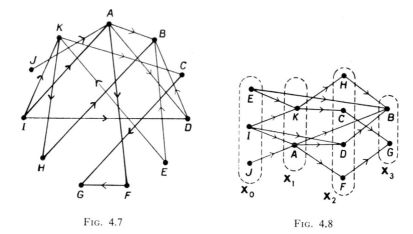

FIG. 4.7   FIG. 4.8

If we take the transpose of this matrix,[14] we obtain the 11×11 matrix shown in Table 4.5 where the zeros have been omitted for clarity.

Let V_A, V_B,..., V_K be the vectors representing the columns, and let us calculate

$$V_0 = V_A + V_B + \cdots + V_K$$

and then transfer the results to the right of the matrix, as in Table 4.5. Vector V_0 contains some zeros, in this case the three corresponding to vertices E, I, and J. These zeros represent the vertices X_r, which have no predecessors (that is, are such that $\Gamma^{-1}X_r = \varnothing$) and form the subset $\mathbf{X}_0$.

We now calculate $V_1 = V_0 - V_E - V_I - V_J$, where we discover two new zeros corresponding to vertices A and K which will form $\mathbf{X}_1$. By calculating $V_2 = V_1 - V_A - V_K$, we obtain four more zeros for vertices C, D, F, and H, which will be $\mathbf{X}_2$. Last, we calculate

$$V_3 = V_2 - V_C - V_D - V_F - V_H,$$

where new zeros appear for B and G which will constitute $\mathbf{X}_3$. Since there are no further vertices, the process is now complete.

If we had used the boolean matrix instead of its transpose for our calculations, we should have found the same partition in an inverse direction. However, in other cases the use of the matrix can result in different partitions.

---

[14] The matrix must not be transposed if we use the definition of the ordinal function given as a reminder before.

SEQUENTIAL GRAPH

We give this name[15] to a graph $G = (\mathbf{X}, \Gamma)$ if it satisfies the following conditions:

(1) G possesses an ordinal function $O(X_r)$ with integral values from 0 to N.

(2)
$$\Gamma \mathbf{X}_n \subset \mathbf{X}_{n+1}, \qquad n = 0, 1, 2, ..., N - 1, \tag{4.15}$$

where
$$\mathbf{X}_n = \{X_r \mid O(X_r) = n\}.$$

Example. The graph of Fig. 4.9 is sequential and its ordinal function is shown in Fig. 4.10.

If G is a sequential graph, we have

$$\Gamma^{-1} \mathbf{X}_{n+1} \subset \mathbf{X}_n, \qquad n = 0, 1, 2, ..., N - 1, \tag{4.16}$$

$$\Gamma \mathbf{X}_n \subset \mathbf{X}_{n+1}, \qquad n = 0, 1, 2, ..., N - 1, \tag{4.17}$$

in other words $\Gamma \mathbf{X}_n = \mathbf{X}_{n+1}$.

As a result, any subgraph

$$G_n = (\mathbf{X}_n \cup \mathbf{X}_{n+1}, \Gamma_{\mathbf{X}_n \cup \mathbf{X}_{n+1}}), \qquad n = 0, 1, 2, .., N - 1 \tag{4.18}$$

is a simple graph.[16]

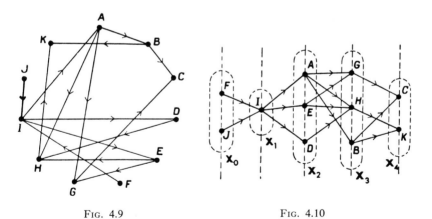

FIG. 4.9   FIG. 4.10

[15] The concept of a sequential graph can be extended to include infinite denumerable graphs with an ordinal function.

[16] A graph $G = (\mathbf{A} \cup \mathbf{B}, \Gamma)$ is simple if the following conditions are satisfied:

(a) $\mathbf{A} \cap \mathbf{B} = \varnothing$,
(b) $\Gamma \mathbf{A} = \mathbf{B}$
(c) $\Gamma \mathbf{B} = \varnothing$.

TABLE 4.6

	A	B	C	D	E	F	G	H	I	J	K	V_0	V_1	V_2	V_3	V_4
A									1			1	1	0	×	×
B	1											1	1	1	0	×
C		1				1						2	2	2	2	0
D								1				1	1	0	×	×
E								1				1	1	0	×	×
F												0	×	×	×	×
G	1				1							2	2	2	0	×
H	1			1	1							3	3	3	0	×
I					1					1		2	0	×	×	×
J												0	×	×	×	×
K		1					1					2	2	2	2	0

Reciprocally, if a graph contains a partition $\mathbf{X}_0$, $\mathbf{X}_1$,..., $\mathbf{X}_N$ of $\mathbf{X}$ such that every subgraph of the form (4.18) is simple, it is sequential.

A method of discovering whether a graph is sequential is to use Demoucron's procedure and to check that there is a single diminution in each line of the table to which the values of the vectors have been transferred. Thus, in line C of Table 4.6 we pass from 2 to 0 in one step, and in line H from 3 to 0, also in one step.

STRUCTURE OF DYNAMIC PROGRAMS

The graph of a dynamic program, as we have seen, is sequential, and we will now consider a system in which the state is marked by a variable and which evolves under the effect of decisions. If the latter are to be chosen by the method of dynamic programming *given by the model* in Section 3, the graph showing the possible evolutions of the system must be sequential.[17]

---

[17] We shall discover in Section 39 that the method of dynamic programming can be generalized for nonsequential structures.

TIMES AND PERIODS OF A PROGRAM

Each vertex of a subset $\mathbf{X}_n$ will represent a "time" equal in value to the ordinal function n, and each pair of consecutive times n and $n + 1$ [that is, each subgraph G_n as defined in (4.18)] will correspond to a "period" $(n + 1)$. Thus, from the examples in Figs. 4.9 and 4.10 we obtain the times and periods shown in Fig. 4.11.

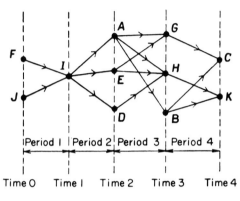

FIG. 4.11

5. Explanation of Certain Difficulties in the Calculations

We shall take the example given in Section 2, this time assuming that the stock must never exceed the value $S = 20$, in order to show that an apparently simple problem can lead to somewhat difficult calculations.

As before, we shall begin with period 6, proceeding from the future toward the past (we could operate inversely, though it is impossible to tell in advance which choice will lead to the easier calculations), and we shall retain the notation of Section 2.

PERIOD 6

Assuming $x_6 = 0$, we will now find the interval over which x_5 can vary. For $n = 5$, in accordance with (2.10),

$$\max(0, x_4 - d_5) \leqslant x_5 \leqslant \min(S - d_5, x_6 + d_6); \qquad (5.1)$$

let

$$\max(0, x_4 - 7) \leqslant x_5 \leqslant \min(20 - 7, 0 + 4), \qquad (5.2)$$

or again,

$$\max(0, x_4 - 7) \leqslant x_5 \leqslant 4. \tag{5.3}$$

The cost for period 6, that is, between times 5 and 6, will be

$$v_6(x_5, x_6) = v_6(x_5, 0) = p_6 a_6 = 40 - 10x_5. \tag{5.4}$$

PERIODS 6 AND 5

In accordance with (2.10), for $n = 4$,

$$\max(0, x_3 - d_4) \leqslant x_4 \leqslant \min(S - d_4, x_5 + d_5); \tag{5.5}$$

let

$$\max(0, x_3 - 2) \leqslant x_4 \leqslant \min(18, x_5 + 7). \tag{5.6}$$

But, in accordance with (5.3),

$$x_5 + 7 \leqslant 11, \tag{5.7}$$

hence (5.6) can be expressed

$$\max(0, x_3 - 2) \leqslant x_4 \leqslant x_5 + 7. \tag{5.8}$$

The expenditure for periods 5 and 6 combined, that is, between times 4 and 6, will be

$$\begin{aligned}
s_{4,6}(x_4, x_6) &= s_{4,6}(x_4, 0) \\
&= p_5 a_5 + v_6(x_5, 0) \\
&= p_5(x_5 + d_5 - x_4) + 40 - 10x_5 \\
&= 20(x_5 + 7 - x_4) + 40 - 10x_5 \\
&= 180 - 20x_4 + 10x_5. \tag{5.9}
\end{aligned}$$

Hence the minimal expenditure will be

$$f_{4,6}(x_4, 0) = \underset{\max(0, x_4 - 7) \leqslant x_5 \leqslant 4}{\text{MIN}} [180 - 20x_4 + 10x_5]. \tag{5.10}$$

The minimum is obtained for

$$x_5{}^* = \max(0, x_4 - 7), \tag{5.11}$$

and we have

$$f_{4,6}(x_4, 0) = 180 - 20x_4 + 10 \max(0, x_4 - 7). \tag{5.12}$$

Further, if we substitute (5.11) in (5.8) we obtain

$$\max(0, x_3 - 2) \leqslant x_4 \leqslant \max(7, x_4). \qquad (5.13)$$

Obviously, the second inequality in (5.13) does not impose any condition on x_4; but, in accordance with (5.3), $x_5 \leqslant 4$ when $x_4 \leqslant 4 + 7 \leqslant 11$. Hence (5.13) becomes

$$\max(0, x_3 - 2) \leqslant x_4 \leqslant 11. \qquad (5.14)$$

PERIODS 6, 5, AND 4

In accordance with (2.10), for $n = 3$,

$$\max(0, x_2 - d_3) \leqslant x_3 \leqslant \min(S - d_3, x_4 + d_4). \qquad (5.15)$$

Let

$$\max(0, x_2 - 3) \leqslant x_3 \leqslant \min(17, x_4 + 2). \qquad (5.16)$$

The expenditure for the two periods will be

$$\begin{aligned}
s_{3,6}(x_3, x_6) &= s_{3,6}(x_3, 0) \\
&= p_4 a_4 + f_{4,6}(x_4, 0) \\
&= 17(x_4 + 2 - x_3) + 180 - 20x_4 + 10 \max(0, x_4 - 7) \\
&= 214 - 17x_3 - 3x_4 + 10 \max(0, x_4 - 7). \qquad (5.17)
\end{aligned}$$

Hence the minimal cost will be

$$f_{3,6}(x_3, 0) = \underset{\max(0, x_3-2) \leqslant x_4 \leqslant 11}{\mathrm{MIN}} [214 - 17x_3 - 3x_4 + 10 \max(0, x_4 - 7)]; \qquad (5.18)$$

again, let

$$f_{3,6}(x_3, 0) = 214 - 17x_3 + \underset{\max(0, x_3-2) \leqslant x_4 \leqslant 11}{\mathrm{MIN}} [\max(-3x_4, 7x_4 - 70)]. \qquad (5.19)$$

If we trace the curves $z_1 = -3x_4$ and $z_2 = 7x_4 - 70$ in the interval $0 \leqslant x_4 \leqslant 11$, we find that the minimum is obtained for $x_4 = 7$. If the lower bound of x_4 is greater than 7 we must take $x_4 = \max(0, x_3 - 2)$. Summing up, we shall have

$$x_4{}^* = \max[7, \max(0, x_3 - 2)] \qquad (5.20)$$

or:

$$x_4{}^* = \max(7, x_3 - 2). \qquad (5.21)$$

(*a*) Let us assume that

$$x_3 - 2 \leqslant 7, \quad \text{or} \quad x_3 \leqslant 9; \tag{5.22}$$

then

$$x_4{}^* = 7 \tag{5.23}$$

and

$$f_{3,6}(x_3, 0) = 214 - 17x_3 - 21 = 193 - 17x_3. \tag{5.24}$$

(*b*) If, on the other hand,

$$x_3 \geqslant 9, \tag{5.25}$$

we have

$$x_4{}^* = x_3 - 2 \tag{5.26}$$

and

$$\begin{aligned}
f_{3,6}(x_3, 0) &= 214 - 17x_3 + 7x_4{}^* - 70 \\
&= 214 - 17x_3 + 7(x_3 - 2) - 70 \\
&= 130 - 10x_3.
\end{aligned} \tag{5.27}$$

Finally, we can say

$$f_{3,6}(x_3, 0) = \max(193 - 17x_3, 130 - 10x_3). \tag{5.28}$$

Also, in accordance with (5.14), we have: $x_4 \leqslant 11$. Hence, from (5.21),

$$\max(7, x_3 - 2) \leqslant 11, \tag{5.29}$$

whence

$$x_3 \leqslant 13. \tag{5.30}$$

If we now examine (5.16), the relation $x_3 \leqslant 17$ is weaker than (5.30), and the relation $x_3 \leqslant x_4 + 2$ already appears in (5.21). Thus, we can now express (5.16) as

$$\max(0, x_2 - 3) \leqslant x_3 \leqslant 13. \tag{5.31}$$

PERIODS 6, 5, 4, AND 3

From (2.10), for $n = 2$:

$$\max(0, x_1 - d_2) \leqslant x_2 \leqslant \min(S - d_2, x_3 + d_3); \tag{5.32}$$

let

$$\max(0, x_1 - 5) \leqslant x_2 \leqslant \min(15, x_3 + 3). \tag{5.33}$$

The minimal cost for the four periods will be

$$s_{2,6}(x_2, x_6) = s_{2,6}(x_2, 0)$$
$$= p_3 a_3 + f_{3,6}(x_3, 0)$$
$$= 13(x_3 + 3 - x_2) + \max(193 - 17x_3, 130 - 10x_3). \quad (5.34)$$

Hence the minimal cost will be

$$f_{2,6}(x_2, 0) = \underset{\max(0,x_2-3) \leqslant x_3 \leqslant 13}{\text{MIN}} [39 - 13x_2 + 13x_3$$
$$+ \max(193 - 17x_3, 130 - 10x_3)]; \quad (5.35)$$

that is,

$$f_{2,6}(x_2, 0) = 39 - 13x_2 + \underset{\max(0,x_2-3) \leqslant x_3 \leqslant 13}{\text{MIN}} [\max(193 - 4x_3, 130 + 3x_3)]. \quad (5.36)$$

If we trace the curves of $z_1 = 193 - 4x_3$ and $z_2 = 130 + 3x_3$ in the interval $0 \leqslant x_3 \leqslant 13$, we find that the minimum is obtained for $x_3 = 9$. If the lower bound of x_3 is greater than 9 we must take

$$x_3 = \max(0, x_2 - 3).$$

To sum up, we shall have

$$x_3{}^* = \max[9, \max(0, x_2 - 3)]; \quad (5.37)$$

that is,

$$x_3{}^* = \max(9, x_2 - 3). \quad (5.38)$$

(*a*) Let us assume that

$$x_2 - 3 \leqslant 9, \quad \text{or} \quad x_2 \leqslant 12; \quad (5.39)$$

then

$$x_3{}^* = 9 \quad (5.40)$$

and

$$f_{2,6}(x_2, 0) = 39 - 13x_2 + 157$$
$$= 196 - 13x_2. \quad (5.41)$$

(*b*) Let us assume, on the contrary, that

$$x_2 - 3 \geqslant 9; \quad (5.42)$$

we then have

$$x_3{}^* = x_2 - 3 \quad (5.43)$$

and

$$f_{2,6}(x_2, 0) = 39 - 13x_2 + 130 + 3x_3{}^*$$
$$= 169 - 13x_2 + 3(x_2 - 3)$$
$$= 160 - 10x_2 . \tag{5.44}$$

Finally, we can say

$$f_{2,6}(x_2, 0) = \max(196 - 13x_2, 160 - 10x_2). \tag{5.45}$$

On the other hand, from (5.31) we have $x_3 \leqslant 13$, so that (5.38) becomes

$$\max(9, x_2 - 3) \leqslant 13, \tag{5.46}$$

whence

$$x_2 \leqslant 16. \tag{5.47}$$

If we now consider (5.33) we must conclude that the relation in it is not modified by (5.47), but $x_2 \leqslant x_3 + 3$ appears in (5.38) and can be suppressed. Hence

$$\max(0, x_1 - 5) \leqslant x_2 \leqslant 15. \tag{5.48}$$

PERIODS 6 TO 2

From (2.10), for $n = 1$:

$$\max(0, x_0 - d_1) \leqslant x_1 \leqslant \min(S - d_1, x_2 + d_2); \tag{5.49}$$

that is,

$$\max(0, 2 - 8) \leqslant x_1 \leqslant \min(12, x_2 + 5), \tag{5.50}$$
$$0 \leqslant x_1 \leqslant \min(12, x_2 + 5). \tag{5.51}$$

The expenditure for periods 6 to 2 will be

$$s_{1,6}(x_1, x_6) = s_{1,6}(x_1, 0)$$
$$= p_2 a_2 + f_{2,6}(x_2, 0)$$
$$= 18(x_2 + 5 - x_1) + \max(196 - 13x_2, 160 - 10x_2). \tag{5.52}$$

Hence the minimal cost will be

$$f_{1,6}(x_1, 0) = \min_{\max(0, x_1 - 5) \leqslant x_2 \leqslant 15} [90 - 18x_1$$
$$+ 18x_2 + \max(196 - 13x_2, 160 - 10x_2)], \tag{5.53}$$

that is,

$$f_{1,6}(x_1, 0) = 90 - 18x_1 + \underset{\max(0, x_1-5) \leqslant x_2 \leqslant 15}{\text{MIN}} [\max(196 + 5x_2, 160 + 8x_2)]. \quad (5.54)$$

If we trace the curves $z_1 = 196 + 5x_2$ and $z_2 = 160 + 8x_2$ in the interval $0 \leqslant x_2 \leqslant 15$, we find that the minimum is obtained for

$$x_2{}^* = \max(0, x_1 - 5). \quad (5.55)$$

(a) Assuming that $x_1 - 5 \leqslant 0$, that is, $x_1 \leqslant 5$, then

$$x_2{}^* = 0$$

and

$$f_{1,6}(x_1, 0) = 90 - 18x_1 + 196 = 286 - 18x_1. \quad (5.56)$$

(b) Assuming, on the contrary, that $x_1 \geqslant 5$, we should have

$$x_2{}^* = x_1 - 5 \quad (5.57)$$

and

$$f_{1,6}(x_1, 0) = 90 - 18x_1 + 196 + 5(x_1 - 5) = 261 - 13x_1. \quad (5.58)$$

Finally, we can say

$$f_{1,6}(x_1, 0) = \max(286 - 18x_1, 261 - 13x_1). \quad (5.59)$$

Also, from (5.48) we have $x_2 \leqslant 15$, so that (5.55) becomes

$$\max(0, x_1 - 5) \leqslant 15, \quad (5.60)$$

whence

$$x_1 \leqslant 20. \quad (5.61)$$

Thus (5.51) is not modified by (5.61), but $x_1 \leqslant x_2 + 5$ appears in (5.55) and can be suppressed:

$$0 \leqslant x_1 \leqslant 12. \quad (5.62)$$

PERIODS 6 TO 1

The expenditure for these six periods will be

$$\begin{aligned} s_{0,6}(x_0, x_6) &= s_{0,6}(2, 0) \\ &= p_1 a_1 + f_{1,6}(x_1, 0) \\ &= 11(x_1 + 8 - 2) + \max(286 - 18x_1, 261 - 13x_1). \quad (5.63) \end{aligned}$$

Hence the minimal cost will be

$$f_{0,6}(2, 0) = \min_{0 \leqslant x_1 \leqslant 12} [66 + 11x_1 + \max(286 - 18x_1, 261 - 13x_1)], \quad (5.64)$$

that is,

$$f_{0,6}(2, 0) = 66 + \min_{0 \leqslant x_1 \leqslant 12} [\max(286 - 7x_1, 261 - 2x_1)]. \quad (5.65)$$

If we trace the curves of $z_1 = 286 - 7x_1$ and $z_2 = 261 - 2x_1$ in the interval $0 \leqslant x_1 \leqslant 12$, the minimum is obtained for

$$x_1^* = 12 \quad (5.66)$$

and we have

$$f_{0.6}(2, 0) = 66 + 237 = 303. \quad (5.67)$$

We can now calculate the optimal values of x_i, y_i, and a_i :

$$
\begin{array}{lll}
x_1^* = 12, & y_1^* = 20, & a_1^* = 18, \\
x_2^* = 7, & y_2^* = 12, & a_2^* = 0, \\
x_3^* = 9, & y_3^* = 12, & a_3^* = 5, \\
x_4^* = 7, & y_4^* = 9, & a_4^* = 0, \\
x_5^* = 0, & y_5^* = 7, & a_5^* = 0, \\
x_6 = 0, & y_6^* = 4, & a_6^* = 4.
\end{array}
\quad (5.68)
$$

As was to be expected, the total optimal expenditure is less than it was for $S = 9$ (303 instead of 357), and in this particular case the results shown in Fig. 5.1 could have been obtained intuitively.

It will be observed that p_6 is the smallest of the p_i terms, and as $x_6 = 0$ we take $x_5^* = 0$. Of the other p_i terms, p_1 is the least; hence the maximum (18) will be bought in period 1 and the remainder (5) in period 3. Nevertheless, this type of reasoning becomes much more subtle in a more complicated case, as we shall now show.

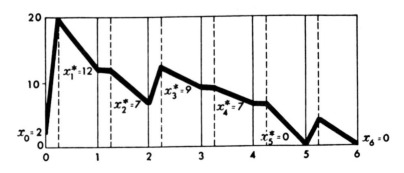

FIG. 5.1

6. A Numerical Example Which Is Nonlinear

In order to render the example which we studied in Sections 2 and 5 less elementary, we shall introduce two modifications, without claiming that even then we will entirely reproduce a practical case. Our aim, however, as already explained, is to familiarize the reader with the methods of dynamic programming and to point out the numerous pitfalls that may be encountered during the calculations.

TABLE 6.1

Period	Purchase price	Selling price
1	4	7
2	6	8
3	15	11
4	3	7
5	2	5
6	9	8

We shall now consider the case of a wholesaler who has periodically to decide not only the quantities he must purchase, but also the amounts which he should sell. In addition, there will be a fixed cost for purchasing, which will be added to the unit purchase price whenever a purchase is made.

Both the purchase and selling prices vary seasonally and are shown in Table 6.1 for the six periods of two months into which we have arbitrarily divided the year. The fixed cost for purchasing is 20 and the stock must never exceed 12 units, while the sales for each period are assumed to take place subsequently to the purchasing in that period. The problem is to find the policy which gives a maximal profit (the difference between the total sales and the total expenditure on purchasing). The initial stock is 10 units and the final stock is to be nil.

In each period there are two decisions to make, but a period may be divided into two fictitious half-periods, one for purchasing and the other for selling. Hence we have a program for 12 semiperiods, but with a single decision (and only one state variable) in each of them.

$S = 12$ upper bound of the stock;

a_n quantity purchased during period n;

$\sigma_n = s_{n-1} + a_n$ stock after purchase a_n (time $n - \frac{1}{2}$);

b_n quantity sold during period n;

$s_n = \sigma_n - b_n$ stock after sale b_n (time n).

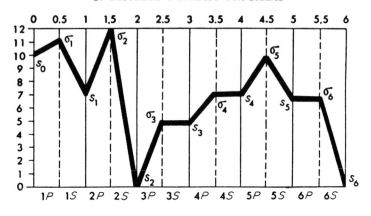

FIG. 6.1

The state variable will be σ_n or s_n, depending on the half-period considered, and we shall begin with period 6. Figure 6.1 shows an arbitrary policy.

The constraints are as follows:

$$0 \leqslant s_n \leqslant S, \qquad n = 0, 1, 2,..., 6;$$
$$0 \leqslant \sigma_n \leqslant S, \qquad n = \quad 1, 2,..., 6;$$
$$s_{n-1} \leqslant \sigma_n, \qquad n = \quad 1, 2,..., 6;$$
$$s_n \leqslant \sigma_n, \qquad n = \quad 1, 2,..., 6.$$

This set can be reduced to the two following:

$$0 \leqslant s_n \leqslant \min[\sigma_n, \sigma_{n+1}], \qquad n = 1, 2,..., 5;$$
$$\max[s_{n-1}, s_n] \leqslant \sigma_n \leqslant S, \qquad n = 1, 2,..., 6.$$

If we use the following notation,

$$\delta(x) = 0 \qquad \text{if} \quad x \leqslant 0,$$
$$= 20 \qquad \text{if} \quad x > 0,$$

then $\delta(a_n)$ represents the cost of filling order a_n for period n.

PERIOD 6. SALES

Let $g_6(\sigma_6)$ be the amount received for period 6:

$$g_6(\sigma_6) = 8b_6 = 8\sigma_6 .$$

For this semiperiod we have

$$\max[s_5, 0] \leqslant \sigma_6 \leqslant 12, \qquad \text{that is,} \quad s_5 \leqslant \sigma_6 \leqslant 12.$$

PERIOD 6. PURCHASES

Let $f_5(s_5)$ represent the profit for period 6 (receipts less expenditure):

$$f_5(s_5) = \max_{s_5 \leqslant \sigma_6 \leqslant 12} [8\sigma_6 - 9(\sigma_6 - s_5) - \delta(\sigma_6 - s_5)]$$

$$= \max_{s_5 \leqslant \sigma_6 \leqslant 12} [-\sigma_6 + 9s_5 - \delta(\sigma_6 - s_5)].$$

We notice that $\delta(x)$ is a nondecreasing function of x, so that $-\delta(\sigma_6 - s_5)$ is a nonincreasing function of σ_6; also, $(-\sigma_6)$ is a decreasing function of σ_6, and the same applies to the expression inside the brackets. Hence the maximum is obtained for $\sigma_6 = s_5$.

For convenience, the results will be entered in the two columns on the right of the following pages.

	Partial results	Final results

Since

$$\sigma_6{}^* = s_5{}^*,$$
$$b_6{}^* = \sigma_6{}^* - s_6{}^*$$
$$= s_5{}^* - 0 = s_5{}^*,$$
$$a_6{}^* = \sigma_6{}^* - s_5{}^* = 0,$$

Partial results:
$$\sigma_6{}^* = s_5{}^*$$
$$b_6{}^* = s_5{}^*$$

Final results:
$$a_6{}^* = 0$$

we therefore have

$$f_5(s_5) = 8s_5.$$

The bounds of s_5 are

$$0 \leqslant s_5 \leqslant \min[\sigma_5, \sigma_6],$$

that is,

$$0 \leqslant s_5 \leqslant \sigma_5.$$

PERIOD 5. S

Let $g_5(\sigma_5)$ be the value in hand before sales b_5:

$$g_5(\sigma_5) = \max_{0 \leqslant s_5 \leqslant \sigma_5} [5(\sigma_5 - s_5) + f_5(s_5)]$$

$$= \max_{0 \leqslant s_5 \leqslant \sigma_5} [5\sigma_5 + 3s_5]$$

$$= 8s_5, \quad \text{with} \quad s_5{}^* = \sigma_5{}^*.$$

Final results:
$$b_5{}^* = 0$$

Partial results:
$$s_5{}^* = \sigma_5{}^*$$
$$\sigma_6{}^* = \sigma_5{}^*$$
$$b_6{}^* = \sigma_5{}^*$$

Partial results	Final results

The bounds of σ_5 are

$$\max[s_4 , s_5] \leqslant \sigma_5 \leqslant 12,$$
$$\max[s_4 , \sigma_5] \leqslant \sigma_5 \leqslant 12,$$
$$s_4 \leqslant \sigma_5 \leqslant 12.$$

PERIOD 5. P

Let $f_4(s_4)$ be the profit for periods 5 and 6:

$$f_4(s_4) = \max_{s_4 \leqslant \sigma_5 \leqslant 12} [-2(\sigma_5 - s_4) + 8\sigma_5 \\ - \delta(\sigma_5 - s_4)]$$

$$= \max_{s_4 \leqslant \sigma_5 \leqslant 12} [2s_4 + 6\sigma_5 \\ - \delta(\sigma_5 - s_4)].$$

The expression enclosed in brackets is an increasing function of σ_5, except for $\sigma_5 = s_4 + 0$ where it makes a jump of -20; hence the maximum corresponds to the highest of the values with the bounds

$$f_4(s_4) = \max_{(\sigma_5 = s_4),(\sigma_5 = 12)} (8s_4 , 52 + 2s_4).$$

The optimal value of σ_5 is shown below the expression corresponding to the maximum. The inequality

$$8s_4 < 52 + 2s_4$$

is equivalent to

$$s_4 < \tfrac{52}{6}.$$

Hence $\sigma_5 = s_4$ if $s_4 \geqslant \tfrac{52}{6}$, and $\sigma_5 = 12$ if $s_4 \leqslant \tfrac{52}{6}$. The bounds of s_4 are

$$0 \leqslant s_4 \leqslant \min(\sigma_4 , \sigma_5).$$

As we have already taken $s_4 \leqslant \sigma_5$ into account, we can express this more simply,

$$0 \leqslant s_4 \leqslant \sigma_4 .$$

if $s_4{}^* \leqslant \tfrac{52}{6}$:

$\sigma_5{}^* = 12$
$s_5{}^* = 12$
$\sigma_6{}^* = 12$
$b_6{}^* = 12$

if $s_4{}^* \geqslant \tfrac{52}{6}$:

$\sigma_5{}^* = s_4{}^*$
$s_5{}^* = s_4{}^*$
$\sigma_6{}^* = s_4{}^*$
$b_6{}^* = s_4{}^*$

	Partial results	Final results

PERIOD 4. S

Still using the same notation:

$$g_4(\sigma_4) = \underset{0 \leqslant s_4 \leqslant \sigma_4}{\text{MAX}} [7(\sigma_4 - s_4) + f_4(s_4)]$$

$$= \text{MAX}[7\sigma_4 - 7s_4 + \max(8s_4, 52 + 2s_4)]$$

$$= 7\sigma_4 + \underset{0 \leqslant s_4 \leqslant \sigma_4}{\text{MAX}} [\max(s_4, 52 - 5s_4)]$$

$$= 7\sigma_4 + \max_{} [\underset{0 \leqslant s_4 \leqslant \sigma_4}{\text{MAX}} (s_4),$$

$$\underset{0 \leqslant s_4 \leqslant \sigma_4}{\text{MAX}} (52 - 5s_4)]$$

$$= 7\sigma_4 + \max[\underset{(s_4=\sigma_4)}{\sigma_4}, \underset{(s_4=0)}{52}].$$

Taking account, in advance, of the constraint $\sigma_4 \leqslant 12$, we obtain

$$g_4(\sigma_4) = 52 + 7\sigma_4,$$

with

$$s_4{}^* = 0 \quad \text{whence} \quad a_5{}^* = \sigma_5{}^* = 12.$$

The bounds of σ_4 are

$$\max(s_3, s_4) \leqslant \sigma_4 \leqslant 12,$$
$$s_3 \leqslant \sigma_4 \leqslant 12.$$

(Final results column:)
$s_4{}^* = 0$
$a_5{}^* = 12$
$\sigma_5{}^* = 12$
$s_5{}^* = 12$
$\sigma_6{}^* = 12$
$b_6{}^* = 12$

PERIOD 4. P

$$f_3(s_3) = \underset{s_3 \leqslant \sigma_4 \leqslant 12}{\text{MAX}} [-3(\sigma_4 - s_3) + g_4(\sigma_4)$$

$$-\delta(\sigma_4 - s_3)]$$

$$= \underset{s_3 \leqslant \sigma_4 \leqslant 12}{\text{MAX}} [-3\sigma_4 + 3s_3 + 7\sigma_4 + 52$$

$$- \delta(\sigma_4 - s_3)]$$

$$= \underset{s_3 \leqslant \sigma_4 \leqslant 12}{\text{MAX}} [3s_3 + 4\sigma_4 + 52$$

$$- \delta(\sigma_4 - s_3)].$$

(Partial results column:)
if $s_3{}^* \leqslant 7$:
$\sigma_4 = 12$
$b_4{}^* = 12$
$a_4{}^* = 12$
$\quad -s_3{}^*$
if $s_3{}^* \geqslant 7$:
$\sigma_4{}^* = s_3{}^*$
$b_4{}^* = s_3{}^*$
$a_4{}^* = 0$

By the same method as for period 5 P, we find

$$f_3(s_3) = \max[7s_3 + 52, 3s_3 + 80],$$

	Partial results	Final results

with

$$\sigma_4{}^* = s_3{}^* \quad \text{if} \quad s_3 \geqslant 7$$

and

$$\sigma_4{}^* = 12 \quad \text{if} \quad s_3 \leqslant 7.$$

From this we deduce the values of

$$b_4{}^* = \sigma_4{}^* - s_4{}^* = \sigma_4{}^* \quad \text{and} \quad a_4{}^* = \sigma_4{}^* - s_3{}^*.$$

The bounds of s_3 are

$$0 \leqslant s_3 \leqslant \min[\sigma_3, \sigma_4],$$
$$0 \leqslant s_3 \leqslant \min[\sigma_3, 12],$$
$$0 \leqslant s_3 \leqslant \sigma_3.$$

PERIOD 3. S

$$
\begin{aligned}
g_3(\sigma_3) &= \max_{0 \leqslant s_3 \leqslant \sigma_3} [11(\sigma_3 - s_3) + f_3(s_3)] \\
&= \max_{0 \leqslant s_3 \leqslant \sigma_3} [11\sigma_3 - 11s_3 \\
&\qquad + \max(7s_3 + 52, 3s_3 + 80)] \\
&= 11\sigma_3 + \max[\max_{0 \leqslant s_3 \leqslant \sigma_3} (52 - 4s_3), \\
&\qquad\qquad \max_{0 \leqslant s_3 \leqslant \sigma_3} (80 - 8s_3)] \\
&= 11\sigma_3 + \max(52, 80) \\
&= 11\sigma_3 + 80 \quad \text{with} \quad s_3{}^* = 0.
\end{aligned}
$$

The bounds of σ_3 are

$$\max[s_2, s_3] \leqslant \sigma_3 \leqslant 12,$$
$$\max[s_2, 0] \leqslant \sigma_3 \leqslant 12,$$
$$s_2 \leqslant \sigma_3 \leqslant 12.$$

PERIOD 3. P

$$
\begin{aligned}
f_2(s_2) &= \max_{s_2 \leqslant \sigma_3 \leqslant 12} [-15(\sigma_3 - s_2) + g_3(\sigma_3) \\
&\qquad\qquad - \delta(\sigma_3 - s_2)] \\
&= \max_{s_2 \leqslant \sigma_3 \leqslant 12} [-15\sigma_3 + 15s_2 + 11\sigma_3 \\
&\qquad\qquad + 80 - \delta(\sigma_3 - s_2)] \\
&= \max_{s_2 \leqslant \sigma_3 \leqslant 12} [15s_2 - 4\sigma_3 + 80 \\
&\qquad\qquad - \delta(\sigma_3 - s_2)] \\
&= 11s_2 + 80, \quad \text{with} \quad \sigma_3{}^* = s_2,
\end{aligned}
$$

Partial results column:

$s_3{}^* = 0$

$\sigma_4{}^* = 12$

$b_4{}^* = 12$

$a_4{}^* = 12$

$\sigma_3{}^* = s_2$

Final results column:

$a_3{}^* = 0$

	Partial results	Final results

whence

$$a_3{}^* = \sigma_3{}^* - s_3{}^* = 0,$$
$$b_3{}^* = \sigma_3{}^* - s_3{}^* = \sigma_3{}^* - 0 = \sigma_3{}^* = s_2 .$$

The bounds of s_2 are

$$0 \leqslant s_2 \leqslant \min[\sigma_2 , \sigma_3],$$
$$0 \leqslant s_2 \leqslant \min[\sigma_2 , s_2],$$
$$0 \leqslant s_2 \leqslant \sigma_2 .$$

PERIOD 2. S

$$g_2(\sigma_2) = \max_{0 \leqslant s_2 \leqslant \sigma_2} [8(\sigma_2 - s_2) + f_2(s_2)]$$
$$= \max_{0 \leqslant s_2 \leqslant \sigma_2} [8\sigma_2 - 8s_2 + 11s_2 + 80]$$
$$= \max_{0 \leqslant s_2 \leqslant \sigma_2} [8\sigma_2 + 3s_2 + 80]$$
$$= 11\sigma_2 + 80 \quad \text{with} \quad s_2{}^* = \sigma_2 ,$$

whence

$$b_2{}^* = \sigma_2{}^* - s_2 = 0.$$

The bounds of σ_2 are

$$\max[s_1 , s_2] \leqslant \sigma_2 \leqslant 12,$$
$$\max[s_1 , \sigma_2] \leqslant \sigma_2 \leqslant 12,$$
$$s_1 \leqslant \sigma_2 \leqslant 12.$$

PERIOD 2. P

$$f_1(s_1) = \max_{s_1 \leqslant \sigma_2 \leqslant 12} [-6(\sigma_2 - s_1) + g_2(\sigma_2)$$
$$- \delta(\sigma_2 - s_1)]$$
$$= \max_{s_1 \leqslant \sigma_2 \leqslant 12} [-6\sigma_2 + 6s_1 + 11\sigma_2 + 80$$
$$- \delta(\sigma_2 - s_1)]$$
$$= \max_{s_1 \leqslant \sigma_2 \leqslant 12} [6s_1 + 5\sigma_2 + 80$$
$$- \delta(\sigma_2 - s_1)]$$
$$= \max[11s_1 + 80, 6s_1 + 120],$$

with

$$\sigma_2{}^* = 12 \quad \text{if} \quad s_1 \leqslant 8,$$
$$\sigma_2{}^* = s_1 \quad \text{if} \quad s_1 \geqslant 8,$$

Side column (Partial results / Final results):

$b_3{}^* = s_2$

$s_2{}^* = \sigma_2$

$\sigma_3{}^* = \sigma_2$ $b_2{}^* = 0$

$b_3{}^* = \sigma_2$

if $s_1 \leqslant 8$:

$\sigma_2{}^* = 12$

$s_2{}^* = 12$

$\sigma_3{}^* = 12$

$b_3{}^* = 12$

$a_2{}^* = 12 - s_1$

if $s_1 \geqslant 8$:

$\sigma_2 = s_1$

$s_2{}^* = s_1$

$\sigma_3{}^* = s_1$

$b_3{}^* = s_1$

	Partial results	Final results

whence we deduce

$$a_2{}^* = \sigma_2 - s_1 .$$
$$b_2{}^* = \sigma_2 - s_3 .$$

The bounds of s_1 are

$$0 \leqslant s_1 \leqslant \min[\sigma_1 , \sigma_2],$$
$$0 \leqslant s_1 \leqslant \sigma_1 .$$

PERIOD 1. S

$$g_1(\sigma_1) = \underset{0 \leqslant s_1 \leqslant \sigma_1}{\text{MAX}} [7(\sigma_1 - s_1) + f_1(s_1)]$$
$$= \underset{0 \leqslant s_1 \leqslant \sigma_1}{\text{MAX}} [7\sigma_1 - 7s_1$$
$$+ \max(11s_1 + 80, 6s_1 + 120)]$$
$$= 7\sigma_1 + \max[\underset{0 \leqslant s_1 \leqslant \sigma_1}{\text{MAX}} (11s_1 + 80),$$
$$\underset{0 \leqslant s_1 \leqslant \sigma_1}{\text{MAX}} (6s_1 + 120)]$$
$$= 7\sigma_1 + \max[4\sigma_1 + 80, 120]$$
$$= \max[11\sigma_1 + 80, 7\sigma_1 + 120],$$

with

$$s_1 = \sigma_1 \quad \text{if} \quad \sigma_1 \geqslant 10,$$
$$s_1 = 0 \quad \text{if} \quad \sigma_1 \leqslant 10.$$

The bounds of σ_1 are

$$\max[s_0 , s_1] \leqslant \sigma_1 \leqslant 12,$$
$$\max[10, s_1] \leqslant \sigma_1 \leqslant 12$$

($s_0 = 10$ by assumption). Since we have already taken into account the condition $s_1 \leqslant \sigma_1$, we can say

$$10 \leqslant \sigma_1 \leqslant 12.$$

PERIOD 1. P

$$f_0(10) = \underset{10 \leqslant \sigma_1 \leqslant 12}{\text{MAX}} [-4(\sigma_1 - 10)$$
$$+ g_1(\sigma_1) - \delta(\sigma_1 - 10)]$$
$$= \underset{10 \leqslant \sigma_1 \leqslant 12}{\text{MAX}} [-4\sigma_1 + 40 + \max(11\sigma_1$$
$$+ 80, 7\sigma_1 + 120) - \delta(\sigma_1 - 10)]$$

Partial results:

$a_2{}^* = 0$

if $\sigma_1{}^* \leqslant 10$:

$s_1{}^* = 0$
$\sigma_2{}^* = 12$
$s_2{}^* = 12$
$\sigma_3{}^* = 12$
$b_3{}^* = 12$
$a_2{}^* = 12$

if $\sigma_1 \geqslant 10$:

$s_1{}^* = \sigma_1$
$\sigma_2{}^* = \sigma_1$
$s_2{}^* = \sigma_1$
$\sigma_3{}^* = \sigma_1$
$b_3{}^* = \sigma_1$
$a_2{}^* = 0$
$b_1{}^* = 0$

Final results:

$\sigma_1{}^* = 10$

(1)

$s_1{}^* = 10$

$\sigma_2{}^* = 10$

	Partial results	Final results

$$= \max\{ \underset{10 \leqslant \sigma_1 \leqslant 12}{\text{MAX}}[7\sigma_1 + 120$$
$$- \delta(\sigma_1 - 10)],$$

$s_2{}^* = 10$

$$\underset{10 \leqslant \sigma_1 \leqslant 12}{\text{MAX}}[3\sigma_1 + 160 - \delta(\sigma_1 - 10)]\}$$

$\sigma_3{}^* = 10$

$$= \max\{\underset{(\sigma_1=10)}{\max}\,(190\,,\,\underset{(\sigma_1=12)}{184})\,,$$

$b_3{}^* = 10$

$$\underset{(\sigma_1=10)}{\max}\,(190\,,\,\underset{(\sigma_1=12)}{176})\}$$

$a_2{}^* = 0$

$$= 190,$$

$b_1{}^* = 0$

with $\sigma_1{}^* = 10$; but the maximum can be obtained either by using the first expression of $g_1(\sigma_1)$, which corresponds to $s_1{}^* = \sigma_1{}^* = 10$, or the second, which corresponds to $s_1{}^* = 0$. Thus, we finally obtain two optimal policies which are given in the right-hand column and are shown in Figs. 6.2 and 6.3.

(2)
$s_1{}^* = 0$
$\sigma_2{}^* = 12$
$s_2{}^* = 12$
$\sigma_3{}^* = 12$
$b_3{}^* = 12$
$a_2{}^* = 12$

We can easily check the value of f_0 which we have found. Using policy 1, we have

$$f_0(10) = 10 \times 11 - 12 \times 3 - 20 + 12 \times 7 - 12 \times 2 - 20 + 12 \times 8$$

$$= 110 - 36 - 20 + 84 - 24 + 20 + 96 = 190.$$

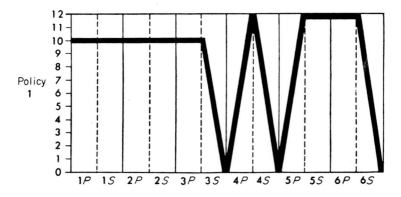

FIG. 6.2

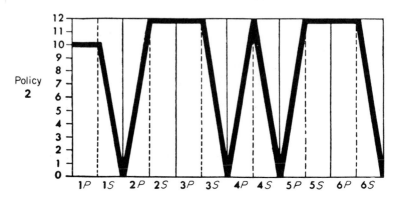

FIG. 6.3

Using policy 2,

$$f_0(10) = 10 \times 7 - 12 \times 6 - 20 + 12 \times 11 - 12 \times 3 - 20 + 12 \times 7$$
$$- 12 \times 2 - 20 + 12 \times 8$$
$$= 70 - 72 - 20 + 132 - 36 - 20 + 84 - 24 - 20 + 96 = 190.$$

7. The Case where the Decision Variable Has More Dimensions than the State Variable

In Section 3 we stated that the state variable may have more components than the decision variable. We shall now see that the opposite condition may exist, but that the number of components in the decision variable can then be reduced by solving "subprograms" of the main dynamic program.

To show that such a case may occur, let us consider a dynamic program in which a scalar x_n is both the decision and state variable. The set of periods n and $n + 1$ can be considered as a single period $[n, n + 1]$, at the end of which the state variable is x_{n+1}, since the constraints of period $n + 2$ and the value of the decision in it only depend on x_{n+1}. But in this double period, the decision variable is (x_n, x_{n+1}) and has two components.

In the example in Section 6, let us consider the two half-periods which, by a concession to the convention of Section 3 that will now appear very natural, we agreed to call a period. For this period throughout the program, the state variable is s_n, but the decision variable (σ_n, s_n) has two dimensions.

In a more general form, we may consider a program in which:

(a) The constraints linking periods $(n - 1)$ and n are of the form

$$y_n \in \Delta_n x_{n-1} \tag{7.1}$$

and

$$x_n = \Omega_n(x_{n-1}, y_n), \tag{7.2}$$

where $\Delta_n x_{n-1}$ is a correspondence (not usually univocal) of the set $\mathbf{X}_{n-1}$ of the states at time $n - 1$ with set $\mathbf{Y}_n$ of the decisions of period n, and where $\Omega_n(x_{n-1}, y_n)$ is a univocal correspondence of the set $\mathbf{X}_{n-1} \times \mathbf{Y}_n$ with $\mathbf{X}_n$.

These constraints can also be expressed in the form

$$x_n \in \Gamma_n' x_{n-1} \quad \text{and} \quad y_n \in \Gamma_n''(x_{n-1}, x_n), \tag{7.3}$$

where $\Gamma_n' x_{n-1}$ is the reunion of the sets $\Omega_n(x_{n-1}, y_n)$ corresponding to the possible decisions $y_n \in \Delta_n x_{n-1}$, and where $\Gamma_n''(x_{n-1}, x_n)$ is the set of the decisions which lead to the state x_n :

$$\Gamma_n''(x_{n-1}, x_n) = \{ y_n \mid y_n \in \Delta_n x_{n-1}, \ \Omega_n(x_{n-1}, y_n) = x_n \}.$$

(b) The present value of period n is

$$v_n(x_{n-1}, y_n). \tag{7.4}$$

It should be observed that the choice of y_n determines x_n, but that several vectors y_n may give the same value for x_n but different values for v_n. It is clear that in such a problem we can use the model in Section 3 by finding the quantities

$$v_n'(x_{n-1}, x_n) = \operatorname*{OPT}_{y_n \in \Gamma_n''(x_{n-1}, x_n)} v_n(x_{n-1}, y_n), \tag{7.5}$$

which represent the optimal value for the period, with x_{n-1} and x_n given. The program defined for $\Gamma_n' x_{n-1}$ and $v_n'(x_{n-1}, x_n)$ is then a dynamic program in the sense of Section 3. The method of optimization used to solve (7.5) clearly depends on the form of the function v_n, and a linear program could be used advantageously if the form of (7.5) is suitable. To take an example, the study of national planning may lead, with certain assumptions, to this type of model in which a sequence of annual plans, each containing the solution of a linear program, is coordinated by dynamic programming,[18] the state variable summing up the objectives of the plan.

[18] Actually, in such a case it would be advisable to use dynamic programs with adaptation, a subject which will be treated in a second volume to be published by Dunod, Paris.

For us the most interesting case is the one where the subprograms to be solved are themselves dynamic programs, a condition which must exist if two or more periods are combined in a dynamic program. The solution of the subprogram (7.5) then consists of finding the optimal subpolicy from x_{n-1} to x_n of the initial program. It is sometimes useful to make such a decomposition, as we shall now discover by resuming the example given in Section 6.

Let us first consider the case where there is a zero fixed cost. A subpolicy from s_{n-1} to s_n (where these are given) is characterized by the value σ_n submitted to the constraint

$$\max(s_{n-1}, s_n) \leqslant \sigma_n \leqslant S. \tag{7.6}$$

If p_n and q_n are the purchase and selling prices for period n, the value of a subpolicy will be

$$v_{n-1}(s_{n-1}, \sigma_n, s_n) = -p_n \cdot (\sigma_n - s_{n-1}) + q_n \cdot (\sigma_n - s_n)$$
$$= p_n s_{n-1} - q_n s_n + (q_n - p_n) s_n. \tag{7.7}$$

The value of the optimal subpolicy will be

$$v_{n-1,n}^*(s_{n-1}, s_n) = \underset{\max(s_{n-1}, s_n) \leqslant \sigma_n \leqslant S}{\mathrm{MAX}} [p_n s_{n-1} - q_n s_n + (q_n - p_n)\sigma_n]. \tag{7.8}$$

(a) If $q_n \geqslant p_n$, we shall have

$$v_{n-1,n}^*(s_{n-1}, s_n) = p_n s_{n-1} - q_n s_n + (q_n - p_n) s_n, \tag{7.9}$$

with

$$\sigma_n{}^* = S. \tag{7.10}$$

(b) If, on the other hand, $q_n \leqslant p_n$, we shall have

$$v_{n-1,n}^*(s_{n-1}, s_n) = p_n s_{n-1} - q_n s_n + (q_n - p_n)[\max(s_{n-1}, s_n)], \tag{7.11}$$

with

$$\sigma_n{}^* = \max(s_{n-1}, s_n). \tag{7.12}$$

Figure 7.1 shows the four possible cases, and also the optimal policies which could, actually, have been found by intuition.

The case where the fixed purchasing cost is not zero is treated in the same way, and we then have

$$v_{n-1,n}(s_{n-1}, s_n) = \underset{\max(s_{n-1}, s_n) \leqslant \sigma_n \leqslant S}{\mathrm{MAX}} [p_n s_{n-1} - q_n s_n + (q_n - p_n)\sigma_n - \delta(\sigma_n - s_{n-1})]. \tag{7.13}$$

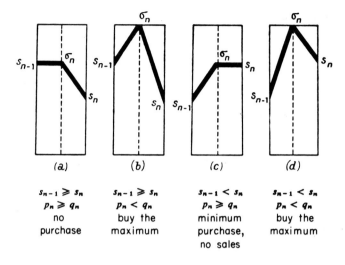

FIG. 7.1

(*a*) If $q_n \leqslant p_n$, the maximum takes place for $\sigma_n = \max(s_{n-1}, s_n)$:

$$\sigma_n^* = s_n \quad \text{and} \quad v_{n-1,n}^*(s_{n-1}, s_n) = p_n(s_{n-1} - s_n) - \delta(>0), \quad \text{if } s_{n-1} < s_n ,$$
(7.14)

$$\sigma_n^* = s_{n-1} \quad \text{and} \quad v_{n-1,n}^*(s_{n-1}, s_n) = q_n(s_{n-1} - s_n), \quad \text{if } s_{n-1} \geqslant s_n \quad (7.15)$$

(taking $\delta(>0)$ for the fixed cost of purchasing).

(*b*) If $q_n \geqslant p_n$, we must compare the values obtained for

$$\sigma_n = \max(s_{n-1}, s_n) \quad \text{and for} \quad \sigma_n = S;$$

(*b*₁) If $s_{n-1} < s_n$, we have

for $\sigma_n = s_n$,

$$v_{n-1,n}(s_{n-1}, s_n, s_n) = p_n(s_{n-1} - s_n) - \delta(> 0);$$

for $\sigma_n = S$,

$$v_{n-1,n}(s_{n-1}, S, s_n) = p_n s_{n-1} - q_n s_n + (q_n - p_n)S - \delta(> 0).$$

The first expression is less than or equal to the second if

$$-p_n s_n \leqslant -q_n s_n + (q_n - p_n)S$$

or

$$s_n \leqslant S,$$

which is always satisfied. Hence we shall find

$$v^*_{n-1,n}(s_{n-1}, s_n) = p_n s_{n-1} - q_n s_n + (q_n - p_n)S - \delta(> 0), \qquad (7.16)$$

with

$$\sigma_n{}^* = S.$$

(b_2) If $s_{n-1} \geqslant s_n$, we have

for $\sigma_n = s_{n-1}$,

$$v_{n-1,n}(s_{n-1}, s_{n-1}, s_n) = q_n(s_{n-1} - s_n);$$

for $\sigma_n = S$,

$$v_{n-1,n}(s_{n-1}, S, s_n) = p_n s_{n-1} - q_n s_n + (q_n - p_n)S - \delta(> 0).$$

The first expression is less than or equal to the second if

$$q_n s_{n-1} \leqslant p_n s_{n-1} + (q_n - p_n)S - \delta(> 0)$$

or

$$\delta(> 0) \leqslant (q_n - p_n)(S - s_{n-1}).$$

Hence we shall have

$$\sigma_n{}^* = S \quad \text{and} \quad v^*_{n-1,n}(s_{n-1}, s_n) = p_n s_{n-1} - q_n s_n + (q_n - p_n)S - \delta(> 0) \quad (7.17)$$

if $\delta(> 0) \leqslant (q_n - p_n)(S - s_{n-1})$;

$$\sigma_n{}^* = s_{n-1} \quad \text{and} \quad v^*_{n-1,n}(s_{n-1}, s_n) = q_n(s_{n-1} - s_n) \qquad (7.18)$$

if $\delta(> 0) \geqslant (q_n - p_n)(S - s_{n-1})$.

Figure 7.2 shows the four possible cases and the optimal subpolicies with the numerical values of Section 6, that is, $S = 12$ and $\delta(>0) = 20$.

If we now assume

$$\Gamma s_{n-1} = \{s_n \mid 0 \leqslant s_n \leqslant S\} \qquad (7.19)$$

and

$$v_n{}'(s_{n-1}, s_n) = v^*_{n-1,n}(s_{n-1}, s_n), \qquad (7.20)$$

where $v^*_{n-1,n}$ is given, according to the case, by (7.14) to (7.17) or (7.18), we are led to the dynamic program defined by the constraints (7.19) and the values (7.20) in which there are only six periods.

To show the comparison between this method and that of Section 6, we shall again commence with period 6, and as the constraints (7.19) are always the same, they will not be given each time.

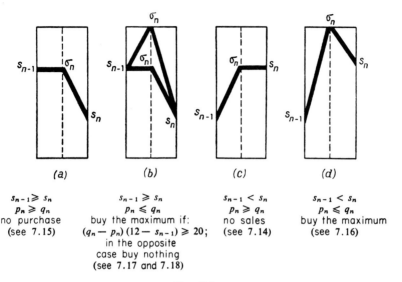

σ_n

s_{n-1} σ_n s_n

(a)

$s_{n-1} \geqslant s_n$
$p_n \geqslant q_n$
no purchase
(see 7.15)

(b)

$s_{n-1} \geqslant s_n$
$p_n \leqslant q_n$
buy the maximum if:
$(q_n - p_n)(12 - s_{n-1}) \geqslant 20$;
in the opposite
case buy nothing
(see 7.17 and 7.18)

(c)

$s_{n-1} < s_n$
$p_n \geqslant q_n$
no sales
(see 7.14)

(d)

$s_{n-1} < s_n$
$p_n \leqslant q_n$
buy the maximum
(see 7.16)

FIG. 7.2

PERIOD 6

Since $s_6 = 0$, we must have $s_5 \geqslant s_6$; also $p_6 > q_6$. Hence we are in case (a) of Fig. 7.2, and in accordance with (7.15) we have

$$\sigma_6{}^* = s_5 \quad \text{and} \quad v_6{}'(s_5 , 0) = 8(s_5 - 0) = 8s_5 .$$

Hence the profit for period 6 is

$$f_5(s_5) = 8s_5 .$$

PERIOD 5

We have $p_5 < q_5$, so that it is either a case of (b) or (d) of Fig. 7.2; in the case of (b) we must compare $\delta(>0) = 20$ and

$$(q_5 - p_5)(S - s_4) = 3(12 - s_4).$$

Hence, for $v_5{}'(s_4 - s_5)$ we have the following expressions

case (b)
$\begin{cases} s_5 \leqslant s_4 \leqslant \frac{16}{3}, & v_5{}'(s_4 , s_5) = 2s_4 - 5s_5 + 16, & \text{with} \quad \sigma_5{}^* = 12; \\ s_5 \leqslant s_4 \text{ and } \frac{16}{3} \leqslant s_4 , & v_5{}'(s_4 , s_5) = 5(s_4 - s_5), & \text{with} \quad \sigma_5{}^* = s_4 ; \end{cases}$

case (d): $s_5 > s_4 , \quad v_5{}'(s_4 , s_5) = 2s_4 - 5s_5 + 16, \qquad\qquad \text{with} \quad \sigma_5{}^* = 12.$

Hence, the maximal profit for periods 5 and 6 will be

$$s_4 \leqslant \tfrac{16}{3}, \quad f_4(s_4) = \underset{0 \leqslant s_5 \leqslant 12}{\text{MAX}}[2s_4 - 5s_5 + 16 + 8s_5]$$
$$= 2s_4 + 52, \quad \text{with} \quad s_5{}^* = 12;$$

$$s_4 \geqslant \tfrac{16}{3}, \quad f_4(s_4) = \max\{\underset{0 \leqslant s_5 \leqslant s_4}{\text{MAX}}[5(s_4 - s_5) + 8s_5],$$

$$\underset{0 \leqslant s_5 \leqslant s_4}{\text{MAX}}[2s_4 - 5s_5 + 16 + 8s_5]\}$$

$$= \max[\underset{(s_5{}^*=s_4)}{8s_4}, \underset{(s_5{}^*=12)}{2s_4 + 52}].$$

For $s_4 \leqslant \tfrac{16}{3}$, we have

$$2s_4 + 52 > 8s_4;$$

hence, whatever the value of s_4, we can say

$$f_4(s_4) = \max[\underset{s_5{}^*=s_4}{8s_4}, \underset{s_5{}^*=12}{2s_4 + 25}].$$

PERIOD 4

Here also $p_4 < q_4$; for case (b) we must compare $\delta(>0) = 20$ with $(q_4 - p_4)(S - s_3) = 4(12 - s_3)$. Whence

$$\text{case (b)} \begin{cases} s_4 \leqslant s_3 \leqslant 7, & v_4'(s_3, s_4) = 3s_3 - 7s_4 + 28, & \text{with } \sigma_4{}^* = 12, \\ s_4 \leqslant s_3 \geqslant 7, & v_4'(s_3, s_4) = 7(s_3 - s_4), & \text{with } \sigma_4{}^* = s_3; \end{cases}$$

$$\text{case (d):} \ s_4 > s_3, \quad v_4'(s_3, s_4) = 3s_3 - 7s_4 + 28, \quad \text{with } \sigma_4{}^* = 12.$$

From this we deduce

$$s_3 \leqslant 7: \ f_3(s_3) = \underset{0 \leqslant s_4 \leqslant 12}{\text{MAX}}[3s_3 - 7s_4 + 28 + \max(8s_4, 2s_4 + 52)]$$

$$= 3s_3 + 28 + \underset{0 \leqslant s_4 \leqslant 12}{\text{MAX}}[\max(s_4, 52 - 5s_4)]$$

$$= 3s_3 + 28 + \max[\underset{(s_4{}^*=12)}{12}, \underset{(s_4{}^*=0)}{52}]$$

$$= 3s_3 + 80, \quad \text{with} \quad s_4{}^* = 0.$$

$$s_3 \geqslant 7: \ f_3(s_3) = \max\{\underset{0 \leqslant s_4 \leqslant s_3}{\text{MAX}}[7s_3 - 7s_4 + \max(8s_4, 2s_4 + 52)],$$

$$\underset{0 \leqslant s_4 \leqslant s_3}{\text{MAX}}[3s_3 - 7s_4 + 28 + \max(8s_4, 2s_4 + 52)]\}$$

$$= \max[\underset{0 \leqslant s_4 \leqslant s_3}{\text{MAX}}(7s_3 + s_4), \underset{0 \leqslant s_4 \leqslant s_3}{\text{MAX}}(7s_3 - 5s_4 + 52),$$

$$\underset{0 \leqslant s_4 \leqslant s_3}{\text{MAX}}(3s_3 + s_4 + 28), \underset{0 \leqslant s_4 \leqslant s_3}{\text{MAX}}(3s_3 - 5s_4 + 80)]$$

$$= \max[\underset{(s_4{}^*=s_3)}{8s_3}, \underset{(s_4{}^*=0)}{7s_3 + 52}, \underset{(s_4{}^*=12)}{3s_3 + 40}, \underset{(s_4{}^*=s_3)}{80 - 2s_3}]$$

$$= 7s_3 + 52, \quad \text{with} \quad s_4{}^* = 0.$$

We can combine the two expressions of $f_3(s_3)$ into a single one:

$$f_3(s_3) = \max[7s_3 + 52, 3s_3 + 80],$$

with $s_4{}^* = 0$ in both cases.

PERIOD 3

We have $p_3 > q_3$, hence case (a) or (c), Fig. 7.2. If

$$s_2 \geqslant s_3, \qquad \sigma_3{}^* = s_2 \quad \text{and} \quad v_3'(s_2, s_3) = 11(s_2 - s_3);$$

$$s_2 \leqslant s_3, \qquad \sigma_3{}^* = s_3 \quad \text{and} \quad v_3'(s_2, s_3) = 15(s_2 - s_3) - 20;$$

whence

$$f_2(s_2) = \max\{\ \underset{0 \leqslant s_3 \leqslant s_2}{\text{MAX}} [11s_2 - 11s_3 + \max(7s_3 + 52, 3s_3 + 80)],$$

$$\underset{0 \leqslant s_3 \leqslant s_2}{\text{MAX}} [15s_2 - 15s_3 - 20 + \max(7s_3 + 52, 3s_3 + 80)]\}$$

$$= \max[\ \underset{0 \leqslant s_3 \leqslant s_2}{\text{MAX}} (11s_2 - 4s_3 + 52), \ \underset{0 \leqslant s_3 \leqslant s_2}{\text{MAX}} (11s_2 - 8s_3 + 80),$$

$$\underset{0 \leqslant s_3 \leqslant s_2}{\text{MAX}} (15s_2 - 8s_3 + 32), \ \underset{0 \leqslant s_3 \leqslant s_2}{\text{MAX}} (15s_2 - 12s_3 + 60)]$$

$$= \max[\underset{(s_3{}^*=0)}{11s_2 + 52}, \ \underset{(s_3{}^*=0)}{11s_2 + 80}, \ \underset{(s_3{}^*=s_2)}{7s_2 + 32}, \ \underset{(s_3{}^*=s_2)}{3s_2 + 60}]$$

$$= 11s_2 + 80, \qquad \text{with} \quad s_3{}^* = 0.$$

PERIOD 2

For $p_2 < q_2$ (case (b) or (d)) we have

$$(q_2 - p_2)(12 - s_1) = 24 - 2s_1.$$

(b): $\begin{cases} s_2 \leqslant s_1 \leqslant 2, \\ s_2 \leqslant s_1 \quad \text{and} \quad 2 - s_1, \end{cases}$ $\quad \sigma_2{}^* = 12 \quad \text{and} \quad v_2'(s_1, s_2) = 6s_1 - 8s_2 + 4;$ $\quad \sigma_2{}^* = s_1 \quad \text{and} \quad v_2'(s_1, s_2) = 8(s_1 - s_2);$

(d): $s_2 > s_1, \qquad \sigma_2{}^* = 12 \quad \text{and} \quad v_2'(s_1, s_2) = 6s_1 - 8s_2 + 4.$

From this we deduce

$$s_1 \leqslant 2: \ f_1(s_1) = \underset{0 \leqslant s_2 \leqslant 12}{\text{MAX}} [6s_1 - 8s_1 + 4 + 11s_2 + 80]$$

$$= 6s_1 + 120, \qquad \text{with} \quad s_2{}^* = 12;$$

$$s_1 \geqslant 2: \ f_1(s_1) = \max\{\ \underset{0 \leqslant s_2 \leqslant s_1}{\text{MAX}} (8s_1 - 8s_2 + 11s_2 + 80),$$

$$\underset{0 \leqslant s_2 \leqslant s_1}{\text{MAX}} (8s_1 - 8s_2 + 4 + 11s_2 + 80)\}$$

$$= \max[\underset{(s_2{}^*=s_1)}{11s_1 + 80}, \ \underset{(s_2{}^*=12)}{6s_1 + 120}].$$

In both cases we have

$$f_1(s_1) = \max_{\substack{(s_2{}^*=s_1) \\ }}[11s_1 + 80, \underset{(s_2{}^*=12)}{6s_1 + 120}].$$

PERIOD 1

$p_1 < q_1$ (case (b) or (d)).
$(q_1 - p_1)(12 - s_0) = 6$ (taking account of the given $s_0 = 10$).
   Since $\delta(>0) > 6$, we apply formula (7.18) in case (b):

$s_1 \leqslant 10$: $\sigma_1{}^* = 10$ and $v_1'(s_0, s_1) = 7(10 - s_1) = 70 - 7s_1$;

$s_1 > 10$: $\sigma_1{}^* = 12$ and $v_1'(s_0, s_1) = 40 - 7s_1 + 16 = 56 - 7s_1$.

Hence we have

$$f_0(10) = \max\{\underset{0 \leqslant s_1 \leqslant 10}{\mathrm{MAX}}[70 - 7s_1 + \max(11s_1 + 80, 6s_1 + 120)],$$

$$\underset{10 \leqslant s_1 \leqslant 12}{\mathrm{MAX}}[56 - 7s_1 + \max(11s_1 + 80, 6s_1 + 120)]$$

$$= \max[\underset{0 \leqslant s_1 \leqslant 10}{\mathrm{MAX}}(150 + 4s_1), \underset{0 \leqslant s_1 \leqslant 10}{\mathrm{MAX}}(170 - s_1),$$

$$\underset{10 \leqslant s_1 \leqslant 12}{\mathrm{MAX}}(136 + 4s_1), \underset{10 \leqslant s_1 \leqslant 12}{\mathrm{MAX}}(176 - s_1)]$$

$$= \max[\underset{(s_1{}^*=10)}{190}, \underset{(s_1{}^*=0)}{190}, \underset{(s_1{}^*=12)}{184}, \underset{(s_1{}^*=10)}{166}]$$

$$= 190, \quad \text{with} \quad s_1{}^* = 10 \quad \text{or} \quad s_1{}^* = 0.$$

   Thus, we have again found the same optimal policies as those obtained in Section 6, and though there is little difference in the length of the calculations, the present method possesses two advantages:

   (1) The fact that the optimal subpolicy for one period applies to all the periods means that this method is somewhat the shorter when there is a larger number of periods.

   (2) The reasons for making the choices are shown more clearly once the internal mechanism for each period has been established.

8. Case where the Final and Initial States Are Not Both Prescribed

   So far we have considered problems in which both the initial and final states x_0 and x_N were given, and in order to find the optimal policies we have had to obtain optimal subpolicies from x_i to x_j ($i, j = 1, 2,..., N$; $i < j$).

We shall now consider the case where either the initial or final state (or both) is indeterminate. Let us assume that x_0, for instance, is given and that we wish to discover, among all the policies leading from x_0 to some state of period N, the one with the optimal value. We say that such a policy is optimal from x_0 to $n = N$, and will represent it as

$$\varpi_{0,N}^*(x_0\,,\,\cdot);$$

an arbitrary policy between these states will be designated as

$$\varpi_{0,N}(x_0\,,\,\cdot)$$

and an arbitrary subpolicy from x_i to $n = j$ as

$$\varpi_{i,j}(x_i\,,\,\cdot).$$

The method explained in Section 3 and applied from the past toward the future will give the optimal policies $\varpi_{0,N}^*(x_0\,,\,x_N)$ from x_0 to x_N for any value of $x_N \in \mathbf{X}_N(x_0\,,\,\cdot)$, and also the total optimal value $f_{0,N}(x_0\,,\,x_N)$. All we need do is compare the policies obtained to find the optimal policy or policies from x_0 to $n = N$:

$$\varpi_{0,N}^{**}(x_0\,,\,\cdot) = \varpi_{0,N}^*(x_0\,,\,x_N{}^*),$$

where $x_N{}^*$ is the value of x_N for which we obtain the optimum in

$$f_{0,N}(x_0\,,\,\cdot) = \underset{x_N \in \mathbf{X}_N(x_0,\cdot)}{\mathrm{OPT}} f_{0,N}(x_0\,,\,x_N),$$

making $f_{0,N}(x_0\,,\,\cdot)$ the optimal value, and using OPT for MAX or MIN, according to the case.

We thus have a method of finding the optimal policies from x_0 to $n = N$, and the case where x_N is prescribed and x_0 is indeterminate is treated in a similar manner, but in the opposite direction, to obtain the optimal policies from x_0 to x_N for every value of $x_0 \in \mathbf{X}_0(\cdot\,,\,x_N)$ in a single operation.

This method can be slightly varied, and we will return to the case where x_0 is prescribed, in order to consider it. Since we are looking for the policies $\varpi_{0,N}^*(x_0\,,\,\cdot)$, it is natural to define the subpolicies $\varpi_{n,N}(x_n\,,\,\cdot)$ from x_0 to $n = N$. For $x_n \in \mathbf{X}_n(x_0\,,\,\cdot)$ the optimal value of such a subpolicy will be

$$f_{n,N}(x_n\,,\,\cdot) = \underset{x_N \in \mathbf{X}_N(x_n,\cdot)}{\mathrm{OPT}} f_{n,N}(x_n\,,\,x_N) \tag{8.1}$$

where $\mathbf{X}_N(x_n\,,\,\cdot)$ is a subset of $\mathbf{X}_N(x_0\,,\,\cdot)$:

$$\mathbf{X}_N(x_n\,,\,\cdot) \subset \mathbf{X}_N(x_0\,,\,\cdot). \tag{8.2}$$

If $\mathbf{X}_N(x_n, \cdot) = \varnothing$, that is to say, if it is not possible to go from x_n to x_N, we shall agree to take $f_{n,N}(x_n, \cdot)$ equal to $(-\infty)$ if we desire the maximum or to $(+\infty)$ if we desire the minimum.

The functions $f_{n,N}(x_n, \cdot)$ satisfy a recurring equation similar to the one which enables us to calculate the functions $f_{n,N}(x_n, x_N)$, and which is derived from the first theorem of optimality:

$$f_{n,N}(x_n, x_N) = \underset{x_{n+1} \in \mathbf{X}_{n+1}(x_n, x_N)}{\mathrm{OPT}} [v_{n+1}(x_n, x_{n+1}) + f_{n+1,N}(x_{n+1}, x_N)]. \quad (8.3)$$

Indeed, if we assume $n < N - 1$, (8.1) can be expressed

$$f_{n,N}(x_n, \cdot) = \underset{x_N \in \mathbf{X}_N(x_n, \cdot)}{\mathrm{OPT}} \{\underset{x_{n+1} \in \mathbf{X}_{n+1}(x_n, x_N)}{\mathrm{OPT}} [v_{n+1}(x_n, x_{n+1}) + f_{n+1,N}(x_{n+1}, x_n)]\}, \quad (8.4)$$

or, by changing the order of optimization,

$$f_{n,N}(x_n, \cdot) = \underset{x_{n+1} \in \Gamma_{n+1} x_n}{\mathrm{OPT}} \{\underset{x_N \in \mathbf{X}_N(x_{n+1}, \cdot)}{\mathrm{OPT}} [v_{n+1}(x_n, x_{n+1}) + f_{n+1,N}(x_{n+1}, x_N)]\}$$

$$= \underset{x_{n+1} \in \Gamma_{n+1} x_n}{\mathrm{OPT}} \{v_{n+1}(x_n, x_{n+1}) + \underset{x_N \in \mathbf{X}_N(x_{n+1}, \cdot)}{\mathrm{OPT}} [f_{n+1,N}(x_{n+1}, x_N)]\},$$

whence, in accordance with (8.1),

$$f_{n,N}(x_n, \cdot) = \underset{x_{n+1} \in \Gamma_{n+1} x_n}{\mathrm{OPT}} [v_{n+1}(x_n, x_{n+1}) + f_{n+1,N}(x_{n+1}, \cdot)]. \quad (8.5)$$

For $n = N - 1$, we have, by referring to definition (8.1),

$$f_{N-1,N}(x_{N-1}, \cdot) = \underset{x_N \in \Gamma_N x_{N-1}}{\mathrm{OPT}} f_{N-1,N}(x_{N-1}, x_N)$$

$$= \underset{x_N \in \Gamma_N x_{N-1}}{\mathrm{OPT}} v_N(x_{N-1}, x_N). \quad (8.6)$$

It will be observed that (8.5) is identical with (8.3), but the first term of the sequence, given by (8.6), usually differs from the function

$$f_{N-1,N}(x_{N-1}, x_N) = v_N(x_{N-1}, x_N).$$

Equation (8.5) can be obtained directly by using the following theorem, which is similar to the one given in Section 3.

THEOREM OF OPTIMALITY 8.1. *Every subpolicy* $\varpi_{i,N}(x_i, \cdot)$ *extracted from a policy* $\varpi_{0,N}^*(x_0, \cdot)$ *optimal from* x_0 *to* $n = N$ *is itself optimal from* x_i *to* $n = N$.

Observation. Since an optimal policy from x_0 to $n = N$ is also optimal from x_0 to state $x_N{}^*$ where it ends, the second theorem of optimality also implies that any subpolicy $\varpi_{0,i}(x_0 , x_i{}^*)$ taken from $\varpi_{0,N}^*$ is optimal from x_0 to $x_i{}^*$; but it is not usually optimal from x_0 to $n = i$.

The amount of calculation when we use the above method is generally about the same as that required for the method given in Section 3, but we must observe two important differences in the result obtained by these methods:

(a) We obtain the optimal policies from x_0 to $n = N$, but not the separate ones from x_0 to x_N .

(b) On the other hand, we obtain the optimal policies from x_0 to $n = N$ for all possible values of x_0 when this variable has several. In contrast, by the method of Section 3, the calculations would have to be repeated for all values of x_0 , which would entail considering the $f_{0,n}(x_0 , x_n)$ as functions of two variables, thus greatly increasing the calculations.

It must further be observed that when we use the method of Section 3 we must carry out the optimization from the past toward the future, whereas in the above method it is carried out in the opposite direction.

The case where x_N is prescribed is treated by adopting an inverse direction, that is, for the method of the present section, from the past toward the future. We define the functions

$$f_{0,n}(\cdot, x_n) = \underset{x_0 \in \mathbf{X}_0(\cdot,x_n)}{\mathrm{OPT}} f_{0,n}(x_0 , x_n), \tag{8.7}$$

which satisfies the recurring equation

$$n > 1, \quad f_{0,n}(\cdot, x_n) = \underset{x_{n-1} \in \Gamma_n^{-1}x_n}{\mathrm{OPT}} [f_{0,x_{n-1}}(\cdot, x_{n-1}) + v_n(x_{n-1} , x_n)], \tag{8.8}$$

with

$$f_{0,1}(\cdot, x_1) = \underset{x_0 \in \Gamma_1^{-1}x_1}{\mathrm{OPT}} v_1(x_0 , x_1). \tag{8.9}$$

By successively solving Eqs. (8.8) from $n = 2$ to $n = N$, we obtain $f_{0,N}(\cdot, x_N)$, that is, the optimal value from $n = 0$ to x_N , as well as the corresponding optimal policies $\varpi_{0,N}^*(\cdot, x_N)$.

Finally, we have the case where both x_0 and x_N are indeterminate, and we are looking for the optimal policies from $n = 0$ to $n = N$. We can then use the method of the present section in either direction and optimize either the function $f_{0,N}(x_0 , \cdot)$ or $f_{0,N}(\cdot, x_N)$, which has been obtained.

Example. We shall rework the example in Section 5, this time assuming that the final stock is not prescribed. We must observe at the outset that, for an optimal policy from $x_0 = 2$ (initial prescribed state) to $n = 6$, the final stock x_6 will be zero, so that we should obtain the same result as in Section 5 where x_6 was prescribed.

We shall use the recurring equations (8.5) and (8.6). In accordance with (2.10) the constraints $x_{n+1} \in \Gamma_{n+1} x_n$ are expressed here as

$$\max(0, x_n - d_{n+1}) \leqslant x_{n+1} \leqslant S - d_{n+1}, \tag{8.10}$$

with $S = 20$; d_n is given by Table (2.1).

PERIOD 6

The expenditure for period 6 is

$$v_6(x_5, x_6) = p_6 a_6 = p_6(x_6 + d_6 - x_5), \tag{8.11}$$

whence

$$v_6(x_5, x_6) = 40 + 10(x_6 - x_5). \tag{8.12}$$

By (8.6), the minimal cost is

$$f_{5,6}(x_5, \cdot) = \underset{\max(0, x_5-4) \leqslant x_6 \leqslant 16}{\text{MIN}} [40 + 10(x_6 - x_5)], \tag{8.13}$$

whence

$$x_6{}^* = \max(0, x_5 - 4), \tag{8.14}$$

and

$$f_{5,6}(x_5, \cdot) = 40 + 10 \max(0, x_5 - 4) - 10x_5, \tag{8.15}$$

or again,

$$f_{5,6}(x_5, \cdot) = 40 + 10 \max(-x_5, -4). \tag{8.16}$$

PERIODS 6 AND 5

In accordance with (8.5), for $n = 4$,

$$f_{4,6}(x_4, \cdot) = \underset{\max(0, x_4-7) \leqslant x_5 \leqslant 13}{\text{MIN}} [v_5(x_4, x_5) + f_{5,6}(x_5, \cdot)], \tag{8.17}$$

whence

$$f_{4,6}(x_4, \cdot) = \underset{\max(0, x_4-7) \leqslant x_5 \leqslant 13}{\text{MIN}} [140 + 20(x_5 - x_4) + 40 + 10 \max(-x_5, -4)]. \tag{8.18}$$

The quantity between brackets is a uniformly increasing function of x_5, and we have

$$x_5{}^* = \max(0, x_4 - 7) \tag{8.19}$$

and

$$f_{4,6}(x_4, \cdot) = 180 - 20x_4 + 10 \max(x_5{}^*, 2x_5{}^* - 4). \qquad (8.20)$$

But we have

$$\max(x_5{}^*, 2x_5{}^* - 4) = \max[\max(0, x_4 - 7), 2\max(0, x_4 - 7) - 4]$$
$$= \max[\max(0, x_4 - 7), \max(-4, 2x_4 - 18)]$$
$$= \max(0, x_4 - 7, -4, 2x_4 - 18)$$
$$= \max(0, x_4 - 7, 2x_4 - 18),$$

whence

$$f_{4,6}(x_4, \cdot) = 180 - 20x_4 + 10 \max(0, x_4 - 7, 2x_4 - 18). \qquad (8.21)$$

PERIODS 6, 5, AND 4

$$f_{3,6}(x_3, \cdot) = \operatorname*{MIN}_{\max(0, x_3 - 2) \leqslant x_4 \leqslant 18} [v_4(x_3, x_4) + f_{4,6}(x_4, \cdot)], \qquad (8.22)$$

whence

$$f_{3,6}(x_3, \cdot) = \operatorname*{MIN}_{\max(0, x_3 - 2) \leqslant x_4 \leqslant 18} [34 + 17(x_4 - x_3) + 180 - 20x_4$$
$$+ 10 \max(0, x_4 - 7, 2x_4 - 18)]$$
$$= \operatorname*{MIN}_{\max(0, x_3 - 2) \leqslant x_4 \leqslant 18} [214 - 17x_3 - 3x_4$$
$$+ 10 \max(0, x_4 - 7, 2x_4 - 18)]. \qquad (8.23)$$

The quantity between brackets is a function of x_4, decreasing for $x_4 < 7$, and increasing for $x_4 > 7$, whence

$$x_4{}^* = \max(7, x_3 - 2) \qquad (8.24)$$

and

$$f_{3,6}(x_3, \cdot) = 214 - 17x_3 - 3x_4{}^* + 10 \max(0, x_4{}^* - 7, 2x_4{}^* - 18). \qquad (8.25)$$

But, as $x_4{}^* \geqslant 7$, we have

$$-3x_4{}^* + 10 \max(0, x_4{}^* - 7, 2x_4{}^* - 18)$$
$$= 10 \max(x_4{}^* - 7, 2x_4{}^* - 18) - 3x_4{}^*$$
$$= \max(7x_4{}^* - 70, 17x_4{}^* - 180)$$
$$= \max[\max(-21, 7x_3 - 84), \max(-61, 17x_3 - 214)]$$
$$= \max(-21, 7x_3 - 84, 17x_3 - 214), \qquad (8.26)$$

whence

$$f_{3,6}(x_3, \cdot) = 214 - 17x_3 + \max(-21, 7x_3 - 84, 17x_3 - 214)$$
$$= \max(193 - 17x_3, 130 - 10x_3, 0). \tag{8.27}$$

PERIODS 6 TO 3

$$f_{2,6}(x_2, \cdot) = \underset{\max(0, x_2-3) \leqslant x_3 \leqslant 17}{\text{MIN}} [v_3(x_2, x_3) + f_{3,6}(x_3, \cdot)], \tag{8.28}$$

whence

$$f_{2,6}(x_2, \cdot) = \underset{\max(0, x_2-3) \leqslant x_3 \leqslant 17}{\text{MIN}} [39 + 13(x_3 - x_2)$$
$$+ \max(193 - 17x_3, 130 - 10x_3, 0)]$$
$$= \underset{\max(0, x_2-3) \leqslant x_3 \leqslant 17}{\text{MIN}} [39 - 13x_2$$
$$+ \max(193 - 4x_3, 130 + 3x_3, 13x_3)]. \tag{8.29}$$

The quantity between brackets is a function of x_3, decreasing for $x_3 < 9$, and increasing for $x_3 > 9$, whence

$$x_3{}^* = \max(9, x_2 - 3) \tag{8.30}$$

and

$$f_{2,6}(x_2, \cdot) = 39 - 13x_2 + \max(193 - 4x_3{}^*, 130 + 3x_3{}^*, 13x_3{}^*). \tag{8.31}$$

But, as $x_3 \geqslant 9$, we have

$$\max(193 - 4x_3{}^*, 130 + 3x_3{}^*, 13x_3{}^*) = \max(130 + 3x_3{}^*, 13x_3{}^*)$$
$$= \max[\max(157, 3x_2 + 121),$$
$$\max(117, 13x_2 - 39)]$$
$$= \max(157, 3x_2 + 121, 13x_2 - 39), \tag{8.32}$$

whence

$$f_{2,6}(x_2, \cdot) = 39 - 13x_2 + \max(157, 3x_2 + 121, 13x_2 - 39)$$
$$= \max(196 - 13x_2, 160 - 10x_2, 0). \tag{8.33}$$

PERIODS 6 TO 2

$$f_{1,6}(x_1, \cdot) = \underset{\max(0, x_1-5) \leqslant x_2 \leqslant 15}{\text{MIN}} [v_2(x_1, x_2) + f_{2,6}(x_2, \cdot)], \tag{8.34}$$

whence

$$f_{1,6}(x_1, \cdot) = \underset{\max(0,x_1-5) \leqslant x_2 \leqslant 15}{\text{MIN}} [90 + 18(x_2 - x_1)$$
$$+ \max(196 - 13x_2, 160 - 10x_2, 0)]$$

$$= \underset{\max(0,x_1-5) \leqslant x_2 \leqslant 15}{\text{MIN}} [90 - 18x_1 + \max(196$$
$$+ 5x_2, 160 + 8x_2, 18x_2)]. \quad (8.35)$$

The quantity between brackets is an increasing function of x_2, whence

$$x_2{}^* = \max(0, x_1 - 5) \quad (8.36)$$

and

$$f_{1,6}(x_1, \cdot) = 90 - 18x_1 + \max(196 + 5x_2{}^*, 160 + 8x_2{}^*, 18x_2{}^*). \quad (8.37)$$

But we have

$$\max(196 + 5x_2{}^*, 160 + 8x_2{}^*, 18x_2{}^*)$$
$$= \max[\max(196, 5x_1 + 171), \max(160, 8x_1 + 120), \max(0, 18x_1 - 90)]$$
$$= \max(196, 5x_1 + 171, 8x_1 + 120, 18x_1 - 90), \quad (8.38)$$

whence

$$f_{1,6}(x_1, \cdot) = 90 - 18x_1 + \max(196, 5x_1 + 171, 8x_1 + 120, 18x_1 - 90)$$
$$= \max(286 - 18x_1, 261 - 13x_1, 210 - 10x_1, 0). \quad (8.39)$$

PERIODS 6 TO 1

$$f_{0,6}(x_0, \cdot) = \underset{\max(0,x_0-8) \leqslant x_1 \leqslant 12}{\text{MIN}} [v_1(x_0, x_1) + f_{1,6}(x_1, \cdot)], \quad (8.40)$$

whence

$$f_{0,6}(2, \cdot) = \underset{0 \leqslant x_1 \leqslant 12}{\text{MIN}} [88 + 11(x_1 - 2) + \max(286 - 18x_1,$$
$$261 - 13x_1, 210 - 10x_1, 0)],$$

$$= \underset{0 \leqslant x_1 \leqslant 12}{\text{MIN}} [66 + \max(286 - 7x_1, 261 - 2x_1, 210 + x_1, 11x_1)]. \quad (8.41)$$

The quantity between brackets is a decreasing function of x_1 for $x_1 < 17$; whence

$$x_1{}^* = 12 \quad (8.42)$$

and

$$f_{0,6}(2, \cdot) = 303. \quad (8.43)$$

Thus, we have obtained the same results as those given by (5.67) and (5.68) in Section 5.

9. Comparison of the Four Methods

To sum up, dynamic programming may lead to four types of recurring equations:

Type I

$$n > 1, \quad f_{0,n}(x_0, x_n) = \underset{x_{n-1} \in \mathbf{X}_{n-1}(x_0, x_n)}{\mathrm{OPT}} [f_{0,n-1}(x_0, x_{n-1}) + v_n(x_{n-1}, x_n)], \quad (9.1)$$

$$f_{0,1}(x_0, x_1) = v_1(x_0, x_1). \quad (9.2)$$

Type II

$$n < N - 1,$$

$$f_{n,N}(x_n, x_N) = \underset{x_{n+1} \in \mathbf{X}_{n+1}(x_n, x_N)}{\mathrm{OPT}} [v_{n+1}(x_n, x_{n+1}) + f_{n+1,N}(x_{n+1}, x_N)], \quad (9.3)$$

$$f_{N-1,N}(x_{N-1}, x_N) = v_N(x_{N-1}, x_N). \quad (9.4)$$

Type III

$$n > 1, \quad f_{0,n}(\cdot, x_n) = \underset{x_{n-1} \in \Gamma_n^{-1} x_n}{\mathrm{OPT}} [f_{0,n-1}(\cdot, x_{n-1}) + v_n(x_{n-1}, x_n)], \quad (9.5)$$

$$f_{0,1}(\cdot, x_1) = \underset{x_0 \in \Gamma_1^{-1} x_1}{\mathrm{OPT}} v_1(x_0, x_1). \quad (9.6)$$

Type IV

$$n < N - 1, \quad f_{n,N}(x_n, \cdot) = \underset{x_{n+1} \in \Gamma_{n+1} x_n}{\mathrm{OPT}} [v_{n+1}(x_n, x_{n+1}) + f_{n+1,N}(x_{n+1}, \cdot)], \quad (9.7)$$

$$f_{N-1,N}(x_{N-1}, \cdot) = \underset{x_N \in \Gamma_N x_{N-1}}{\mathrm{OPT}} v_N(x_{N-1}, x_N). \quad (9.8)$$

Table 9.1 sums up the main features of the methods corresponding to the four types of recurring equations,[19] and we shall now consider which of these formulas to use in different types of problem.

The initial state can be:

(a) Prescribed and single.
(b) Prescribed but capable of assuming several values; in other words,

---

[19] For types I and II, we assume that the functions $f_{0,n}(x_0, x_n)$ or $f_{n,N}(x_n, x_N)$ are those of a single variable x_n, the quantity x_0 or x_N having the same value.

we are seeking the policies leaving a prescribed initial state x_0, but we wish to solve the problem for several possible values of x_0.
(c) The subject of a choice.

In the same way, the final state may be:

(α) Prescribed and single.
(β) Prescribed but capable of assuming several values.
(γ) The subject of a choice.

The methods which we can use are:

(1) The method of Section 3 in the direction past $\rightarrow$ future (equations of type I).
(2) This method applied in the opposite direction (type II).
(3) The method of Section 8 in the direction past $\rightarrow$ future (type III).
(4) This method used in the opposite direction (type IV).

TABLE 9.1

PRINCIPAL CHARACTERISTICS OF THE METHODS USED

Type	Section	Function of value	Direction	Results
I	3	$f_{0,n}(x_0, x_n)$	past $\rightarrow$ future	$\varpi_{0,N}^*(x_0, x_N)$: optimal policies from x_0 to x_N, for a single value of x_0 and for all $x_N \in \mathbf{X}_N(x_0, \cdot)$ $\varpi_{0,N}^*(x_0, \cdot)$: optimal policies from x_0 to $n = N$, for a single value of x_0
II	3	$f_{n,N}(x_n, x_N)$	future $\rightarrow$ past	$\varpi_{0,N}^*(x_0, x_N)$: optimal policies from x_0 to x_N for a single value of x_N and for all $x_0 \in \mathbf{X}_0(\cdot, x_N)$ $\varpi_{0,N}^*(\cdot, x_N)$: optimal policies from $n = 0$ to x_N for a single value of x_N
III	8	$f_{0,n}(\cdot, x_n)$	past $\rightarrow$ future	$\varpi_{0,N}^*(\cdot, x_N)$: optimal policies from $n = 0$ to x_N for all given values of $x_N \in \mathbf{X}_N$ $\varpi_{0,N}^*(\cdot, \cdot)$: optimal policies from $n = 0$ to $n = N$
IV	8	$f_{n,N}(x_n, \cdot)$	future $\rightarrow$ past	$\varpi_{0,N}^*(x_0, \cdot)$: optimal policies from x_0 to $n = N$ for all given values of $x_0 \in \mathbf{X}_0$ $\varpi_{0,N}^*(\cdot, \cdot)$: optimal policies from $n = 0$ to $n = N$

By considering Table 9.1 and with the help of the observations given at the end of Sections 3 and 8, we can decide the simplest method or methods for solving any of the nine types of problem that can arise from a combination of the three possible initial states with the three possible final ones. From this, Table 9.2 is obtained.

TABLE 9.2

	Initial state x_0		
Final state x_N	(a) Prescribed and single	(b) Prescribed and multiple	(c) To be chosen
(α) Prescribed and single	Type I or II	Type II	Type II or III
(β) Prescribed and multiple	Type I	Type I or II with several repetitions	Type III
(γ) To be chosen	Type I or IV	Type IV	Type III or IV

It must be observed that the result to be obtained should not be the sole criterion for the method to adopt. The decisions in Table 9.2 are only valid when the four methods appear likely in advance to entail about the same length of calculation. This would not, for example, be the case if the constraints $x_n \in \Gamma_n x_{n-1}$ were difficult to invert, that is, if their inverted form were a complicated one. In this event we ought to choose type IV in which there are no inverted constraints.

10. Stationary Programs. Convergence. Permanent Policies

The problems of industrial management, which are one of the main uses for dynamic programming, are often of a repetitive type. Every week or month, or even year, the person in charge has to make a decision in conditions which are always similar if not exactly alike. It will be useful, therefore, to give additional particulars about the methods we have been studying.

We say that a deterministic dynamic program is *stationary* when the two following conditions are satisfied for all values of n on which the program is based (except perhaps for the extreme values):

$$\Gamma_n x_n = \Gamma x_n , \tag{10.1}$$

$$v_n(x_{n-1} , x_n) = v(x_{n-1} , x_n); \tag{10.2}$$

that is to say, the correspondence which defines the constraints and the value assigned to each decision do not depend on period n which is being considered.

For example, the program in Section 2 is not stationary, but would be if the demand d_i (condition 10.1) and the purchase price p_i (condition 10.2) had a uniform value independent of i. The program of Section 4 satisfies (10.1), but (10.2) would imply that $v_n(u_n)$ must be independent of n:

$$v_n(u_n) = v(u_n).$$

A program is *semistationary* if it satisfies condition (10.1) only.

In a stationary program, the set of possible values of the state variable x_n which may be reached from an initial state x_0 is

$$\mathbf{X}_n(x_0, \cdot) = \Gamma^{(n)}x_0, \tag{10.3}$$

where $\Gamma^{(n)}x_0$ is the set obtained by n repetitions of the correspondence Γ. In the same way,

$$\mathbf{X}_n(\cdot, x_N) = \Gamma^{-(N-n)}x_0 \tag{10.4}$$

and

$$\mathbf{X}_n(x_0, x_N) = \Gamma^{(n)}x_0 \cap \Gamma^{-(N-n)}x_N. \tag{10 5}$$

But we also have, whatever the value of k (provided the periods being considered are a part of the periods for which the program is defined):

$$\mathbf{X}_{n+k}(x_k, x_{n'+k}) = \Gamma^{(n)}x_k \cap \Gamma^{-(n'-n)}x_{n'+k}. \tag{10.6}$$

Hence the expression

$$\mathbf{X}_{n+k}(x_k = x, x_{n'+k} = x') = \mathbf{X}_n(x_0 = x, x_{n'} = x') \tag{10 7}$$

is independent of k, and will be called[20] $\mathbf{X}_{n,n'-n}(x, x')$:

$$\mathbf{X}_{n,n'-n}(x, x') = \mathbf{X}_{n+k}(x_k = x, x_{n'+k} = x'). \tag{10.8}$$

Furthermore, still with the assumption of a stationary program, the recurring equations (9.3) and (9.4) of type II will be expressed

$$n < N - 1, \quad f_{n,N}(x_n, x_N) = \underset{x_{n+1} \in \mathbf{X}_{n+1}(x_n, x_N)}{\text{OPT}} [v_{n+1}(x_n, x_{n+1}) + f_{n+1,N}(x_{n+1}, x_N)], \tag{10.9}$$

with

$$f_{N-1,N}(x_{N-1}, x_N) = v_N(x_{N-1}, x_N). \tag{10.10}$$

---

[20] The notation which we have used for the sake of shortness in the preceding sections is incomplete in the sense that the initial and final times are not explicitly defined, and it would have been more correct to have used $\mathbf{X}_{0,n,N}(x_0, x_N)$.

In accordance with (10.2) we have

$$f_{n-1,N}(x_{N-1}, x_N) = v(x_{N-1}, x_N); \tag{10.11}$$

hence

$$f_{N-1,N}(x, x')$$

does not depend on N. Moreover, (10.9) can be expressed:

$$f_{n,N}(x_n, x_N) = \underset{x_{n+1} \in \mathbf{X}_{1.N-n-1}(x_n, x_N)}{\text{OPT}} [v(x_n, x_{n+1}) + f_{n+1,N}(x_{n+1}, x_N)]. \tag{10.12}$$

We can then progressively show that $f_{n,N}(x, x')$ only depends on $n' = N - n$. In other words, the optimal value of x to x' (for $n' = N - n$ periods) is independent of n or N. It is also clear that each subpolicy $\{x^{(0)}, x^{(1)}, ..., x^{(n)}\}$ has a value independent of the number of the period with which this value commences, a property that changes the preceding one into a generalization. To show this property clearly, we shall assume

$$f_k(x, x') = f_{n,n+k}(x, x'). \tag{10.13}$$

The recurring equation (10.12) is then expressed:

$$f_n(x, x'') = \underset{x' \in \mathbf{X}_{1.(n-1)}(x, x'')}{\text{OPT}} [v(x, x') + f_{n-1}(x, x'')]. \tag{10.13'}$$

The same reasoning can be applied to the other types of equations and the four types now become:

Type I

$$n > 1, \quad f_n(x, x'') = \underset{x' \in \mathbf{X}_{(n-1).1}(x, x'')}{\text{OPT}} [f_{n-1}(x, x') + v(x', x'')], \tag{10.14}$$

$$f_1(x, x'') = v(x, x''). \tag{10.15}$$

Type II

$$n > 1, \quad f_n(x, x'') = \underset{x' \in \mathbf{X}_{1.(n-1)}(x, x'')}{\text{OPT}} [v(x, x') + f_{n-1}(x', x'')], \tag{10.16}$$

$$f_1(x, x'') = v(x, x''). \tag{10.17}$$

Type III

$$n > 1, \quad f_n(\cdot, x'') = \underset{x' \in \Gamma^{-1}x''}{\text{OPT}} [f_{n-1}(\cdot, x') + v(x', x'')], \tag{10.18}$$

$$f_1(\cdot, x'') = \underset{x' \in \Gamma^{-1}x''}{\text{OPT}} v(x', x''). \tag{10.19}$$

Type IV

$$n > 1, \quad f_n(x, \cdot) = \underset{x' \in \Gamma x}{\mathrm{OPT}} [v(x, x') + f_{n-1}(x', \cdot)], \tag{10.20}$$

$$f_1(x, \cdot) = \underset{x' \in \Gamma x}{\mathrm{OPT}} \; v(x, x'). \tag{10.21}$$

Let us recall that by definition (see Section 8)

$$f_n(x, \cdot) = \underset{x'' \in \Gamma^{(n)}x}{\mathrm{OPT}} f_n(x, x''), \tag{10.22}$$

$$f_n(\cdot, x'') = \underset{x \in \Gamma^{(-n)}x''}{\mathrm{OPT}} f_n(x, x''). \tag{10.23}$$

By way of an example, we shall again take the program of Sections 6 and 7, assuming on this occasion that the purchase price p and the selling price q remain the same for all the periods, with $p < q$. If we proceed as in Section 7 by complete periods (purchase-sale), the constraint is expressed as $0 \leqslant s \leqslant S$, whatever the value of s in the preceding period. If s and s' are the stock at two consecutive times, we see, by referring to Fig. 7.2, that:

(1) If $s \geqslant s'$, we are in case (b) and, in accordance with (7.17) and (7.18),

$$v(s, s') = ps - qs' + (q - p)S - \delta(>0) \quad \text{if} \quad \delta(>0) \leqslant (q - p)(S - s),$$

$$v(s, s') = q(s - s') \quad \text{if} \quad \delta(>0) \geqslant (q - p)(S - s),$$

relations which we can also express by assuming

$$\alpha = S - \frac{\delta(>0)}{q - p} :$$

$$v(s, s') = ps - qs' + (q - p)\alpha \quad \text{if} \quad s \leqslant \alpha,$$

$$= q(s - s') \quad \text{if} \quad s \geqslant \alpha. \tag{10.24}$$

(2) If $s < s'$, we are in case (d) and, in accordance with (7.16),

$$v(s, s') = ps - qs' + (q - p)\alpha. \tag{10.25}$$

Figure 10.1 summarizes these data, in the assumption, which we shall adopt, that $\alpha > 0$.

To find the optimal policies from s_0 to $n = N$, we shall, in conformity with what is indicated by Table 9.2, use method IV (Eqs. (10.20) and (10.21)). It follows:

$$f_1(s, \cdot) = \underset{0 \leqslant s' \leqslant S}{\mathrm{MAX}} \; v(s, s'). \tag{10.26}$$

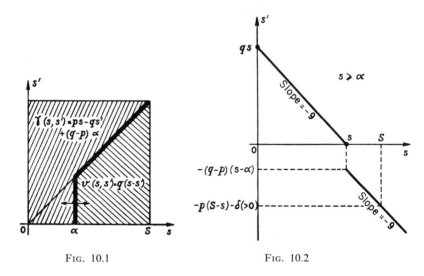

FIG. 10.1   FIG. 10.2

The simplest way to find the optimum is to consider Fig. 10.1, where we must choose a point (defined by the corresponding value of s') on a straight line parallel to the $0s'$ axis. If $s \leqslant \alpha$, $v(s, s')$ has only one expression, and the maximum is obtained for $s' = 0$,

$$s \leqslant \alpha: \quad f_1(s, 0) = ps + (q - p)\alpha \quad \text{with} \quad s'^* = 0. \qquad (10.27)$$

If $s \geqslant \alpha$, the optimum is still obtained for $s' = 0$, as is shown in Fig. 10.2:

$$s \geqslant \alpha: \quad f_1(s, 0) = qs \quad \text{with} \quad s'^* = 0. \qquad (10.28)$$

The function $f_1(s, \cdot)$ is shown in Fig. 10.3. We next calculate

$$f_2(s, \cdot) = \underset{0 \leqslant s' \leqslant S}{\text{MAX}} [v(s, s') + f_1(s', \cdot)].$$

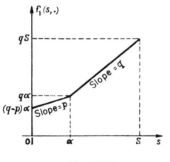

FIG. 10.3

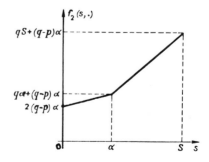

FIG. 10.4

We shall now successively consider the cases where $s \leqslant \alpha$ and $s \geqslant \alpha$.

(a) $\quad s \leqslant \alpha$: $\quad f_2(s, \cdot) = \underset{0 \leqslant s' \leqslant S}{\text{MAX}} [ps - qs' + (q - p)\alpha + f_1(s', \cdot)]$.

The quantity between brackets is linear in parts; for $s' \leqslant \alpha$ the slope is $(-q + p) < 0$; for $s' \geqslant \alpha$ the slope is $(-q + q) = 0$. Hence the maximum is obtained for $s' = 0$:

$$s \leqslant \alpha: \quad f_2(s, \cdot) = ps + 2(q - p)\alpha \qquad \text{with} \quad s'^* = 0. \qquad (10.29)$$

(b) $s \geqslant \alpha$.

Here the slope of $v(s, s')$ is always $(-q)$, the quantity between brackets is nonincreasing, and the optimum is again obtained for $s' = 0$:

$$s \geqslant \alpha: \quad f_2(s, \cdot) = qs + (q - p)\alpha \qquad \text{with} \quad s'^* = 0. \qquad (10.30)$$

By comparing (10.29) and (10.30) respectively with (10.27) and (10.28), we find that $f_2(s, \cdot)$ is obtained by merely adding $(q - p)\alpha$ to $f_1(s, \cdot)$. Indeed, we have discovered that the optimal policy for two periods always passes through the value $s' = 0$ at the end of the first period, whatever the initial value of s. The value for the second period is therefore always $f_1(0, \cdot) = (q - p)\alpha$. By continuing the calculation we should discover the generalization

$$f_n(s, \cdot) = (n - 1)(q - p)\alpha + f_1(s, \cdot), \qquad (10.31)$$

as can easily be shown by recurrence.

This result can be interpreted as follows: The assumption $\alpha > 0$ means that the maximal gross profit for a period $(q - p)S$ is greater than the fixed purchase charge δ (>0), so that the net profit is positive when the quantity S is bought for immediate sale. It is therefore clear that it is to our advantage to perform this operation in each period and to reduce the stock at the end of each period to zero.

In this simple example (which could, in fact, have been solved intuitively) we have seen the appearance of what may be termed a "permanent policy" from the time of the second period, and it would appear in the first period, provided there is a zero initial stock.

CHAPTER 2

DISCRETE DYNAMIC PROGRAMS WITH A CERTAIN FUTURE AND AN UNLIMITED HORIZON

---

11. Introduction

The use of the model of finite dynamic programming given in Chapter 1 is often open to major objections. In most cases, certainly where we are dealing with stationary programs, the economic horizon is not limited to a fixed number of periods N, and logic then requires that we should treat the problem in the assumption that their number is infinite.[1]

Let us consider a dynamic program defined by the model of Section 3 of which we shall retain the notation. For simplification, we shall assume that the initial state x_0 is single and prescribed. In order to be able to treat the problem over an unlimited number of periods, it is clearly necessary that:

(a) The correspondence $\Gamma_n x_{n-1}$ must be defined for every $n > 0$ and every $x_{n-1} \in \mathbf{X}_{n-1}(x_0 , \cdot)$.

(b) The value $v_n(x_{n-1} , x_n)$ must be defined for every $n > 0$, every $x_{n-1} \in \mathbf{X}_{n-1}(x_0 , \cdot)$, and every $x_n \in \Gamma x_{n-1}$.

We assume these conditions are satisfied, and a policy will consist of a clearly defined sequence

$$\cdot \varpi = (x_0 , x_1 ,..., x_n ,...).$$

But when we seek to discover whether there is one or several optimal policies we must ask ourselves what is the meaning of the word "optimal" in this context. We must first observe that if, in a program with N periods, we sought the optimal policies from x_0 to x_N , there is no meaning in prescribing a final value when the number of periods is infinite.[2] In addition, let us assume, to be more precise, that we wish

---

[1] See P. Massé, *Le Choix des Investissements*. Dunod, 1964.

[2] Let us observe that this statement enables us to exclude from now on the use of any equations except those of type IV.

to maximize the values. In the case of a program with N periods, an optimal policy from x_0 to $n = N$ is a policy of which the value cannot be exceeded. But the value of a policy may well be infinite in the case considered here, so that we might be tempted to call any such policy optimal, a result that would be meaningless.

Let us again consider the example in Section 2, where the quantity of merchandise to be purchased in order to satisfy the demand has to be decided in each period, and let us assume that after period 6 we discover, for each group of six periods, the same values for the demand and for the purchase price as we found in the first group, and always in the same order. We are here trying to minimize the expenditure, and the value of N periods, whatever policy is chosen, is an increasing function of N which approaches infinity.

The previous example proves that such a definition of an optimal policy would lead in certain cases to all the policies being considered as equivalent, which would not be very satisfactory. Indeed, two policies that each have an infinite value may be different in the sense that, for each finite value of N, the portion $(0, N)$ may have a greater value in one of them than in the other. Hence we may ask if there is a policy

$$\varpi^* = \{x_0, x_1{}^*, ..., x_n{}^*, ...\},$$

such that any policy

$$\varpi_{0,n}^* = \{x_0, x_1{}^*, ..., x_n{}^*\}$$

is optimal from x_0 to n for every value of n, or at least where n is greater than a certain number N.

Let us assume that a policy ϖ^* has this property for a certain value $n > N$, and that the subpolicy $\varpi_{0,n}^*$ is optimal from x_0 to n, with $x_i{}^*$ the state through which this subpolicy causes the system to pass at time i $(N < i < n)$. The subpolicy

$$\varpi_{0,i}^* = \{x_0, x_1{}^*, ..., x_i{}^*\}$$

taken from ϖ^* will be optimal from x_0 to $x_i{}^*$ by the first theorem of optimality, but it will not usually be optimal from x_0 to $n = i$, and the policy ϖ^* will not be optimal in the sense described above.

It can be seen that there are very delicate problems associated with dynamic programs with an unlimited horizon, especially if the function of value $f_n(x_0, \cdot)$ has no finite limit. The difficulties we have encountered arise essentially from two causes. First, we have been considering a nonstationary program, but it is clear that the behavior of such a program depends on that of Γ_n and v_n and that the latter must be clearly defined. Secondly, the case where the function of value increases indefinitely excludes any comparison of policies. Accordingly, in this chapter we shall consider certain typical special cases, being careful to define a function of value possessing bounds, and confining our examination to stationary or semistationary programs, where the latter are obtained by a simple modification of the former.[3]

Chapter 4 will also help to clarify this question of programs with an unlimited horizon, and the random character of the model which will be studied in it should produce some instructive comparisons.

12. Convergence by "Narrowing" the Domain of Decision

We shall begin by considering a class of dynamic programs whose structure is such that the optimal value $f_n(x_0, \cdot)$ for n periods has a finite limit $f(x_0, \cdot)$ as $n \to \infty$, both because the domain of the possible states $\mathbf{X}_n(x_0, \cdot)$ is reduced at the limit to a point and because the value of this point is zero. Figure 12.1 represents a system where the set of possible states narrows as n increases.

Bellman [10] gives the following example:

A certain quantity of equipment has to be bought periodically. If, at the beginning of period n, the sum x_{n-1} is available, it should be divided into two quantities y_n and $x_{n-1} - y_n$, for purchasing equipment of type A and type B respectively. During period n, the two types of equipment will perform $g(y_n)$ and $h(x_{n-1} - y_n)$ hours of work, where $g(0) = h(0) = 0$. In addition, their resale at the end of period n will produce a sum equal to

$$[ay_n + b(x_{n-1} - y_n)],$$

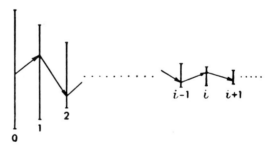

$$i-1 \quad i \quad i+1$$

FIG. 12.1

[3] R. Fortet [31] has given some results for nonstationary programs.

with $0 < a < 1$ and $0 < b < 1$. This is the sum available at the beginning of period $n + 1$ for the purchase of new equipment:

$$x_n = ay_n + b(x_{n-1} - y_n). \qquad (12.1)$$

The use of the auxiliary decision variable y_n is convenient but by no means necessary. Instead of choosing a value y_n between 0 and x_{n-1}, we can at once choose the value x_n between ax_{n-1} and bx_{n-1}. Hence, using the notation of Section 3, we have a dynamic program which is defined as follows:

$$\Gamma_n x_{n-1} = \{x_n \mid bx_{n-1} \leqslant x_n \leqslant ax_{n-1}\}, \qquad (12.2)$$

$$v_n(x_{n-1}, x_n) = g(y_n) + h(x_{n-1} - y_n)$$

$$= g\left(\frac{x_n - bx_{n-1}}{a - b}\right) + h\left(\frac{ax_{n-1} - x_n}{a - b}\right). \qquad (12.2')$$

We have assumed, when expressing these relations, that $0 \leqslant b < a < 1$, and have ignored the valueless case where $a = b$.

This program is stationary, and if we start with a given sum x_0, the recurring equations of type IV [(10.20) and (10.21)] enable us to calculate progressively the optimal (maximal) value for n periods:

$$f_n(x_0, \cdot) = \underset{bx \leqslant x' \leqslant ax}{\text{MAX}} [v(x, x') + f_{n-1}(x', \cdot)], \qquad (12.3)$$

with

$$f_0(x_0, \cdot) = 0. \qquad (12.4)$$

It is clear that, whatever policy is chosen, x_n and $v_n(x_{n-1}, x_n)$ approach zero as n increases indefinitely. Further on, we shall see that v_n decreases so rapidly that f_n remains finite.

During the remainder of this section we shall study a rather more common class of dynamic program than the one just described, namely, stationary ones[4] in which the decision variable has only one dimension and where the constraint Γx_{n-1} is of the form (12.2):

$$\Gamma x_{n-1} = \{x_n \mid bx_{n-1} \leqslant x_n \leqslant ax_{n-1}\}, \qquad (12.5)$$

where

$$0 \leqslant b < a < 1;$$

the value $v(x_{n-1}, x_n)$ is not necessarily of the form (12.2').

---

[4] The stationary property will simplify the proofs, but the results of this section can be extended to certain semistationary or even nonstationary problems.

Relying on Bellman's work, we shall show that in this case, and making certain assumptions, the sequence $f_n(x_0, \cdot)$ is convergent, with the result that there is an optimal policy in the sense given to it in Chapter 1.

To simplify the notation, we shall asume

$$f_n(x, \cdot) = f_n(x),\tag{12.6}$$

so that (12.3) becomes

$$f_n(x) = \underset{bx \leqslant x' \leqslant ax}{\text{MAX}}[v(x, x') + f_{n-1}(x')],\tag{12.7}$$

with $f_0(x) = 0$.

EXISTENCE OF A SOLUTION

Let us first show that the functional equation

$$f(x) = \underset{bx \leqslant x' \leqslant ax}{\text{MAX}}[v(x, x') + f(x')],\tag{12.8}$$

formally obtained by making n approach ∞ in (12.7), under certain conditions has a solution $f(x)$ continuous for $x = 0$ and zero at this point.

The first assumption that we shall make about the value $v(x, x')$ is that this function is continuous in relation to the two variables. Hence the function

$$f_1(x) = \underset{bx \leqslant x' \leqslant ax}{\text{MAX}} v(x, x')\tag{12.9}$$

is continuous. It is then easy to show by recurrence that $f_n(x)$ is also continuous. To study the convergence of the sequence $f_n(x)$, we shall examine the differences $[f_n(x) - f_{n+1}(x)]$.

Let $x'^*_{n-1}(x)$ be the first decision for $n \geqslant 1$ of an optimal policy for n periods, in other words, a value[5] of x' which produces the maximum in (12.7). By definition of this quantity, for $n \geqslant 0$, we have

$$f_{n+1}(x) = v(x, x'^*_n) + f_n(x'^*_n) \qquad \text{where} \quad bx \leqslant x'^*_n \leqslant ax,\tag{12.10}$$

and

$$f_{n+2}(x) = v(x, x'^*_{n+1}) + f_{n+1}(x'^*_{n+1}) \qquad \text{where} \quad bx \leqslant x'^*_{n+1} \leqslant ax.\tag{12.11}$$

But, since $bx \leqslant x'^*_{n+1} \leqslant ax$, we also have

$$f_{n+1}(x) \geqslant v(x, x'^*_{n+1}) + f_n(x'^*_{n+1}),\tag{12.12}$$

_____

[5] We must observe that $x'^*_n(x)$ need not be a univocal and continuous function, since $[v(x, x') + f_{n-1}(x')]$ may contain a straight line parallel to the Ox' axis.

and in the same way,

$$f'_{n+2}(x) \geqslant v(x, x'^*_n) + f'_{n+1}(x'^*_n). \qquad (12.13)$$

From (12.12) and (12.11) we obtain

$$f'_{n+1}(x) - f'_{n+2}(x) \geqslant f'_n(x'^*_{n+1}) - f'_{n+1}(x'^*_{n+1}), \qquad (12.14)$$

and, beginning with (12.10) and (12.13),

$$f'_{n+1}(x) - f'_{n+2}(x) \leqslant f'_n(x'^*_n) - f'_{n+1}(x'^*_n). \qquad (12.15)$$

Further, if we consider three real numbers, a, b, and c such that $a \leqslant b \leqslant c$, we can easily prove

$$|b| \leqslant \max(|a|, |c|).$$

Hence, from (12.14) and (12.15) we obtain

$$|f'_{n+1}(x) - f'_{n+2}(x)| \leqslant \max[|f'_n(x'^*_{n+1}) - f'_{n+1}(x'^*_{n+1})|, |f'_n(x'^*_n) - f'_{n+1}(x'^*_n)|]. \qquad (12.16)$$

Let us now assume

$$u_n(x) = \max_{0 \leqslant z \leqslant x} |f'_n(z) - f'_{n+1}(z)|, \qquad n \geqslant 0, \qquad (12.17)$$

and let $z^*_{n+1}(x)$ be such that $0 \leqslant z^*_{n+1} \leqslant x$, and that

$$|f'_{n+1}(z^*_{n+1}) - f'_{n+2}(z^*_{n+1})| \equiv u_{n+1}(x).^6 \qquad (12.18)$$

If we apply inequality (12.16), replacing x by z^*_{n+1}, we obtain

$$u_{n+1}(x) \leqslant \max[|f'_n(z'^*_{n+1}) - f'_{n+1}(z'^*_{n+1})|, |f'_n(z'^*_n) - f'_{n+1}(z'^*_n)|], \qquad (12.19)$$

where z'^*_{n+1} and z'^*_n are two numbers which satisfy the inequalities

$$bz^*_{n+1} \leqslant z'^*_{n+1} \leqslant az^*_{n+1} \leqslant ax, \qquad (12.20)$$

$$bz^*_{n+1} \leqslant z'^*_n \leqslant az^*_{n+1} \leqslant ax. \qquad (12.21)$$

But, by definition (12.17), the inequality $z'^*_{n+1} \leqslant ax$ implies

$$|f'_n(z'^*_{n+1}) - f'_{n+1}(z'^*_{n+1})| \leqslant u_n(ax), \qquad (12.22)$$

---

^{6} The sign $\equiv$ means that (12.18) is true for any value of x.

and in the same way,

$$|f_n(z_n'^*) - f_{n+1}(z_n'^*)| \leqslant u_n(ax). \tag{12.23}$$

Hence the second member is at most equal to $u_n(ax)$, whence

$$u_{n+1}(x) \leqslant u_n(ax), \tag{12.24}$$

and in consequence,

$$u_n(x) \leqslant u_0(a^n x). \tag{12.25}$$

Also, in accordance with (12.17) and taking into account $f_0(x) = 0$, we have

$$u_0(x) = \underset{0 \leqslant z \leqslant x}{\text{MAX}} |f_1(z)| = \underset{0 \leqslant z \leqslant x}{\text{MAX}} |\underset{bz \leqslant z' \leqslant az}{\text{MAX}} v(z, z')|. \tag{12.26}$$

We are therefore led to make a second assumption concerning $v(x, x')$, namely, that the function $u_0(x)$ given by (12.26) is such that

$$\sum_{n=0}^{\infty} u_0(a^n x) < \infty \qquad \text{for every } x \geqslant 0. \tag{12.27}$$

If this condition is satisfied, the series with the general term $u_n(x)$, which is bounded by the series $u_0(a^n x)$, is convergent. Hence

$$f_N(x) = [f_N(x) - f_{N-1}(x)] + [f_{N-1}(x) - f_{N-2}(x)] + \cdots$$
$$+ [f_2(x) - f_1(x)] + [f_1(x) - f_0(x)], \tag{12.28}$$

which means that $f_N(x)$ is the sum of the first N terms of the series with the general term $[f_n(x) - f_{n-1}(x)]$, and in virtue of (12.17), we have

$$|f_n(x) - f_{n-1}(x)| \leqslant u_{n-1}(x); \tag{12.29}$$

whence

$$|f_N(x)| \leqslant \sum_{n=0}^{N-1} u_n(x). \tag{12.30}$$

The sequence $f_N(x)$ is therefore fully and uniformly convergent in any finite interval. Since it is also continuous, there is a function

$$f(x) = \lim_{N \to \infty} f_N(x), \tag{12.31}$$

which is continuous. In addition, since the convergence is uniform, this function is the solution of Eq. (12.8).

A necessary condition for ensuring convergence is that $u_0(0) = 0$; from this we deduce $u_n(0) = 0$, and in consequence that $f_n(0) = 0$, $n > 0$, and $f(0) = 0$.

PERMANENT POLICIES

The first decision of an optimal policy is given by the function $x'^*(x)$ which leads to the maximum in Eq. (12.8), and which can be nonunivocal, since for a given value of x there may be several values of x' leading to the maximal one. The above function completely defines the set of optimal policies. Indeed, if we start from an initial value $x = x_0$, the first decision is given by $x_1 \in x'^*(x_0)$. But, in general, the nth decision may be regarded as the first decision of an optimal policy for an infinitude of periods where the initial value is x_{n-1}. Hence we have

$$x_n \in x'^*(x_{n-1}), \qquad n \geqslant 1. \tag{12.32}$$

All the optimal policies

$$\varpi^* = \{x_0, x_1, ..., x_n, ...\} \tag{12.33}$$

are thus given by (12.32) in which we shall eventually be required each time to choose one of the values of $x'^*(x)$.

We shall apply the term "permanent policy" to a policy such that the decision taken during a period (at the beginning of which the state is x) is $y(x)$, a univocal function which is independent of the period considered, and is called the "decision function." Obtaining the function (12.32) therefore amounts to obtaining the set of permanent optimal policies.

THE SOLUTION IS UNIQUE

We shall now show that the function defined by (12.31) is, with the assumptions made earlier, the sole solution of Eq. (12.8), defined for every value of x, continuous for $x = 0$, and zero at this point.

Indeed, let us assume that there is another function $\varphi(x)$ which fulfills these conditions, that $y(x)$ is one of the values of x' which leads to the maximum in (12.8), and that $\xi(x)$ is a similar quantity corresponding to the function $\varphi(x)$. With the reasoning used above, we show that

$$f(x) = v(x, y) + f(y) \geqslant v(x, \xi) + f(\xi), \tag{12.34}$$

$$\varphi(x) = v(x, \xi) + \varphi(\xi) \geqslant v(x, y) + \varphi(y), \tag{12.35}$$

whence

$$|f(x) - \varphi(x)| \leqslant \max[|f(\xi) - \varphi(\xi)|, |f(y) - \varphi(y)|], \qquad (12.36)$$

where $bx \leqslant y \leqslant ax$ and $bx \leqslant \xi \leqslant ax$.

Let us assume

$$u(x) = \sup_{0 \leqslant z \leqslant x} |f(z) - \varphi(z)|, \qquad (12.37)$$

where SUP $g(x)$ means[7] "upper bound of" $g(x)$.

With the assumptions made as to $\varphi(x)$, and the properties of $f(x)$, the function $u(x)$ is continuous for $x = 0$ and zero at this point. Now let z^* be a value of z between 0 and x such that

$$|f(z^*) - \varphi(z^*)| \geqslant u(x) - \epsilon, \qquad (12.38)$$

where ϵ is an arbitrarily small number. Applying the relation (12.36) with x replaced by z^*, and making ϵ approach zero, we obtain

$$u(x) \leqslant u(ax),$$

whence

$$u(x) \leqslant u(a^n x) \qquad \text{whatever} \quad n \geqslant 1.$$

As $u(x)$ is continuous for $x = 0$, and zero at this point, we must have $u(x) \equiv 0$, and in consequence $f(x) \equiv \varphi(x)$.

Hence we have proved the following theorem:

THEOREM 12.1. *Let a and b be two numbers such that* $0 \leqslant b < a < 1$. *If:*

(α) $v(x, x')$ *is continuous in relation to the set of its variables,*
(β) *the function*

$$u_0(x) = \max_{0 \leqslant z \leqslant x} |\max_{bz \leqslant z' \leqslant az} v(z, z')| \qquad (12.39)$$

satisfies the relation

$$\sum_{u=0}^{\infty} u_0(a^n x) < \infty$$

---

[7] As the function $\varphi(x)$ is, by assumption, defined for all values of x, the second member of (12.37) has an upper bound. But as $\varphi(x)$ need not be continuous, this bound may not actually be reached, which is why we do not use the sign MAX.

for every $x \geqslant 0$, *which implies, in particular, that* $v(0,0) = 0$. *The functional equation* (12.8) *has a solution, and one only,* $f(x)$, *which is continuous for* $x = 0$ *and zero at this point. The optimal value for n periods* $f_n(x)$ *of the dynamic program, defined by the constraint* $bx \leqslant x' \leqslant ax$ *and by the value* $v(x, x')$, *which is given by* (12.7), *is uniformly convergent towards* $f(x)$.

To discover whether assumption (β) is satisfied, we first calculate the optimal value for a period:

$$f_1(x) = \underset{bx \leqslant x' \leqslant ax}{\text{MAX}} v(x, x'), \tag{12.40}$$

then the function

$$u_0(x) = \underset{0 \leqslant z \leqslant x}{\text{MAX}} |f_1(z)|, \tag{12.41}$$

and we study the series with the general term $u_0(a^n x)$.

Example.   Let

$$v(x, x') = \frac{x}{x'^\alpha} \quad \text{with} \quad 0 < \alpha < 1. \tag{12.42}$$

It follows:

$$f_1(x) = \underset{bx \leqslant x' \leqslant ax}{\text{MAX}} \frac{x}{x'^\alpha} = \frac{x^\beta}{b^\alpha} \quad \text{with} \quad \beta = 1 - \alpha > 0, \tag{12.43}$$

$$u_0(x) = \underset{0 \leqslant z \leqslant x}{\text{MAX}} \left| \frac{z^\beta}{b^\alpha} \right| = \frac{x^\beta}{b^\alpha}, \tag{12.44}$$

$$u_0(a^n x) = \frac{(a^n x)^\beta}{b^\alpha} = (a^\beta)^n \frac{x^\beta}{b^\alpha}. \tag{12.45}$$

As $a^\beta < 1$, the series is uniformly convergent in any interval, and the theorem applies.

Bellman has made a detailed study [10] of the case where the value $v(x, x')$ has the form shown in the example at the beginning of this section, and he has shown in particular the form taken by $f(x)$ when the value reveals certain properties of convexity or concavity.

APPROXIMATION IN THE SPACE OF THE POLICIES

We have seen that, with certain assumptions, the sequence $f_n(x)$ defined by (12.7) converges uniformly towards a single solution $f(x)$ of (12.8). It is useful to observe, as Bellman has pointed out, that this property is still true if we replace the initial function $f_0(x) = 0$ by an arbitrary function continuous for $x > 0$ and zero for $x = 0$, the proof being identical with the one given above.

This property enables us to shorten the process of successive approximations by which we obtain $f(x)$, if we know $f_0(x)$ which is close to it. Although it is often difficult to make an a priori choice of such a function, we can usually obtain, through intuition or experience, a permanent policy $y_0(x)$ which is close to the optimal policy $y(x)$. The value of this policy $y_0(x)$ is given by

$$f_0(x) = v[x, y_0(x)] + f_0[y_0(x)]. \tag{12.46}$$

It might seem that we are making a blunder, for the solution of this equation also usually requires a sequence of approximations; but it is a much simpler equation than (12.8), where two functions $f(x)$ and $x'^*(x)$ have to be found, whereas (12.46) only requires one. Once we have calculated $f_0(x)$, we make this function our point of departure and use (12.7) to find a new policy $y_1(x)$:

$$f_1(x) = \max_{bx \leqslant y \leqslant ax} [v(x, y) + f_0(y)]. \tag{12.47}$$

But, if we compare this relation with (12.46), we see that $f_1(x) \geqslant f_0(x)$ for every x. If $f_1(x) \equiv f_0(x)$, the policy $y_0(x)$, which was first chosen, is optimal and the problem is solved. If not, we calculate $f_2(x), f_3(x)$, and so on. The property $f_n(x) \geqslant f_{n-1}(x)$ is satisfied for $n = 1$. Let us therefore assume that it is satisfied up to $n - 1$. Then

$$f_{n-1}(x) = v[x, y_{n-1}(x)] + f_{n-2}[y_{n-1}(x)] \leqslant v[x, y_{n-1}(x)] + f_{n-1}[y_{n-1}(x)] \leqslant f_n(x). \tag{12.48}$$

Hence the sequence $\{f_n(x)\}$ is a monotone increasing one, which gives added usefulness to the method.

Another method is as follows: Once $f_0(x)$ has been calculated as above, and we have found the policy (or one of the policies) which maximizes the expression between brackets in (12.47), we calculate its value by an equation similar to (12.46), and it is this value we substitute in (12.7) expressed for $n = 2$ in order to find the new policy; and so on, returning each time to the area of the policies. We shall study this method further in Section 22.

Example. Let us again take the example given at the beginning of this section, this time with

$$g(x) = x(2 - x), \qquad h(x) = x(6 - x); \tag{12.49}$$

$$a = 0.8, \qquad b = 0.6. \tag{12.50}$$

Hence we have a dynamic program in which the constraint is

$$0.6x \leqslant x' \leqslant 0.8x, \qquad (12.51)$$

and the present value, in accordance with (12.2′), is

$$v(x, x') = g\left(\frac{x' - 0.6x}{0.2}\right) + h\left(\frac{0.8x - x'}{0.2}\right), \qquad (12.52)$$

whence we calculate, taking (12.49) into account,

$$
\begin{aligned}
v(x, x') &= (5x' - 3x)(2 - 5x' + 3x) + (4x - 5x')(6 - 4x + 5x') \\
&= -50x'^2 + (70x - 20)x' + x(18 - 25x).
\end{aligned} \qquad (12.53)
$$

We will assume that the maximum is required only when

$$0 \leqslant x \leqslant 1. \qquad (12.54)$$

Let us first verify that Theorem 12.1 is applicable. Assumption (α) causes no difficulty. To check assumption (β) let us first calculate the optimal value for a period. Function $v(x, x')$ is a trinomial in x'; it is also concave, and we have

$$
\begin{aligned}
v(x; 0.6x) &= x(6 - x) \geqslant 0, \\
v(x; 0.8x) &= x(2 - x) \geqslant 0.
\end{aligned} \qquad (12.55)
$$

The roots are therefore external in the interval $(0.6x; 0.8x)$. Their average is

$$\frac{70x - 20}{100} = 0.7x - 0.2,$$

and we find that it is always less than $0.6x$ for $0 \leqslant x \leqslant 1$. Hence the function $v(x, x')$ is decreasing, and

$$\underset{0.6x \leqslant x' \leqslant 0.8x}{\text{MAX}} v(x, x') = v(x; 0.6x) = x(6 - x). \qquad (12.56)$$

The function $u_0(x)$ defined by (12.41) then becomes

$$u_0(x) = \underset{0 \leqslant z \leqslant x}{\text{MAX}} [z(6 - z)] = x(6 - x), \qquad (12.57)$$

whence

$$u_0(a^n x) = (0.8)^n x[6 - (0.8)^n x] \leqslant 6(0.8)^n x. \qquad (12.58)$$

The series with the standard term $u_0(a^n x)$ is therefore convergent. Theorem 12.1 now enables us to state that the maximal total value is a function $f(x)$, continuous for $x = 0$ and zero at this point. To find this function, and the policy or policies which correspond to it, we shall employ the second method of approximation given above in the area of the policies.

First Iteration:

(1) For our initial policy, let us take the policy[8]

$$y_0 = 0.6x, \qquad (12.59)$$

which is equivalent to buying only equipment of type B, by the interpretation given earlier. We then have

$$v(x, y_0) = h(x) = x(6 - x). \qquad (12.60)$$

The functional equation (12.46), which gives the total value of this policy, is expressed as:

$$f_0(x) = v(x, y_0) + f_0(y_0), \qquad (12.61)$$

in other words,

$$f_0(x) = x(6 - x) + f_0(0.6x). \qquad (12.62)$$

Let us attempt a solution of the form

$$f_0(x) = \alpha x + \beta x^2. \qquad (12\ 63)$$

By substituting this expression in (12.62), we find

$$\alpha = 15 \quad \text{and} \quad \beta = -1/0.64 = -1.5625. \qquad (12.64)$$

Hence we have a solution

$$f_0(x) = x(15 - 1.5625x), \qquad (12.65)$$

zero for $x = 0$ and continuous at this point; we know that it is the only solution.

(2) Let us now seek a new policy y_1 which maximizes the function

$$Z = v(x, y) + f_0(y), \qquad (12.66)$$

---

[8] We are only considering permanent policies, and the adjective is to be understood in the following discussion.

that is to say, such that

$$v(x, y_1) + f_0(y_1) = \underset{0.6x \leqslant y \leqslant 0.8x}{\text{MAX}} [v(x, y) + f_0(y)]. \qquad (12.67)$$

Function Z is, like v and f_0, concave and nonnegative in the interval $0.6x \leqslant y \leqslant 0.8x$. The half-sum of the roots is

$$\frac{70x - 5}{103.125} = 0.678x - 0.0485.$$

This quantity is always less than 0.8; it is less than 0.6 for $x < 0.956$ and greater than 0.6 for $x > 0.956$.

(a) If $x \leqslant 0.956$, Z is decreasing and we shall take

$$y_1 = 0.6x. \qquad (12.68)$$

(b) If $x \geqslant 0.956$, the maximum of Z is obtained for

$$y_1 = 0.678x - 0.0485. \qquad (12.69)$$

Second Iteration:

(1) Let us find the value of policy y_1, that is to say, the solution of

$$f_1(x) = v(x, y_1) + f_1(y_1). \qquad (12.70)$$

(a) For $x \leqslant 0.956$, we have

$$y_1 = 0.6x = y_0 < 0.956,$$

and in consequence,

$$v(x, y_1) = x(6 - x),$$

as in the first iteration. Hence we shall have as before,

$$f_1(x) = x(15 - 1.5625x). \qquad (12.71)$$

(b) For $1 \geqslant x \geqslant 0.956$, we have

$$y_1 = 0.678x - 0.0485 < 0.956,$$

hence

$$f_1(y_1) = y_1(15 - 1.5625y_1).$$

The equation can then be expressed:

$$f_1(x) = v(x, y_1) + y_1(15 - 1.5625y_1). \qquad (12.72)$$

Replacing y_1 by its expression (12.69), we find

$$f_1(x) = 0.119 - 14.61x - 1.244x^2. \tag{12.73}$$

(2) Let us now find a new policy y_2 such that

$$v(x, y_2) + f_1(y_2) = \max_{0.6x \leqslant y \leqslant 0.8x}[v(x, y) + f_1(y)]. \tag{12.74}$$

But we have

$$y \leqslant 0.8x \leqslant 0.8 < 0.956.$$

The expression of f_1 which appears in the second member is that given by (12.71), and Eq. (12.74) is identical with (12.67). Hence the optimum is obtained, and the definitive results are

$$y(x) = 0.6x, \qquad\qquad 0 \leqslant x \leqslant 0.956,$$

$$= 0.678x - 0.0485, \quad 0.956 \leqslant x \leqslant 1. \tag{12.75}$$

The value of this optimal policy is given, according to the value of x, by (12.71) or (12.73).

13. The Criterion of the Present Value

It is obvious that programs in which convergence is obtained solely by narrowing the domain of the decisions represent a very special case. Much more frequently, the value $f_n(x)$ of an optimal policy for n periods becomes infinite as n increases indefinitely, and we are then confronted with the difficulties outlined in Section 11. Fortunately there is a procedure which enables us to overcome this obstacle, a procedure which might appear very artificial were it not justified on economic grounds in the great majority of cases; this is the introduction of a discount rate.[9]

This is not the place to discuss the economic validity of the introduced rate, and for this subject the reader is referred to the works cited in the footnote.[10] Let us recall only that a sum s to be spent over n years can be considered as equivalent to the sum

$$s' = \frac{s}{(1+i)^n}$$

[9] The reason we did not introduce the discounted value in Chapter 1 is that it in no way alters the method of calculation. In point of fact, the economic considerations we have mentioned are equally valid for a program with N periods, provided their total duration is not too short.

[10] P. Massé, *Le choix des investissements*. Dunod, 1964; J. Lesourne, *Technique économique et gestion industrielle*. Dunod, 1960.

expendable immediately, if the rate of interest on the money (assumed constant over these n years) is i. By borrowing this sum s', we could, in fact, use it at once, and after n years would have to repay a sum $(1 + i)^n s' = s$, equal to the sum which would then be availabe to us. The value s' is called the "present value" or "discounted value" of s. If we introduce the parameter

$$r = \frac{1}{1 + i} < 1,$$

called the "coefficient of the introduced rate," the above relation becomes

$$s' = r^n s. \tag{13.1}$$

If, in a dynamic program, the value for each period is a sum of money, or a convertible asset, it is only logical to compare two policies by their total discounted values. Hereafter we shall assume that the value $v_n(x_{n-1}, x_n)$ of a decision during period n is to be understood for time n (end of period n). If we agree to take time 0 as that of reference, the present value of this decision will be

$$r^n v_n(x_{n-1}, x_n);$$

in particular, the discounted value of the first decision will be

$$r v_1(x_0, x_1).$$

Let us now consider a stationary program, defined by the model in Section 3. The introduction of discounted values will modify this model,[11] and if we call the discounted value of an optimal policy for n periods $f_n(x, r)$, the equations of type IV will now become

$$f_n(x, r) = r \max_{x' \in \Gamma x}[v(x, x') + f_{n-1}(x', r)]. \tag{13.2}$$

To sum up, $f_n(x, r)$ is the optimal value for n periods, discounted at the beginning of the first one: the sign MAX in the second member represents this same value discounted at the end of the first period. The quantity r is the coefficient of the introduced rate *for a period*.

It must be emphasized that the optimal policy as defined in this section, that is to say, the policy corresponding to the maximal or minimal value, usually depends on the coefficient of the introduced rate r. This is economically sound; in fact, "the transfer to a different time

---

[11] The new model obtained is semistationary in the sense of Section 10.

of the disposal of a given asset is the same as the exchange of two different assets, and the rate of this exchange is equivalent to a relation to price."[12] In an economic situation where the rate of interest is low (that is, where r approximates to 1), we should prefer a long-dated policy, whereas in the contrary situation, where it is high, it would be advantageous to gain money quickly in order to reinvest it. This does not entail any contradiction, but only a recognition of the economic circumstances.

Discounting has the effect of an exponential reduction of the values as the periods to which they correspond progress towards the future, and we can therefore conclude that the discounted value is usually convergent. The proof that there is a solution, and one only, is very similar to the one in the previous section. As the theorem is also a special case of one propounded by Bellman and proved in Section 21, we shall confine ourselves to its enunciation.

THEOREM 13.1.   *Given a dynamic program where Γx is defined for every $x \in \mathbf{X}$, where $\Gamma x \subset \mathbf{X}$, and where $v(x, x')$ is defined for all $x \in \mathbf{X}$ and every $x' \in \Gamma x$. If:*

(a) *$v(x, x')$ is uniformly bounded for every x such that $x \in \mathbf{X}$ and $| x | \leqslant c$, and[13] every $x' \in \Gamma x$:*

$$| v(x, x')| \leqslant m(c);$$

(b) *$x' \in \Gamma x$ implies $| x' | \leqslant | x |$ for each $x \in \mathbf{X}$;   or,   if   we   prefer,*

$$x \in \mathbf{X}   \text{implies} | x | \leqslant c';$$

the functional equation

$$f(x, r) = r \operatorname*{OPT}_{x' \in \Gamma x} [v(x, x') + f(x', r)], \tag{13.3}$$

where $0 \leqslant r < 1$, has one and only one solution which is uniformly bounded for every x such that $| x | \leqslant c$. The sequence $\{f_n(x, r)\}$ defined by

$$f_0(x, r) = 0, \tag{13.4}$$

$$f_n(x, r) = r \operatorname*{OPT}_{x' \in \Gamma(x)} [v(x, x') + f_{n-1}(x', r)], \tag{13.5}$$

converges towards $f(x, r)$. Finally, if $v(x, x')$ is continuous, $f(x, r)$ is also continuous.

---

[12] P. Massé, *op. cit.*
[13] If x is a vector $\{_1x, _2x,..., _kx\}$, the expression $| x |$ represents the modulus of x:

$$| x | = \sqrt{_1x^2 + _2x^2 + \cdots + _kx^2}.$$

112759

The assumptions in this theorem require some explanation. They cover, in fact, two classes of dynamic program. In the first, the correspondence Γx is such that $| x' | \leqslant x$ and is similar to that in Section 12 ($x' \leqslant ax$, or $a < 1$), but wider in scope; as a result of an introduced rate it is sufficient if the domain of decision does not increase, but the initial state x_0 is not bounded. The second class is that where the domain of decision is bounded but may increase temporarily.

What we stated in the previous section about approximation in the area of the strategies is always valid, and we shall not repeat it.

Finally, we may ask what happens when the coefficient of the rate r approaches 1 (a rate of interest close to zero). As a rule, $f_n(x, r) \to \infty$; but to what does the policy $y(x)$, which we obtain at the limit, then correspond? We shall answer this question in the next section.

14. Criterion of the Average Value per Period

We now have to consider the case where we do not wish to introduce a discount rate.

In a case of this kind, the average value for a period is often used as the criterion, and to define this concept more precisely let us return briefly to programs for N periods. Let $\varpi = \{x_0, x_1, ..., x_N\}$ be an arbitrary policy, and let

$$s_N = \sum_{n=1}^{N} v_n(x_{n-1}, x_n) \tag{14.1}$$

be the value of this policy. The average value per period is, by definition,

$$\sigma_N = \frac{1}{N} \sum_{n=1}^{N} v_n(x_{n-1}, x_n) = \frac{s_N}{N}. \tag{14.2}$$

When we compare two policies for N periods, it is clearly the same whether we consider the total value or the average value for a period; in other words, the criterion of the average value and that of the total value, used in Chapter 1, are equivalent. If $\varphi_N(x)$ is the optimal average value per period for an arbitrary initial state x,

$$\varphi_N(x) = \frac{1}{N} f_N(x). \tag{14.3}$$

If we assume, for simplification, that the program is stationary, the recurring equation of type IV for $\varphi_N(x)$ is deduced from (10.20) and (10.21) as

$$\varphi_n(x) = \underset{x' \in \Gamma x}{\text{OPT}} \left[\frac{v(x, x')}{n} + \frac{n-1}{n} \varphi_{n-1}(x') \right]. \tag{14.4}$$

When $n \to \infty$, and agreeing that the sequence $\{\varphi_n(x)\}$ converges towards a function $\varphi(x)$ representing the average value for a period of an optimal policy for an infinitude of periods, we obtain

$$\varphi(x) = \underset{x' \in \Gamma x}{\text{OPT}}[\varphi(x')]. \tag{14.5}$$

This equation prescribes certain conditions for the function $\varphi(x)$ (for example, if the constraint is of the form $0 \leqslant x' \leqslant x$, it is nondecreasing), but it does not completely determine it, since the value $v(x, x')$ does not enter the equation. However, $\varphi(x)$ can be obtained by successive approximations, using (14.4).

INTRODUCED RATE AND AVERAGE VALUE OF A PERIOD

The use of the criterion of average value can be justified, to the extent that any criterion can be, by the fact that it is equivalent, for all finite values, to that of the total value. But we may well ask what relation it has to the criterion of the discounted value. The problem has some importance in practice, for with equal rates of interest the coefficient of the discounted value approaches 1 as the length of each period decreases. If a decision has to be made every day, or every week, it would be pointless to introduce a rate with a coefficient in the region of 0.999 to 0.990. We shall see that in a case of this type the use of the criterion of the average value is justified, if only as an approximation.

With this purpose, let ϖ be a policy for an infinite number of periods with corresponding values v_1, v_2 ,..., v_n , and let the initial state x be the sole one, though the proof can be extended to the case where this is not so. Let us further assume that, for the given policy ϖ:

(a) The sequence $| v_n |$ is uniformly bounded, that is to say, whatever n may be, we have $| v_n | \leqslant m$.

(b) The series with the general term v is divergent, with the result that the total value (without an introduced rate) of ϖ is infinite.

Then, if we discount the values at time 0, the discounted value of ϖ will be

$$s(r) = \sum_{n=1}^{\infty} r^n v_n \tag{14.6}$$

and the series $s(r)$ is strictly and uniformly convergent for $0 \leqslant r < 1$, so that $s(r)$ is continuous in this interval and has a radius of convergence equal to 1.

Let $\sigma_N(r)$ be a quantity such that a sequence of N payments of this sum at times $1, 2,..., N$ has the same discounted value as the first N payments of policy

$$\sum_{n=1}^{N} r^n \sigma_N(r) = \sum_{n=1}^{N} r^n v_n ,\qquad (14.7)$$

whence

$$\sigma_N(r) = \frac{\sum_{n=1}^{N} r^n v_n}{\sum_{n=1}^{N} r^n} = \frac{1-r}{1-r^N} \sum_{n=1}^{N} r^{n-1} v_n .\qquad (14.8)$$

In accordance with (14.6), $\sigma_N(r)$ converges uniformly (for $N \to \infty$ and in the interval $0 \leqslant r < 1$) towards a function $\sigma(r)$:

$$\sigma(r) = \lim_{N\to\infty} \sigma_N(r) = (1-r) \sum_{n=1}^{\infty} r^{n-1} v_n = \frac{1-r}{r} s(r).\qquad (14.9)$$

In addition, as $r \to 1$, we have, whatever the value of N, and observing that

$$\frac{1-r}{1-r^N} = \frac{1}{1 + r + \cdots + r^{N-1}} ,$$

$$\sigma_N = \lim_{r\to 1} \sigma_N(r) = \frac{1}{N} \sum_{n=1}^{N} v_n .\qquad (14.10)$$

Hence σ_N is the average value for the first N periods. But in this case what happens to $\sigma(r)$ as $r \to 1$? We have

$$\lim_{r\to 1} \sigma(r) = \lim_{r\to 1} \lim_{N\to\infty} \sigma_N(r).\qquad (14.11)$$

Since $\sigma_N(r)$ converges *uniformly*, in the interval $0 \leqslant r < 1$, toward $\sigma(r)$ as $N \to \infty$, we can invert the order of the limits:

$$\lim_{r\to 1} \sigma(r) = \lim_{N\to\infty} \lim_{r\to 1} \sigma_N(r) = \lim_{N\to\infty} \frac{1}{N} \sum_{n=1}^{N} v_n .\qquad (14.12)$$

Thus we have

$$\left| \frac{1}{N} \sum_{n=1}^{N} v_n \right| \leqslant \frac{1}{N} \sum_{n=1}^{N} | v_n | \leqslant \frac{1}{N} \sum_{n=1}^{N} m = m.\qquad (14.13)$$

Hence the limit that appears in the last member of (14.12) exists, and we have

$$\sigma = \lim_{r\to 1} \sigma(r) = \lim_{N\to\infty} \frac{1}{N} \sum_{n=1}^{N} v_n .\qquad (14.14)$$

The limit in the second member is, in accordance with (14.9), the limit of

$$\frac{(1 - r)s(r)}{r},$$

or, more simply, the limit of $(1 - r)s(r)$. From this we obtain a first theorem:

THEOREM 14.1. *For every policy ϖ such that the values v_n are uniformly bounded, the discounted value $s(r)$ of ϖ, and the expression $(1 - r)s(r)$ approach the average value of a period for this policy, as $r \to 1$.*

Let us now assume that the v_n terms are uniformly bounded for *every* policy ϖ belonging to set $\mathbf{\Pi}$ of the possible policies:

$| v_n | \leqslant m$ for every $n > 0$ and every $\varpi \in \mathbf{\Pi}$, and let $\varpi^*(r)$ be an optimal policy as defined in Section 13. The value $f(r)$ of this policy is such that

$$f(r) = \operatorname*{OPT}_{\varpi \in \Pi} s_\varpi(r), \tag{14.15}$$

if we now call $s_\varpi(r)$ the discounted value of any policy ϖ. As a result, for every $r < 1$,

$$\frac{1 - r}{r} f(r) = \operatorname*{OPT}_{\varpi \in \Pi} \frac{1 - r}{r} s_\varpi(r) = \operatorname*{OPT}_{\varpi \in \Pi} \sigma_\varpi(r), \tag{14.16}$$

and at the limit,[14]

$$\varphi = \operatorname*{OPT}_{\varpi \in \Pi} \sigma_\varpi, \tag{14.17}$$

where φ is the average value of a period of the policy $\varpi^*(1)$.

THEOREM 14.2. *Let $\varpi^*(r)$ be an optimal policy as defined by the criterion of the discounted value and ϖ^* its limit as $r \to 1$. If $| v_n | < m$ for every n and every $\varpi \in \mathbf{\Pi}$, the policy ϖ^* is optimal in the above sense, and the average value of a period of the policy is given by*

$$\varphi = \lim_{r \to 1} (1 - r)f(r), \tag{14.18}$$

where $f(r)$ is the total discounted value of $\varpi^*(r)$.

---

[14] This reasoning will be developed more strictly in Section 26.

In practice, the method of finding the optimal policies by the criterion of the total present value in order to find them by that of the average value of a period is not to be recommended. In Section 36 we shall give a much more convenient algorithm, which is designed for the far more frequent case of a random future, but which can only be used when the number of possible states is finite.

CHAPTER 3

DISCRETE DYNAMIC PROGRAMS WITH A RANDOM[1] FUTURE AND LIMITED HORIZON

15. Introduction

The dynamic programs that we studied in the first two chapters have important uses. Nevertheless, most human activities, industrial, commercial, military, and so forth, are subject to an uncertain future or, where sufficiently accurate estimates are possible, to a random one in which future events can be forecast in terms of probability. With a random future, the systems under consideration are subject to external factors over which it is impossible to have complete control, and they evolve under the dual influence of the decisions and of these external factors. Hence the latter must be taken into account, assuming, of course, that they are sufficiently regular and well enough known for us to be able to assign a priori laws to them. In a forthcoming volume* we shall treat the case where the laws of probability have to be constructed progressively by making use in each period of the results of the previous ones (programs with adaptation), as well as the case where the external factors to some extent depend on the decisions of an adversary.

As in the last two chapters, we shall begin with a simple numerical example to familiarize the reader with the problems to be studied, though of course the method of optimization employed has to be justified in the more general form which we shall consider later. In the present example, the state of the system at the end of a period depends both on the decision and the random factor, the latter only entering after the decision has been taken. Later on, in Section 18, we shall examine programs where this order is inverted.

---

[1] Mr. Kaufmann prefers "random" as the translation of the French *aléatoire* to "uncertain" or the coined "incertain" used by some American writers. [Translator's note.]

* To be published by Dunod. Paris.

16. An Example of D.H. (Décision-Hasard) Dynamic Program

An article is restocked every three months, and our problem concerns the annual policy for restocking, in which the value of the stock at the end of the year is not taken into consideration. The quarterly demand u is random and its law of probability $\varphi(u)$ is given by Table 16.1 in which the cumulative probability $\Phi(u)$ is also given; this law of probability is treated as stationary to simplify the problem, in other words, it is the same for the four quarters.

The cost of stocking an article for a unit of time is $C_1 = 4$, and when the stock is exhausted there is a scarcity charge of $C_2 = 3C_1 = 12$. The orders that are not completed are lost, in other words, are not carried forward to the next period. In addition, the stock cannot exceed $S = 3$ articles, owing to considerations of space.

The cost of purchasing is proportional to the quantity bought, and the unit purchase price is the same in each period, so that it can be disregarded. The problem consists of minimizing the expected value of the sum of the cost of stocking and of the scarcity charge. The following notation will be used:

s_i stock at the end of period i,
σ_i stock at the beginning of period i (after purchase),
$a_i = \sigma_i = s_{i-1}$ purchase at the beginning of period i
u_i random demand in period i,
S maximal stock ($S = 3$).

TABLE 16.1

u	$\varphi(u)$	$\Phi(u)$
0	0.2	0.2
1	0.3	0.5
2	0.4	0.9
3	0.1	1
$\geqslant 3$	0	1

This problem of stocking can be represented as shown in Fig. 16.1, and the two distinct situations which may arise are given in Fig. 16.2.

situation (a): $u_i \leqslant \sigma_i$; then

$$s_i = \sigma_i - u_i = s_{i-1} + a_i - u_i ;$$

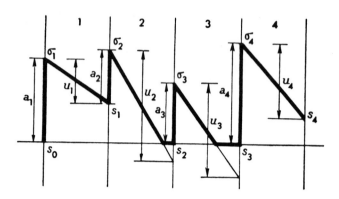

FIG. 16.1

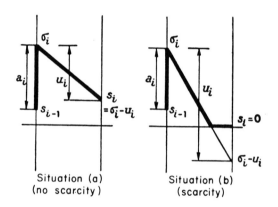

FIG. 16.2

the corresponding cost is equal to

$$C_1(\sigma_i - u_i/2) = 4(\sigma_i - u_i/2). \tag{16.1}$$

situation (b): $u_i \geqslant \sigma_i$; then $s_i = 0$;
the corresponding cost is equal to

$$\frac{1}{2} C_1 \frac{\sigma_i^2}{u_i} + C_2(u_i - \sigma_i) = 2 \frac{\sigma_i^2}{u_i} + 12(u_i - \sigma_i). \tag{16.2}$$

The following constraints enter:

$$s_{i-1} \leqslant \sigma_i \leqslant S; \tag{16.3}$$

that is,

$$s_{i-1} \leqslant a_i + s_{i-1} \leqslant S, \tag{16.4}$$

or

$$0 \leqslant a_i \leqslant S - s_{i-1}. \tag{16.5}$$

Let

$$q(\sigma_i) = \sum_{u_i=0}^{\sigma_i-1} 4\left(\sigma_i - \frac{u_i}{2}\right) \varphi(u_i) + \sum_{u_i=\sigma_i}^{3} \left[2\frac{\sigma_i^2}{u_i} + 12(u_i - \sigma_i)\right] \varphi(u_i)$$

be the expected value of the cost in period i.
    Let us begin with period 4.

PERIOD 4

At the beginning of period 4 we know the value s_3 of the stock. The expected value of the cost for period 4 is, for the optimal strategy,

$$f_1(s_3) = \underset{s_3 \leqslant \sigma_4 \leqslant 3}{\text{MIN}} q(\sigma_4). \tag{16.6}$$

If we calculate the values of q for $\sigma_4 = 0, 1, 2, 3$, we obtain

$$q(0) = \sum_{u_4=0}^{3} 12u_4\varphi(u_4) = (12)[(1)(0.3) + (2)(0.4) + (3)(0.1)] = 16.80,$$

$$q(1) = 4\varphi(0) + \sum_{u_4=1}^{3} \left[\frac{2}{u_4} + 12(u_4 - 1)\right] \varphi(u_4)$$
$$= (4)(0.2) + (2)(0.3) + (13)(0.4) + (74/3)(0.1) = 9.07,$$

$$q(2) = \sum_{u_4=0}^{1} 4\left(2 - \frac{u_4}{2}\right) \varphi(u_4) + \sum_{u_4=2}^{3} \left[\frac{8}{u_4} + 12(u_4 - 2)\right] \varphi(u_4)$$
$$= (8)(0.2) + (6)(0.3) + (4)(0.4) + (44/3)(0.1) = 6.47,$$

$$q(3) = \sum_{u_4=0}^{2} 4\left(3 - \frac{u_4}{2}\right) \varphi(u_4) + \sum_{u_4=3}^{3} \left[\frac{18}{u_4} + 12(u_4 - 3)\right] \varphi(u_4)$$
$$= (12)(0.2) + (10)(0.3) + (8)(0.4) + (6)(0.1) = 9.20. \tag{16.7}$$

Thence,

$$f_1(0) = \underset{0 \leqslant \sigma_4 \leqslant 3}{\text{MIN}} q(\sigma_4) = q(2) = 6.47,$$

$$f_1(1) = \underset{1 \leqslant \sigma_4 \leqslant 3}{\text{MIN}} q(\sigma_4) = q(2) = 6.47,$$

$$f_1(2) = \underset{2 \leqslant \sigma_4 \leqslant 3}{\text{MIN}} q(\sigma_4) = q(2) = 6.47, \tag{16.8}$$

$$f_1(3) = \underset{\sigma_4=3}{\text{MIN}} q(\sigma_4) = q(3) = 9.20.$$

PERIODS 4 AND 3

Let us now place ourselves at the beginning of period 3; s_2 is known, but so far, not s_3. On the other hand, for every decision σ_3 there is a corresponding distribution of probability of s_3. If we let the expected value of $f_1(s_3)$ be $\bar{f}_1(\sigma_3)$, calculated after this distribution of probability, we shall obtain the following results:

$$f_2(s_2) = \underset{s_2 \leqslant \sigma_3 \leqslant 3}{\text{MIN}} [q(\sigma_3) + \bar{f}_1(\sigma_3)]. \qquad (16.9)$$

We have:

$$\bar{f}_1(0) = f_1(0) = 6.47,$$
$$\bar{f}_1(1) = f_1(1) \cdot \varphi(0) + f_1(0)[\varphi(1) + \varphi(2) + \varphi(3)]$$
$$= (6.47)(0.2) + (6.47)(0.8) = 6.47,$$
$$\bar{f}_1(2) = f_1(2) \cdot \varphi(0) + f_1(1) \cdot \varphi(1) + f_1(0)[\varphi(2) + \varphi(3)] \qquad (16.10)$$
$$= (6.47)(0.2) + (6.47)(0.3) + (6.47)(0.5) = 6.47,$$
$$\bar{f}_1(3) = f_1(3) \cdot \varphi(0) + f_1(2) \cdot \varphi(1) + f_1(1) \cdot \varphi(2) + f_1(0) \cdot \varphi(3)$$
$$= (9.2)(0.2) + (6.47)(0.8) = 7.02.$$

Let us again use the notation

$$q_2(\sigma_3) = q(\sigma_3) + \bar{f}_1(\sigma_3); \qquad (16.11)$$

it follows

$$q_2(0) = 16.80 + 6.47 = 23.27,$$
$$q_2(1) = 9.07 + 6.47 = 15.54,$$
$$q_2(2) = 6.47 + 6.47 = 12.94, \leftarrow \qquad (16.12)$$
$$q_2(3) = 9.20 + 7.02 = 16.22.$$

Thence,

$$f_2(0) = \underset{0 \leqslant \sigma_3 \leqslant 3}{\text{MIN}} q_2(\sigma_3) = 12.94 \qquad \text{with} \quad \sigma_3 = 2,$$

$$f_2(1) = \underset{1 \leqslant \sigma_3 \leqslant 3}{\text{MIN}} q_2(\sigma_3) = 12.94 \qquad \text{with} \quad \sigma_3 = 2,$$

$$f_2(2) = \underset{2 \leqslant \sigma_3 \leqslant 3}{\text{MIN}} q_2(\sigma_3) = 12.94 \qquad \text{with} \quad \sigma_3 = 2, \qquad (16.13)$$

$$f_2(3) = \underset{\sigma_3 = 3}{\text{MIN}} q_2(\sigma_3) = 16.32 \qquad \text{with} \quad \sigma_3 = 3.$$

Let us proceed in the same manner and with the same notation.

PERIODS 4, 3, AND 2

$$f_3(s_1) = \underset{s_1 \leqslant \sigma_2 \leqslant 3}{\text{MIN}} [q(\sigma_2) + f_2(\sigma_2)]. \qquad (16.14)$$

We have

$$\tilde{f}_2(0) = f_2(0) = 12.94,$$
$$\tilde{f}_2(1) = f_2(1) \cdot \varphi(0) + f_2(0)[\varphi(1) + \varphi(2) + \varphi(3)] = 12.94,$$
$$\tilde{f}_2(2) = f_2(2) \cdot \varphi(0) + f_2(1) \cdot \varphi(1) + f_2(0)[\varphi(2) + \varphi(3)] = 12.94, \qquad (16.15)$$
$$\tilde{f}_2(3) = f_2(3) \cdot \varphi(0) + f_2(2) \cdot \varphi(1) + f_2(1) \cdot \varphi(2) + f_2(0) \cdot \varphi(3) = 13.60.$$

$$q_3(0) = 16.80 + 12.94 = 29.74,$$
$$q_3(1) = 9.07 + 12.94 = 22.01,$$
$$q_3(2) = 6.47 + 12.94 = 19.41, \leftarrow \qquad (16.16)$$
$$q_3(3) = 9.20 + 13.60 = 22.80.$$

Thence,

$$f_3(0) = \underset{0 \leqslant \sigma_2 \leqslant 3}{\mathrm{MIN}}\, q_3(\sigma_2) = 19.41 \qquad \text{with} \quad \sigma_2 = 2,$$
$$f_3(1) = \underset{1 \leqslant \sigma_2 \leqslant 3}{\mathrm{MIN}}\, q_3(\sigma_2) = 19.41 \qquad \text{with} \quad \sigma_2 = 2,$$
$$f_3(2) = \underset{2 \leqslant \sigma_2 \leqslant 3}{\mathrm{MIN}}\, q_3(\sigma_2) = 19.41 \qquad \text{with} \quad \sigma_2 = 2, \qquad (16.17)$$
$$f_3(3) = \underset{\sigma_2 = 3}{\mathrm{MIN}}\, q_3(\sigma_2) = 22.80 \qquad \text{with} \quad \sigma_2 = 3.$$

PERIODS 4, 3, 2, AND 1

$$f_4(s_0) = \underset{s_0 \leqslant \sigma_1 \leqslant 3}{\mathrm{MIN}}[q(\sigma_1) + \tilde{f}_3(\sigma_1)]. \qquad (16.18)$$

We have

$$\tilde{f}_3(0) = f_3(0) = 19.41,$$
$$\tilde{f}_3(1) = f_3(1) \cdot \varphi(0) + f_3(0)[\varphi(1) + \varphi(2) + \varphi(3)] = 19.41,$$
$$\tilde{f}_3(2) = f_3(2) \cdot \varphi(0) + f_3(1) \cdot \varphi(1) + f_3(0) \cdot [\varphi(2) + \varphi(3)] = 19.41, \qquad (16.19)$$
$$\tilde{f}_3(3) = f_3(3) \cdot \varphi(0) + f_3(2) \cdot \varphi(1) + f_3(1) \cdot \varphi(2) + f_3(0) \cdot \varphi(3).$$
$$= 20.08.$$

$$q_4(0) = 16.80 + 19.41 = 36.21,$$
$$q_4(1) = 9.07 + 19.41 = 28.48,$$
$$q_4(2) = 6.47 + 19.41 = 25.88, \leftarrow \qquad (16.20)$$
$$q_4(3) = 9.20 + 20.08 = 29.28.$$

Thence

$$f_4(0) = \underset{0 \leqslant \sigma_1 \leqslant 3}{\text{MIN}} q_4(\sigma_1) = 25.88 \qquad \text{with} \quad \sigma_1 = 2,$$

$$f_4(1) = \underset{1 \leqslant \sigma_1 \leqslant 3}{\text{MIN}} q_4(\sigma_1) = 25.88 \qquad \text{with} \quad \sigma_1 = 2,$$

$$f_4(2) = \underset{2 \leqslant \sigma_1 \leqslant 3}{\text{MIN}} q_4(\sigma_1) = 25.88 \qquad \text{with} \quad \sigma_1 = 2, \qquad (16.21)$$

$$f_4(3) = \underset{\sigma_1 = 3}{\text{MIN}} q_4(\sigma_1) = 29.28 \qquad \text{with} \quad \sigma_1 = 3.$$

Finally, the following strategies[2] are selected:

PERIOD 1

$$s_0 = 0, \qquad \sigma_1 = 2, \qquad \text{hence} \quad a_1 = \sigma_1 - s_0 = 2.$$

PERIOD 2

$$
\begin{array}{llll}
s_1 = 0: & \sigma_2 = 2, & \text{hence} \quad a_2 = \sigma_2 - s_1 = 2, \\
 = 1: & = 2 & \phantom{\text{hence} \quad a_2 = \sigma_2 - s_1} = 1, \\
 = 2: & = 2 & \phantom{\text{hence} \quad a_2 = \sigma_2 - s_1} = 0, \\
 = 3: & = 3 & \phantom{\text{hence} \quad a_2 = \sigma_2 - s_1} = 0.
\end{array}
$$

PERIOD 3

$$
\begin{array}{llll}
s_2 = 0: & \sigma_3 = 2, & \text{hence} \quad a_3 = \sigma_3 - s_2 = 2, \\
 = 1: & = 2 & \phantom{\text{hence} \quad a_3 = \sigma_3 - s_2} = 1, \\
 = 2: & = 2 & \phantom{\text{hence} \quad a_3 = \sigma_3 - s_2} = 0, \\
 = 3: & = 3 & \phantom{\text{hence} \quad a_3 = \sigma_3 - s_2} = 0.
\end{array}
$$

PERIOD 4

$$
\begin{array}{llll}
s_3 = 0: & \sigma_4 = 2, & \text{hence} \quad a_4 = \sigma_4 - s_3 = 2, \\
 = 1: & = 2 & \phantom{\text{hence} \quad a_4 = \sigma_4 - s_3} = 1, \\
 = 2: & = 2 & \phantom{\text{hence} \quad a_4 = \sigma_4 - s_3} = 0, \\
 = 3: & = 3 & \phantom{\text{hence} \quad a_4 = \sigma_4 - s_3} = 0.
\end{array}
$$

The optimal strategy lies in buying two articles in period 1, and in the three other periods: two articles if $s_i = 0$, one article if $s_i = 1$, and not to purchase anything if s_i is 2 or 3. Hence the expected value of the minimal cost is 25.88.

It is to be observed that in this problem the partial strategies for periods 2, 3, and 4 are the same, but we must not generalize and assume

---

[2] The concept of a strategy will be defined in Section 17.

that this will always be the case. Nevertheless, we shall make an analytic study of the present problem and show that the optimal policy for one period is optimal for the others. Later, we shall examine another problem where this is not the case.

To simplify the study, we shall assume that the quantities in stock need not be integral and that the distribution of the demand is continuous. The consideration of the discrete case, of which we have just seen a numerical example, would be exactly similar.

Let $h(u)$ be the density of probability of the demand u and

$$H(u) = \int_0^u h(\lambda) \, d\lambda, \qquad (16.22)$$

the corresponding distributive function. The maximal stock will be S and the number of periods N. Let

$$q(\sigma) = \int_0^\sigma C_1 \left(\sigma - \frac{u}{2}\right) h(u) \, du + \int_\sigma^\infty \left[C_2(u - \sigma) + C_1 \frac{\sigma^2}{2u} \right] h(u) \, du \quad (16.23)$$

be the expected value of the cost for a certain period during which the decision σ has been taken.

Let $f_{N-n+1}(s_{n-1})$ be the expected value of the cost of the last $(N - n + 1)$ periods when the stock at the end of period $(n - 1)$ is s_{n-1} and we are deciding on an optimal strategy. Let $\bar{f}_{N-n+1}(\sigma_{n-1})$ be the expected value of the cost of the $(N - n + 1)$ periods when we have made the decision σ_{n-1} at the beginning of period $(n - 1)$ and are finding an optimal strategy during the $(N - n + 1)$ last periods. We take $\bar{f}_0(\sigma) = 0$.

Let us assume that in period n we take decision σ and that in the following periods we adopt an optimal strategy; the costs for the last $(N - n + 1)$ periods will be

$$q_{N-n+1}(\sigma) = q(\sigma) + f_{N-n}(\sigma). \qquad (16.24)$$

Hence we obtain the recurring equation

$$f_{N-n+1}(s_{n-1}) = \operatorname*{MIN}_{s_{n-1} \leqslant \sigma \leqslant S} q_{N-n+1}(\sigma), \qquad n = 1, 2, 3,..., N. \qquad (16.25)$$

Let us begin with period N.

PERIOD N

We have

$$f_1(s_{N-1}) = \operatorname*{MIN}_{s_{N-1} \leqslant \sigma \leqslant S} q_1(\sigma) = \operatorname*{MIN}_{s_{N-1} \leqslant \sigma \leqslant S} q(\sigma). \qquad (16.26)$$

Let us study the function $q(\sigma)$.

$$q(\sigma) = \int_0^\sigma C_1 \left(\sigma - \frac{u}{2}\right) h(u)\, du + \int_\sigma^\infty \left[C_2(u - \sigma) + C_1 \frac{\sigma^2}{2u}\right] h(u)\, du, \quad (16.27)$$

$$q'(\sigma) = \frac{dq}{d\sigma} = C_1 \left(\sigma - \frac{u}{2}\right) h(\sigma) + C_1 \int_0^\sigma h(u)\, du$$

$$- C_1 \left(\frac{\sigma}{2}\right) h(\sigma) + \int_\sigma^\infty \left(-C_2 + C_1 \frac{\sigma}{u}\right) h(u)\, du \quad (16.28)$$

$$= (C_1 + C_2)H(\sigma) - C_2 + C_1 \sigma \int_\sigma^\infty \frac{h(u)}{u}\, du.$$

$$q''(\sigma) = \frac{d^2 q}{d\sigma^2} = (C_1 + C_2)h(\sigma) + C_1 \int_\sigma^\infty \frac{h(u)}{u}\, du - C_1 h(\sigma)$$

$$= C_2 h(\sigma) + C_1 \int_\sigma^\infty \frac{h(u)}{u}\, du > 0. \quad (16.29)$$

We observe that

$$\int_\sigma^\infty \frac{h(u)}{u}\, du < \int_\sigma^\infty \frac{h(u)}{\sigma}\, du = \frac{1 - H(\sigma)}{\sigma} \quad (16.30)$$

for $\sigma > 0$, and hence the integral $\int_\sigma^\infty [h(u)/u]\, du$ is convergent for all $\sigma > 0$. It follows that

$$\lim_{\sigma \to \infty} q''(\sigma) = 0. \quad (16.31)$$

In addition,

$$\sigma \int_\sigma^\infty \frac{h(u)}{u}\, du < 1 - H(\sigma), \quad (16.32)$$

thus

$$\lim_{\sigma \to \infty} q'(\sigma) = C_1. \quad (16.33)$$

Hence the curve $q(\sigma)$ has for $\sigma \to \infty$ an asymptote with a positive slope. Again, if $h(0) = h_0 > 0$, we have, for $u \to 0$,

$$\frac{h(u)}{u} \approx \frac{h_0}{u}, \quad (16.34)$$

and for $\sigma \to 0$,

$$\int_\sigma^\infty \frac{h(u)}{u}\, du \approx -h_0 \log \sigma; \quad (16.35)$$

and in consequence,

$$\lim_{\sigma \to 0} \sigma \int_\sigma^\infty \frac{h(u)}{u}\, du = 0; \quad (16.36)$$

thus,

$$\lim_{\sigma \to 0} q'(\sigma) = -C_2 .$$ (16.37)

Hence $q(\sigma)$ has the aspect shown in Fig. 16.3. This function is convex and has a sole minimum $q(\sigma)$ attained for a certain value $\sigma = \sigma_m$. We can distinguish two cases.

First case (Fig. 16.4). $S \geqslant \sigma_m$.

$$f_1(s_{N-1}) = \operatorname*{MIN}_{s_{N-1} \leqslant \sigma \leqslant S} q(\sigma)$$

$$= q(\sigma_m) \quad \text{if} \quad 0 \leqslant s_{N-1} \leqslant \sigma_m ,$$

$$= q(s_{N-1}) \quad \text{if} \quad \sigma_m \leqslant s_{N-1} \leqslant S,$$ (16.38)

with

$$\sigma_N{}^* = \sigma_m \quad \text{if} \quad 0 \leqslant s_{N-1} \leqslant \sigma_m ,$$

$$= s_{N-1} \quad \text{if} \quad \sigma_m \leqslant s_{N-1} \leqslant S.$$ (16.39)

Second case (Fig. 16.5). $S \leqslant \sigma_m$.

$$f_1(s_{N-1}) = q(S)$$ (16.40)

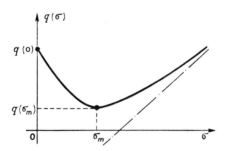

FIG. 16.3

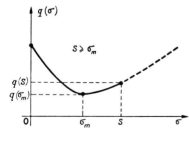

FIG. 16.4

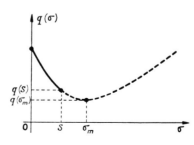

FIG. 16.5

with

$$\sigma_N{}^* = S \quad \text{for} \quad 0 \leqslant s_{N-1} \leqslant S.$$

OTHER PERIODS

First case. $S \geqslant \sigma_m$.

Let us assume that for the $(N - n + 1)$ last periods we have

$$f_{N-n+1}(s_{n-1}) = q_{N-n+1}(\sigma_m) \quad \text{if} \quad 0 \leqslant s_{n-1} \leqslant \sigma_m ,$$
$$= q_{N-n+1}(s_{n-1}) \quad \text{if} \quad \sigma_m \leqslant s_{n-1} \leqslant S, \qquad (16.41)$$

and that $q_{N-n+1}(\sigma)$ has, like $q(\sigma)$, a sole minimum for $\sigma = \sigma_m$ in the interval $0 \leqslant \sigma \leqslant S$, or, to be more precise,

$$dq_{N-n+1}(\sigma)/d\sigma \leqslant 0 \quad \text{for} \quad \sigma \leqslant \sigma_m ,$$
$$\geqslant 0 \quad \text{for} \quad \sigma \geqslant \sigma_m . \qquad (16.42)$$

Then again, for $\check{f}_{N-n+1}(\sigma)$, we have the following expression:

$$\check{f}_{N-n+1}(\sigma) = \int_0^\sigma f_{N-n+1}(\sigma - u)h(u)\, du + f_{N-n+1}(0)[1 - H(\sigma)]. \quad (16.43)$$

For $0 \leqslant \sigma \leqslant \sigma_m$, it follows:

$$\check{f}_{N-n+1}(\sigma) = q_{N-n+1}(\sigma_m)H(\sigma) + q_{N-n+1}(\sigma_m)[1 - H(\sigma)]$$
$$= q_{N-n+1}(\sigma_m). \qquad (16.44)$$

For $\sigma_m \leqslant \sigma \leqslant S$:

$$\check{f}_{N-n+1}(\sigma) = \int_0^{\sigma - \sigma_m} f_{N-n+1}(\sigma - u)h(u)\, du$$
$$+ \int_{\sigma - \sigma_m}^\sigma f_{N-n+1}(\sigma - u)h(u)\, du + f_{N-n+1}(0)[1 - H(\sigma)]$$
$$= \int_0^{\sigma - \sigma_m} q_{N-n+1}(\sigma - u)h(u)\, du + q_{N-n+1}(\sigma_m)[1 - H(\sigma - \sigma_m)] \quad (16.45)$$

and

$$d\check{f}_{N-n+1}\frac{(\sigma)}{d\sigma} = \int_0^{\sigma - \sigma_m} q'_{N-n+1}(\sigma - u)h(u)\, du \geqslant 0. \qquad (16.46)$$

It follows that the function

$$q_{N-n+2}(\sigma) = q(\sigma) + \check{f}_{N-n+1}(\sigma)$$

has, like $q_{N-n+1}(\sigma)$, a sole minimum for $\sigma = \sigma_m$ and that, in consequence,

$$f_{N-n+2}(s_{n-2}) = \underset{s_{n-2} \leqslant \sigma \leqslant S}{\text{MIN}} q_{N-n+2}(\sigma)$$

$$= q_{N-n+2}(\sigma_m) \qquad \text{for} \quad 0 \leqslant s_{n-2} \leqslant \sigma_m ,$$

$$= q_{N-n+2}(s_{n-2}) \qquad \text{for} \quad \sigma_m \leqslant s_{n-2} \leqslant S, \qquad (16.47)$$

and

$$\sigma_{n-1}^{*} = \sigma_m \qquad \text{if} \quad 0 \leqslant s_{n-2} \leqslant \sigma_m ,$$

$$= s_{n-2} \qquad \text{if} \quad \sigma_m \leqslant s_{n-2} \leqslant S. \qquad (16.48)$$

Since the assumption which we made earlier, namely,

$$f_{N-n+1}(s_{n-1}) = q_{N-n+1}(\sigma_m) \qquad \text{if} \quad 0 \leqslant s_{n-1} \leqslant \sigma_m ,$$

$$= q_{N-n+1}(s_{n-1}) \qquad \text{if} \quad \sigma_m \leqslant s_{n-1} \leqslant S, \qquad (16.49)$$

is satisfied for $n = N$, we have thus shown by recurrence that, whatever the value of n, the optimal strategy is the one we have already obtained for a single period, namely, period N. In addition, this strategy leads (several periods later) to our taking $\sigma_n^{*} = \sigma_m$, whatever the value of n. Thus, in the case where $S \geqslant \sigma_m$, even if at the beginning of the calculations s_0 is greater than σ_m, the optimal strategy is not to make any purchase until s_n becomes less than σ_m; then in each period we restock in order to reconstitute σ_m.

Second case. $S \leqslant \sigma_m$.

As in the first case, we assume that $f_{N-n+1}(s_{n-1})$ has a similar expression to that of $f_1(s_{N-1})$:

$$f_{N-n+1}(s_{n-1}) = q_{N-n+1}(S). \qquad (16.50)$$

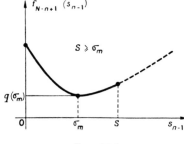

FIG. 16.6

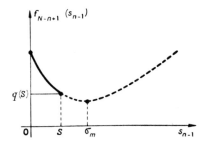

FIG. 16.7

We also assume that

$$q_{N-n+1}(S) = (N - n + 1)q(S),$$

a relation that is satisfied by $n = N$, since, by definition $q_1(\sigma) = q(\sigma)$. We then have, whatever $\sigma(0 \leqslant \sigma \leqslant S)$ may be,

$$\bar{f}_{N-n+1}(\sigma) = q_{N-n+1}(S) \tag{16.51}$$

and

$$q_{N-n+2}(\sigma) = q(\sigma) + \bar{f}_{N-n+1}(\sigma)$$
$$= q(\sigma) + q_{N-n+1}(S), \tag{16.52}$$

whence

$$f_{N-n+2}(s_{n-2}) = \underset{s_{n-2} \leqslant \sigma \leqslant S}{\text{MIN}} q_{N-n+2}(\sigma) = (N - n + 2)q(S) \tag{16.53}$$

and

$$\sigma_{n-1}^{*} = S. \tag{16.54}$$

Hence, whatever the value of n, the optimal strategy is the one which is optimal for only one period; it is always (if $S \leqslant \sigma_m$) to increase the stock to the value of S.

17. Mathematical Model of a D.H. Dynamic Program. Decomposed Form

In a general manner, we shall consider a system in which the state at time n is defined[3] by a "state variable" x_n .

At the beginning of period n (which starts at time $n - 1$ and finishes at time n), we know x_{n-1} and must decide to choose a quantity y_n , which we call the "decision variable." The domain of the possible decisions usually depends on x_{n-1} ; hence we assume

$$y_n \in \varDelta_n x_{n-1} . \tag{17.1}$$

This decision y_n does not entirely determine the state variable x_n , owing to the random influence of external factors, but we shall assume that the distribution of the conditional probability of x_n is

$$\text{pr}\{x_n \leqslant x \mid x_{n-1}, y_n\} = H_n(x \mid x_{n-1}, y_n). \tag{17.2}$$

---

[3] We shall not specifically study programs where the state variable and/or the decision variable have more than one dimension. In such cases the principle remains the same, but the numerical calculations become too lengthy for present-day computers if there are more than 2 or 3 dimensions.

The constraints which usually control the system are naturally more complicated to express than in the case where the future is certain. Let $\Omega_n(x_{n-1}, y_n)$ be the set defined by

$$x_n \in \Omega_n(x_{n-1}, y_n) \qquad \Leftrightarrow \qquad dH_n(x_n \mid x_{n-1}, y_n) > 0, \qquad (17.3)$$

that is, the set of the values of x_n to which the pair (x_{n-1}, y_n) may lead, or to be more precise, the set of values of x_n, where we have:

(a) either

$$\lim_{\substack{\epsilon \to 0 \\ \epsilon > 0}} \{H_n(x_n \mid x_{n-1}, y_n) - H_n(x_n - \epsilon \mid x_{n-1}, y_n)\} > 0, \qquad (17.4)$$

which means that the probability of x_n is positive;

(b) or the above limit is zero, but

$$\lim_{\substack{\epsilon \to 0 \\ \epsilon > 0}} \frac{H_n(x_n \mid x_{n-1}, y_n) - H_n(x_n - \epsilon \mid x_{n-1}, y_n)}{\epsilon} > 0, \qquad (17.5)$$

which means that the density of probability of x_n is finite but not zero.

For the set of possible decisions, the domain of the possible states x_n will be

$$\Gamma_n x_{n-1} = \bigcup_{y_n \in \Delta_n x_{n-1}} \Omega_n(x_{n-1}, y_n). \qquad (17.6)$$

Step by step we can define the domain of possible states at time n as a function of the initial state x_0 by a successive use of the correspondences $\Gamma_1, \Gamma_2, ..., \Gamma_n$:

$$\mathbf{X}_{0,n}(x_0) = \Gamma_n \cdot \Gamma_{n-1} \cdot \cdots \cdot \Gamma_1 x_0, \qquad n > 0. \qquad (17.7)$$

Given a set $\mathbf{X}_0$ of possible initial states, we take $\mathbf{X}_{0,n}$ for the corresponding set at time n:

$$\mathbf{X}_{0,n} = \Gamma_n \cdot \Gamma_{n-1} \cdot \cdots \cdot \Gamma_1 \mathbf{X}_0, \qquad n > 0. \qquad (17.8)$$

When we refer to a possible state at time n without further definition, it will be assumed to belong to set $\mathbf{X}_{0,n}$.

It is convenient to define a set of reference $\mathbf{X}$ containing all the possible values of the variables x_n, such that

$$\mathbf{X} \supset \left(\bigcup_n \mathbf{X}_{0,n} \right).$$

To each trinomial (x_{n-1}, y_n, x_n) such that

$$x_{n-1} \in \mathbf{X}_{0,n-1}, \qquad y_n \in \varDelta_n x_{n-1} \qquad \text{and} \qquad x_n \in \Omega_n(x_{n-1}, y_n),$$

is assigned[4] a present value $v_n(x_{n-1}, y_n, x_n)$; when x_{n-1} and y_n are given but x_n is not yet known, this value is a random variable. This implies that we cannot adopt the criteria of optimization used when the future is certain without altering them. We shall return shortly to this point, but before doing so we wish to emphasize the two properties which characterize dynamic programs, and which enable us to prove a theorem of optimality similar to those given earlier. These properties are:

(a) The distribution of probability of x_n depends only on x_{n-1} and y_n ; it is independent of the manner by which the system reached state x_{n-1} .

(b) In the same way, the value v_n of period n does not depend on what occurred before x_{n-1} .

For every sequence of decisions $\{y_n\}$, assumption (a) means that the random process $\{x_n\}$ is a Markovian process. Let us recall that in the discrete case we are considering, and always for given decisions, the random process $\{x_n\}$ is the mathematical model that enables us to calculate the distribution of conditional probability for x_n if we know the values of x_0 , x_1 ,..., x_{n-1} . A random process $\{x_n\}$ is Markovian if this distribution depends only, in fact, on the value of x_{n-1} , which is the exact assumption we have made. The model that we are studying in this chapter generalizes the concept of a random process in two ways, both logically connected. On the one hand, the state variable is a random function not only of time n, but also of the decisions taken; on the other hand (which is necessary so that we can define a criterion of choice for the possible decisions), we attach a certain value to all the changes of state of the system, which are the result both of the decision taken and of hazard.[5] A model of this kind is called a "decisional random process";

---

[4] In some problems hazard enters in the shape of a random variable z_n for which the distribution of probability depends on x_{n-1} and y_n . The state variable is then a nonrandom function of x_{n-1} , y_n , and z_n . The value v_n will be given in the general case as a function of these three variables. We shall eventually discover that v_n , in fact, only enters as its expected value $q_n(x_{n-1}, y_n)$, in which z_n is absent. This is why we did not consider it useful to give the general form of the model.

[5] The word "hazard" has been chosen, after discussion with one of the co-authors, as the most suitable (if not entirely satisfactory) rendering of the French *hasard*, and it must be stressed that it is used in the sense of "chance" and NOT of "risk" or "danger." The term *probability*, used by some writers (no doubt because of the law of probability associated with the word in operations research), was discarded by M. Kaufmann because of its numerical suggestion, and "chance" was likewise discarded. [Translator's note.]

dynamic programming under these conditions can then be defined as the study of these processes which possess the Markovian property.

To return to the definition of the criterion of optimization, let us assume a program with N periods, where N is finite. The initial state variable x_0 may be prescribed, or we may choose it, or its distribution of probability may be given. Unless the contrary is indicated, we shall assume that it is prescribed, but that we wish to solve the problem for a set $\mathbf{X}_0$ of states x_0. On the other hand, there can be no question of prescribing the value of x_N, for this is random, though not necessarily indifferent. The choice of $\varDelta_N x_{N-1}$ and of $v_N(x_{N-1}, y_N, x_N)$ will always enable us to take account of the eventual preferences with regard to x_N.

At the start of period n we know the quantities $x_0, y_1, x_1, ..., y_{n-1}$, x_{n-1}, but whatever criterion is chosen, the decision y_n cannot be logically based on them. The most common definition of a strategy, that is, of a set of rules which determine the decision to be taken in each period, regardless of the state of the system, is

$$\varpi_{0,N}(x_0) = \{y_1(x_0), y_2(x_0, y_1), ..., y_N(x_0, y_1, x_1, ..., y_{N-1}, x_{N-1})\}, \quad (17.9)$$

where the x_n and y_n terms satisfy the constraints deduced from (17.1) and (17.3). The total value $s_{0,N}(\varpi)$ of a strategy ϖ for a given initial state x_0 is not known in advance; but we can, at time 0, calculate a distribution of probability of this value: from (17.9) we deduce y_1, from which, by means of (17.2), we deduce the distribution of x_1, and as a result that of $v_1(x_0, y_1, x_1)$. Hence, step by step, we can calculate the distributions of $v_2, ..., v_{N-1}, v_N$ and thereby that of their sum[6] $s_{0,N}$. The different strategies cannot be compared except by means of a typical value of this distribution of probability,[7] and we shall assume that the expected value is used as the means of comparison. Hence we say that a strategy $\varpi_{0,N}^*(x_0)$ is optimal from x_0 to $n = N$ [for all values of x_0, since we introduced x_0 as a parameter in definition (17.7)], if the expected total value corresponding to it, such as it can be calculated in advance, is maximal or minimal. If Π is the set of possible strategies, the probable optimal value is

$$f_{0,N}(x_0) = q_{0,N}(x_0, \varpi^*) = \underset{\varpi \in \Pi}{\mathrm{OPT}}\, q_{0,N}(x_0, \varpi), \quad (17.10)$$

---

[6] In the same way, we can, at each time n, calculate a new distribution of probability of $s_{0,N}$, taking into account the variables which we know at that time. As the random progressively gives way to the known, the distribution contracts and at time N, the exact value of $s_{0,N}$ is known.

[7] In fact, if a policy ϖ_1 always leads to a greater value than that of a policy ϖ_2, the comparison is present; since we are not finding an optimum in the sense of Pareto, this observation does not provide a sufficient criterion.

where ϖ^* is an optimal strategy and $q_{0,N}(x_0, \varpi)$ the expected value of ϖ when the initial state is x_0.

Let us now place ourselves at time n; since x_{N-1} is given, with $x_{n-1} \in \mathbf{X}_{0,n-1}$, we are dealing with a subprogram for the $(N - n + 1)$ periods numbered $n, n + 1, ..., N$. In virtue of assumptions (a) and (b) above, this may be considered as an independent dynamic program, since the quantities $x_0, y_1, x_1, ..., y_{n-1}$ do not enter into it. Let us express in the form

$$\varpi_{0,N}^* = \{\varpi_{0,n-1}, \varpi_{n-1,N}\} \tag{17.11}$$

an optimal strategy of the initial program for N periods, where $\varpi_{0,n-1}$ represents the first $(n - 1)$ functions in the second member of (17.9) and $\varpi_{n-1,N}$ the remainder. We can consider $\varpi_{n-1,N}$ as a strategy of the subprogram defined above, although as such it does not satisfy definition (17.9) because of the appearance of the variables $x_0, y_1, ..., y_{n-1}$. To take an example, nothing can prevent us from choosing a stock of sewing machines by taking account of the global production of matches the previous year, although at first sight this behavior would not seem to be logical.

In the same way, we can separate the probable optimal value $f_{0,N}(x_0)$ from two terms. Let

$$\Phi(x_{n-1} \mid x_0, \varpi_{0,n-1})$$

be the distributive function of the law of probability of x_{n-1} when we leave x_0 and apply the strategy ϖ^* (or rather the first part of this strategy with which we are alone concerned), and let $q_{0,n-1}(x_0)$ be the expected sum of the first $(n - 1)$ periods, still retaining the same assumptions. In accordance with what we stated above, the sum of the probable values of the last $(N - n + 1)$ periods, which is none other than the probable value of the strategy $\varpi_{n-1,N}$ in the subprogram, only depends on x_{n-1}. Hence we can say

$$f_{0,N}(x_0) = q_{0,n-1}(x_0) + \int_{x_{n-1}} q_{n-1,N}(x_{n-1}, \varpi_{n-1,N}) \, d\Phi(x_{n-1} \mid x_0, \varpi_{0,n-1}). \tag{17.12}$$

If $\varpi_{n-1,N}(x_{n-1})$ would satisfy the following condition for maximization,

$$f_{n-1,N}(x_{n-1}) \geqslant q_{n-1,N}(x_{n-1}, \varpi_{n-1,N}), \tag{17.13}$$

which does not satisfy the equality, at least for certain values of x_{n-1}. But then the strategy

$$\varpi_{0,N}' = \{\varpi_{0,n-1}, \varpi_{n-1,N}^*\} \tag{17.14}$$

applied to the initial program would produce a probable value,

$$q_{0,n-1}(x_0) + \int_{x_{n-1}} f_{n-1,N}(x_{n-1})\, d\Phi(x_{n-1} \mid x_0, \varpi_{0,n-1}) > f_{0,N}(x_0), \quad (17.15)$$

which contradicts the assumption that the strategy $\varpi_{0,N}^{*}$ is optimal. Hence we have proved the following theorem which generalizes that of Section 8 for the case of a random future.

THEOREM OF OPTIMALITY 17.1.   *Any substrategy $\varpi_{i,N}^{*}(x_i)$ extracted from a strategy $\varpi_{0,N}^{*}(x_0)$ which is optimal from x_0 to $n = N$ is itself optimal from x_i to $n = N$.*

From (17.9) the above substrategy is expressed,

$$\varpi_i{}^{*}{}_N(x_i) = \{y_{i+1}(x_0, y_1, ..., x_i), ..., y_N(x_0, y_1, x_1, ..., y_{N-1}, x_{N-1})\}. \quad (17.16)$$

But the fact that it is optimal implies that the functions $y_n (n > i)$ do not depend on the variables $x_0, y_0, ..., x_{i-1}$. Since this is true for any value of n, and for any value of i less than n, we obtain the following obvious corollary:

COROLLARY.   *Every optimal strategy is of the form*

$$\varpi_0{}^{*}{}_N(x_0) = \{y_1{}^{*}(x_0), y_2{}^{*}(x_1), ..., y_N{}^{*}(x_{N-1})\}. \quad (17.17)$$

We shall take as the decision function for period n any function $y_n(x)$ defined in $\mathbf{X}_{0,n}$ and such that $y_n(x) \in \varDelta_{n,x_{n-1}}$ for every $x_{n-1} \in \mathbf{X}_{0,n-1}$. If $\mathbf{D}_n$ is the set of the decision functions for period n, the above corollary can then be enunciated:

Any optimal strategy from x_0 to $n = N$ is part of the set

$$\Pi' = \mathbf{D}_1 \times \mathbf{D}_2 \times \cdots \times \mathbf{D}_N$$

of the strategies formed by N decision functions.

Again, the proof of the theorem of optimality implies that relation (17.13) is, in fact, an identity, with the result that (17.12) can be expressed,

$$f_{0,N}(x_0) = q_{0,n-1}(x_0) + \int_{x_{n-1}} f_{n-1,N}(x_{n-1})\, d\Phi(x_{n-1} \mid x_0, \varpi_{0,n-1}). \quad (17.18)$$

If we apply this relation for $n = 2$, where $q_{0,1}(x_0)$ is the expected value of the first period, we have

$$q_{0,1}(x_0) = \int_{x_1 \in \Omega_1[x_0, y_1^*(x_0)]} v_1[x_0, y_1^*(x_0), x_1] \, dH_1[x_1 \mid x_0, y_1^*(x_0)]; \quad (17.19)$$

and, on the other hand, we have

$$\Phi(x_1 \mid x_0, \varpi_{0,1}) = H_1[x_1 \mid x_0, y_1^*(x_0)]. \quad (17.20)$$

Hence, the relation (17.18) becomes

$$f_{0,N}(x_0) = q_{0,1}(x_0) + \int_{x_1 \in \Omega_1[x_0, y_1^*(x_0)]} f_{1,N}(x_1) \, dH_1[x_1 \mid x_0, y_1^*(x_0)]. \quad (17.21)$$

Let us now assume that in the first period we take an arbitrary decision $y_1(x_0)$ instead of the optimal decision $y_1^*(x_0)$, but that we then adopt a substrategy $\varpi_{1,N}^*$ which is optimal from x_1 to $n = N$ and is taken from the strategy $\varpi_{0,N}^*$; the probable present value of the first period will be

$$q_1(x_0, y_1) = \int_{x_1 \in \Omega_1(x_0, x_1)} v_1(x_0, y_1, x_1) \, dH_1(x_1 \mid x_0, y_1). \quad (17.22)$$

The value $f_{0,N}(x_0)$ being optimal, we can say,

$$f_{0,N}(x_0) = \underset{y_1 \in \Delta_1 x_0}{\mathrm{OPT}} \left[q_1(x_0, y_1) + \int_{x_1 \in \Omega(x_0, y_1)} f_{1,N}(x_1) \, dH_1(x_1 \mid x_0, y_1) \right]. \quad (17.23)$$

Applied to the subprogram (n, N), this relation becomes

$$n < N - 1, \quad f_{n,N}(x_n) = \underset{y_{n+1} \in \Delta_{n+1} x_n}{\mathrm{OPT}} \left[q_{n+1}(x_n, y_{n+1}) \right.$$
$$\left. + \int_{x_{n+1} \in \Omega_{n+1}(x_n, y_{n+1})} f_{n+1,N}(x_{n+1}) \, dH_{n+1}(x_{n+1} \mid x_n, y_{n+1}) \right]. \quad (17.24)$$

We have thus obtained a recurring equation which generalizes the equation of type IV (9.7); for $n = N - 1$, we shall use the relation

$$f_{N-1,N}(x_0) = \underset{y_N \in \Delta_N x_{N-1}}{\mathrm{OPT}} q_N(x_{N-1}, y_N). \quad (17.25)$$

Let us recall the definition of the probable present value:

$$q_n(x_{n-1}, y_n) = \int_{x_n \in \Omega_n(x_{n-1}, y_n)} v_n(x_{n-1}, y_n, x_n) \, dH_n(x_n \mid x_{n-1}, y_n). \quad (17.26a)$$

As in the case of a certain future, we now have an algorithm which enables us to construct progressively the optimal policy or policies and at the same time determine their value. We apply (17.25), then (17.24) for decreasing values of n. But we have been able to obtain only a single type of recurring equation, the reason being that the first three types of equation in Section 9 introduce the final value, whereas the concept of an optimal policy from x_0 to x_N or from $n = 0$ to x_N is difficult to generalize in a random case.

On the other hand, we can imagine the case where x_0 has to be chosen, and if $\varpi_{0,N}^*(x_0)$ is an optimal strategy from x_0 to $n = N$, it is evident that the strategy

$$\varpi_{0,N}^* = \{x_0^*, \varpi_{0,N}^*(x_0^*)\} \tag{17.26b}$$

is optimal if x_0^* is the solution of the equation

$$f_{0,N} = \mathop{\mathrm{OPT}}_{x_0 \in \mathbf{X}_0} f_{0,N}(x_0). \tag{17.27}$$

In certain cases, a distribution of probability can be prescribed for x_0 ; if we assume that the precise value of x_0 is known at the moment when decision y_1 must be taken, the probable optimal value will be

$$f_{0,N}(H_0) = \int_{x_0 \in \mathbf{X}_0} f_{0,N}(x_0) \cdot dH_0(x_0), \tag{17.28}$$

where $H_0(x)$ is the prescribed distribution of x_0 .

THE CASE OF STATIONARY D.H. PROGRAMS

A dynamic program is called stationary if the following conditions are satisfied for $n > 0$:

$$\Delta_n x_{n-1} = \Delta x_{n-1}, \tag{17.29}$$

$$H_n(x \mid x_{n-1}, y_n) = H(x \mid x_{n-1}, y_n), \tag{17.30}$$

$$v_n(x_{n-1}, y_n, x_n) = v(x_{n-1}, y_n, x_n). \tag{17.31}$$

The subprogram defined by the extreme times $(k, n + k)$ is then identical with the subprogram $(0, n)$ except for the domain of definition of the initial state variable. The conditions (17.29) and (17.30) mean that the correspondences $\Omega_n(x_{n-1}, y_n)$ and $\Gamma_n x_{n-1}$ must also be independent of n. To be more precise, it is easy to show by recurrence that, if the domain of possible states at times $(n - 1)$ and n have a common portion, the correspondences Ω_n and Ω_{n+1}, on the one hand, and Γ_n

and Γ_{n+1}, on the other hand, are respectively identical in this domain, that is to say,

$$\Omega_{n+1}(x, y) = \Omega_n(x, y) \qquad \text{for} \quad x \in \mathbf{X}_{0,n} \cap \mathbf{X}_{0,n-1} \quad \text{and} \quad y \in \Delta x, \quad (17.32)$$

$$\Gamma_{n+1}x = \Gamma_n x \qquad \text{for} \quad x \in \mathbf{X}_{0,n} \cap \mathbf{X}_{0,n-1}. \quad (17.33)$$

Hence there is nothing to prevent our assuming

$$\Omega(x, y) = \Omega_{n+1}(x, y) \quad \text{and} \quad \Gamma x = \Gamma_{n+1}x \qquad (17.34)$$

$$\text{for} \quad x \in \mathbf{X}_{0,n} \quad \text{and} \quad y \in \Delta x, \quad (17.35)$$

$$\Omega(x, y) = \Omega_n(x, y) \quad \text{and} \quad \Gamma x = \Gamma_n x \qquad (17.36)$$

$$\text{for} \quad x \in \mathbf{X}_{0,n-1} \quad \text{and} \quad y \in \Delta x. \quad (17.37)$$

Step by step, we shall thus define correspondences Ω and Γ identical with each of the correspondences Ω_n and Γ_n in the domain of definition of the latter. Let $\mathbf{X}$ be this domain:

$$\mathbf{X} = \bigcup_{n \geqslant 0} \mathbf{X}_{0,n}. \qquad (17.38)$$

We observe that

$$\Omega(x, y) \subset \mathbf{X} \qquad \text{for all} \quad x \in \mathbf{X} \quad \text{and all} \quad y \in \Delta x. \qquad (17.39)$$

The stationary property enables us to simplify the notation, and we shall use $f_n(x)$ for the total optimal value of n periods when the initial state is x, and $q(x, y)$ for the probable present value of the decision y. Hence Eqs. (17.24) and (17.25) can now be expressed,

$$n > 1, \qquad f_n(x) = \underset{y \in \Delta x}{\text{OPT}} \left[q(x, y) + \int_{x' \in \Omega(x,y)} f_{n-1}(x') \, dH(x' \mid x, y) \right], \quad (17.40)$$

$$f_1(x) = \underset{y \in \Delta x}{\text{OPT}} \, q(x, y), \qquad (17.41)$$

with

$$q(x, y) = \int_{x' \in \Omega(x,y)} v(x, y, x') \, dH(x' \mid x, y). \qquad (17.42)$$

In addition, by assuming $f_0(x) = 0$, we can use relation (17.40) for $n = 1$.

An optimal strategy for N periods will be of the form

$$\varpi_N{}^*(x_0) = \{y_1{}^*(x_0), y_2{}^*(x_1), \dots, y_N{}^*(x_{N-1})\}, \qquad (17.43)$$

where $y_n{}^*(x_{n-1})$ is the first decision of an optimal strategy for $(N - n + 1)$ periods, and only, in fact, depends on $(N - n)$. Expressed differently, the strategy $\varpi_N{}^*(x_0)$ can also be defined as

$$\varpi_N{}^*(x_0) = \{y_1{}^*(x_0), \varpi_{N-1}^*(x_1)\}, \tag{17.44}$$

where $\varpi_{N-1}^*(x_1)$ is an optimal strategy over $(N - 1)$ periods when the initial state is x_1. It is this property (which is only a special form of the theorem of optimality) which is expressed by the recurring equation (17.40).

The term *semistationary program* is applied to one in which relations (17.29) and (17.30) only are satisfied.

Example of a stationary program. The example in Section 16 deals with a stationary program. The state variable $x_i y$ is represented by s_i, the decision variable y_i by σ_i (we might equally have used a_i, as will be seen from the two final lines of the present section), while hazard enters in the form of a random variable u_i.

D.H. DECOMPOSED FORM

Most practical problems have a simpler form than the one discussed at the beginning of this section. This form, which is called the D. H. decomposed form, is characterized, for the general nonstationary case, by the following properties:

$$\forall n: \quad H_n(x \mid x_{n-1}, y_n) = H_n(x \mid y_n), \tag{17.45}$$

$$\forall n: \quad v_n(x_{n-1}, y_n, x_n) = a_n(x_{n-1}, y_n) + b_n(y_n, x_n). \tag{17.46}$$

Relation (17.45) means that the distribution of x_n depends only on y_n. The transition from a point in the space $\mathbf{Y}$ of the decisions to a point in the space $\mathbf{X}$ of the states therefore has a Markovian property. In a similar way, relation (17.46) implies that the present value of each period contains two terms respectively attached to the decision (transition $\mathbf{X} \to \mathbf{Y}$) and to the hazard (transition $\mathbf{Y} \to \mathbf{X}$).

When these properties are satisfied, the recurring equation (17.24) can be put in a slightly different form, so that we then have

$$\Omega_n(x_{n-1}, y_n) = \Omega_n(y_n) \tag{17.47}$$

and

$$q_n(x_{n-1}, y_n) = \int_{x_n \in \Omega_n(y_n)} v_n(x_{n-1}, y_n, x_n)\, dH_n(x_n \mid y_n)$$

$$= a_n(x_{n-1}, y_n) + \int_{x_n \in \Omega_n(y_n)} b_n(y_n, x_n)\, dH_n(x_n \mid y_n), \quad (17.48)$$

whence

$$f_{n,N}(x_n) = \operatorname*{OPT}_{y_{n+1} \in \Delta_{n+1}x_n} \Big\{ a_{n+1}(x_n, y_{n+1}) + \int_{x_{n+1} \in \Omega_{n+1}(y_{n+1})} [b_{n+1}(y_{n+1}, x_{n+1})$$

$$+ f_{n+1,N}(x_{n+1})]\, dH_{n+1}(x_{n+1} \mid y_{n+1}) \Big\}. \quad (17.49)$$

The solution of (17.24) or of its equivalent (17.49) is greatly simplified by the fact that the integral in the second member depends only on the parameter y_{n+1}, whereas in the generalization it also depends on x_n.

Observation. Theoretically a program can always be changed to the decomposed form. We need only take as the new decision variable the vector

$$y_n' = \{x_{n-1}, y_n\} \quad (17.50)$$

and, in (17.46), take

$$a_n(x_{n-1}, y_n) = 0 \quad \text{and} \quad b_n(y_n', x_n) = v_n(x_{n-1}, y_n, x_n). \quad (17.51)$$

But this only amounts to a change of notation, which will evidently not simplify matters.

In a D. H. program with a decomposed form, each period includes two stages corresponding respectively to the decision and the hazard, which we shall designate (n, D) and (n, H), where n is the number of the period. We shall make an arbitrary agreement to consider that the decision y_n is taken at time $(n - \tfrac{1}{2})$, though this is not necessarily the case in the actual process. Figure 17.1 shows these conventions.

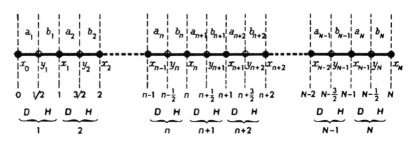

FIG. 17.1

Equation (17.49) can then be used in the following manner: after obtaining the expected optimal value at time $(n + 1)$ between that time and N, we calculate the probable optimal value from $N + \frac{1}{2}$ to N, taking into account the random value b_{n+1} of stage $(N + 1, H)$ for any given decision y_{n+1}. We then calculate the optimal value between times n and N, choosing the optimal decision y_{n+1}^* for each state x_n.

This procedure amounts to applying the theorem of optimality with the stage, and not the period, taken as the unit of time. We can easily show that it is legitimate to do so, by referring to assumptions (17.45) and (17.46).

Example. The example in Section 16 has a decomposed form; the value a_n attached to each stage of decision y is zero.

18. Mathematical Model of an H. D. Dynamic Program. Decomposed Form

So far we have considered that in any period hazard enters after the decision has been taken, but the order may equally be reversed, and we then obtain the following model.

With the system starting from a state y_{n-1}, which is really the value of the decision variable in the previous period, hazard causes it to pass to state x_n, in accordance with the law of probability:

$$\mathrm{pr}(x_n \leqslant x \mid y_{n-1}) = H_n(x \mid y_{n-1}). \tag{18.1}$$

The set $\Omega_n(y_{n-1})$ of the possible values of x_n is defined by

$$x_n \in \Omega_n(y_{n-1}) \quad \Leftrightarrow \quad dH_n(x_n \mid y_{n-1}) > 0. \tag{18.2}$$

We next take a decision y_n which satisfies the constraint

$$y_n \in \Delta_n(y_{n-1}, x_n). \tag{18.3}$$

With the trinomial (y_{n-1}, x_n, y_n) there is associated a present value $u_n(y_{n-1}, x_n, y_n)$.

The time diagram representing these conventions is given in Fig. 18.1.

We shall take $g_{n,N}(y_n)$ for the optimal expected value for periods $n + 1$ to N, that is, between times n and N, when the initial state is y_n. A recurring equation similar to (17.24) can then be obtained in the following manner. If, during period $(n + 1)$, hazard leads to state

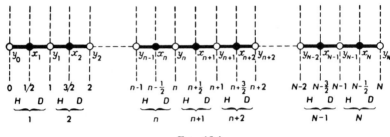

FIG. 18.1

x_{n+1}, if we take the arbitrary decision y_{n+1}, and if, finally, we adopt an optimal strategy during the following periods, the total value for periods $(n + 1)$ to N will be

$$u_{n+1}(y_n , x_{n+1} , y_{n+1}) + g_{n+1,N}(y_{n+1}).$$

The optimal value for state x_{n+1} is therefore given by

$$\underset{y_{n+1}\in\Delta_{n+1}(y_n,x_{n+1})}{\text{OPT}}[u_{n+1}(y_n , x_{n+1} , y_{n+1}) + g_{n+1,N}(y_{n+1})]. \qquad (18.4)$$

Finally, the probable optimal value is

$$0 \leqslant n < N, \quad g_{n,N}(y_n) = \int_{x_{n+1}\in\Omega_{n+1}(y_n)} \{ \underset{y_{n+1}\in\Delta_{n+1}(y_n,x_{n+1})}{\text{OPT}}[u_{n+1}(y_n , x_{n+1} , y_{n+1})$$

$$+ g_{n+1,N}(y_{n+1})]\} \, dH_{n+1}(x_{n+1} \mid y_n), \quad (18.5)$$

with

$$g_{N,N}(y_N) \equiv 0. \qquad (18.6)$$

It will be observed that Eq. (18.5) is obtained by reversing in (17.24) the order of the optimization and the calculation of the expected value.

DECOMPOSED H. D. FORM

We say that the program has this form if the following conditions are satisfied:

$$\forall n: \quad \Delta_n(y_{n-1} , x_n) \quad = \Delta_n(x_n), \qquad (18.7)$$

$$\forall n: \quad u_n(y_{n-1} , x_n , y_n) = b_n(y_{n-1} , x_n) + a_n(x_n , y_n). \qquad (18.8)$$

In the stationary case, we have

$$\forall y, x \in \Omega(y): \quad \Delta(y, x) = \Delta x, \qquad (18.9)$$

$$u(y, x, y') = b(y, x) + a(x, y'). \qquad (18.10)$$

Hence Eq. (18.5) becomes

$$g_n(y) = \int_{x \in \Omega(y)} \left\{ \underset{y' \in \Delta x}{\text{OPT}} [b(y, x) + a(x, y') + g_{n-1}(y')] \right\} dH(x \mid y), \quad (18.11)$$

where $g_n(y)$ is the probable optimal value for n periods when the initial state is y. This equation can further be expressed,

$$g_n(y) = \int_{x \in \Omega(y)} \left\{ b(y, x) + \underset{y' \in \Delta x}{\text{OPT}} [a(x, y') + g_{n-1}(y')] \right\} \cdot dH(x \mid y)$$

$$= \bar{b}(y) + \int_{x \in \Omega(y)} \left\{ \underset{y' \in \Delta x}{\text{OPT}} [a(x, y') + g_{n-1}(y')] \right\} \cdot dH(x \mid y), \quad (18.12)$$

with

$$\bar{b}(y) = \int_{x \in \Omega(y)} b(y, x) \, dH(x \mid y). \quad (18.13)$$

GENERALIZATION OF THE DECOMPOSED FORM

A comparison of the models of decomposed form described in Sections 17 and 18 shows that in all cases:

(a) The random transition from space **Y** into space **X** possesses the Markovian property; for example, in the D. H. program the distribution of the conditional probability of x_n when y_n is known is identical with that when y_n, x_{n-1}, y_{n-1} are known,

(b) The decisional transition from **X** to **Y** has a similar property, since in the D. H. programs the set Δ of the possible decisions y_n depends on x_{n-1} alone,

(c) Each of these two stages has a value which depends solely on the state before and after the transition.

The only difference between the two forms is that in the D. H. program the first stage is a decision and in the H. D. program it is a random one. In both cases the number of stages is even, but we can easily btain a generalization by considering a program with N' stages, where

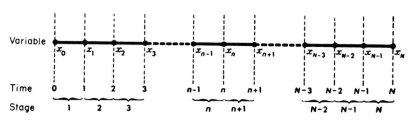

FIG. 18.2

N' is not necessarily even. Neither need stages H and D be alternate; hence we arrive at the following model.

We are considering a system where the state at time n is defined by a state variable x_n . The interval between times $(n - 1)$ and n is called "stage n." The stages are of two kinds:

(a) Stage D, in the course of which we must decide the state variable x_n , the possible values of which are a set known in advance:

$$x_n \in \Gamma_n x_{n-1} . \tag{18.14}$$

(b) Stage H, a random stage, during which x_n is determined by a law of probability depending on x_{n-1} :

$$\mathrm{pr}(x_n \leqslant x \mid x_{n-1}) = H_n(x \mid x_{n-1}). \tag{18.15}$$

Each stage of both types has a value $v_n(x_{n-1} , x_n)$ which can be zero. **N** will be the set of the numbers of the stages, **D** the set of the decision stages, **H** that of the random ones. Hence we have

$$\mathbf{N} = \{1, 2,..., N\}, \tag{18.16}$$

$$\mathbf{D} \cup \mathbf{H} = \mathbf{N}, \tag{18.17}$$

$$\mathbf{D} \cap \mathbf{H} = \varnothing . \tag{18.18}$$

A strategy will then be defined, as in Section 17, as a set of decision functions

$$\varpi_{0,N}(x_0) = \{x_{\alpha_1}(x_{\alpha_1-1}), x_{\alpha_2}(x_{\alpha_2-1}),..., x_{\alpha_d}(x_{\alpha_d-1})\}, \tag{18.19}$$

where $\alpha_1 , \alpha_2 ,..., \alpha_d$ are the elements of **D**.

The algorithm to be used for optimization is directly derived from our previous observations. If $f_{n,N}(x_n)$ is the total optimal expected value for $(n + 1)$ to N stages (that is, between times n and N), we then have:

If $(n + 1) \in$ **D**:

$$f_{n,N}(x_n) = \operatorname*{OPT}_{x_{n+1} \in \Gamma_{n+1} x_n} [v_{n+1}(x_n , x_{n+1}) + f_{n+1,N}(x_{n+1})]. \tag{18.20}$$

If $(n + 1) \in$ **H**:

$$f_{n,N}(x_n) = \int_{x_{n+1} \in \Gamma_{n+1} x_n} [v_{n+1}(x_n , x_{n+1}) + f_{n+1,N}(x_{n+1})] \, dH_n(x_{n+1} \mid x_n). \tag{18.21}$$

The reader can easily verify, in spite of the changed notation, that Eqs. (17.50) and (18.12) are found from the successive use of (18.20) and (18.21) in the correct order.

When $\mathbf{H} = \emptyset$ we have the model given in Chapter 1, and (18.20) is equivalent to (9.7). When $\mathbf{D} = \emptyset$ we have a random Markovian process.

19. Examples

(1) H.D. DYNAMIC PROGRAM[8]

The problem to be studied deals with the operation of machinery over a period of a year. Every three months the machinery is examined, and an estimate is made for repairs, on the basis of which a decision must be made whether to overhaul or to replace the old machinery by new. A discarded machine has a negligible value and the cost of a new one is $A = 10$. We know, as a function of the age i of the machinery, the law of probability for the rise in the cost of repairs. The aim in this problem is to minimize the expected value of the combined cost of purchases and repairs.

Our unit of time is three months, y_n is the age of the machinery at the beginning of a period (immediately after renewal or repair), and x_{n+1} is the increase in the estimate for repairs at the end of the period.

We assume the cumulative probability function $H(x \mid y_n)$ is known for x_{n+1}. When the latter is obtained, the decision is made either to repair the machinery, when we have $y_{n+1} = y_n + 1$, or to renew it, when we have $y_{n+1} = 0$. Hence

$$\Delta(y_n, x_{n+1}) = \{0, y_n + 1\}. \tag{19.1}$$

The present value is

$$u(y_n, x_{n+1}, y_{n+1}) = A \quad \text{for} \quad y_{n+1} = 0,$$
$$= x_{n+1} \quad \text{for} \quad y_{n+1} = y_n + 1. \tag{19.2}$$

Hence we have a stationary H. D. dynamic program, and Eq. (18.5) can be expressed here as

$$0 \leqslant n < N, \quad g_{n,N}(y_n)$$

$$= \int_{x_{n+1}}^{\infty} \min[A + g_{n+1,N}(0), x_{n+1} + g_{n+1,N}(y_n + 1)] \, dH(x_{n+1} \mid y_n), \tag{19.3}$$

where the first term in the brackets represents the decision $y_{n+1} = 0$, and the second, $y_{n+1} = y_n + 1$.

[8] This example was suggested by an article by P. Gardent and L. Nonat in the *Revue Française de Recherche Opérationnelle* (1963).

In working the problem, let us assume that

$$H(x \mid y) = 0, \qquad\qquad x < 1;$$
$$= 0, 2, \qquad 1 \leqslant x < y + 1;$$
$$= 1, \qquad\qquad x \geqslant y + 1, \qquad\qquad (19.4)$$

that is to say that the increase x of the estimate for maintenance can only have the value 1 and $y + 1$ with respective probabilities 0.2 and 0.8.

As the program is stationary, we shall take $g_n(y)$ as the expected total optimal value for n periods when the initial age is y, and $y'*$ as the optimal decision. We then have:

One period

$$g_1(y) = 0.2 \min(10; 1) + 0.8 \min(10; y + 1). \qquad (19.5)$$

If $x = 1$, repairs should be undertaken, so we take $y'* = y + 1$; if $x = y + 1$, the optimal decision is the same when $y \leqslant 9$ and is equal to 0 when $y \geqslant 9$. From which

$$g_1(y) = 0.2 + 0.8(y + 1) = 1 + 0.8y, \qquad y \leqslant 9;$$
$$= 0.2 + (0.8)(10) = 8.2, \qquad\qquad y \geqslant 9. \qquad (19.6)$$

Two periods

$$g_2(y) = 0.2 \min[10 + g_1(0); 1 + g_1(y + 1)]$$
$$+ 0.8 \min[10 + g_1(0); y + 1 + g_1(y + 1)]. \quad (19.7)$$

Let us first assume $y \leqslant 8$. Then

$$g_2(y) = 0.2 \min(11; 2.8 + 0.8y) + 0.8 \min(11; 2.8 + 1.8y).$$

In the first term we always have $2.8 + 0.8y < 11$, so that when $x = 1$ we must take $y'* = y + 1$. In the second term the inequality $2.8 + 1.8y < 11$ is equivalent to $y < 4.56$; hence the optimal decision is $y + 1$ if $y \leqslant 4.56$ and 0 if $4.56 \leqslant y \leqslant 8$. It follows, therefore, that

$$g_2(y) = 2.8 + 1.6y, \qquad\qquad y \leqslant 4.56;$$
$$= 9.36 + 0.16y, \qquad 4.56 \leqslant y \leqslant 8.$$

On the other hand, if $y \geqslant 8$, we have

$$g_2(y) = 0.2 \min(11; 9.2) + 0.8 \min(11; y + 9.2).$$

If $x = 1$, we must choose $y'^* = y + 1$; if $x = y + 1$, we must take $y'^* = 0$, and we have

$$g_2(y) = 0.2 \times 9.2 + 0.8 \times 11 = 10.64.$$

Hence, to sum up, we find

$$\begin{aligned} g_2(y) &= 2.8 + 1.6y, & y \leqslant 4.56 \\ &= 9.36 + 0.16y, & 4.56 \leqslant y \leqslant 8; \\ &= 10.64, & y \geqslant 8. \end{aligned} \quad (19.8)$$

Three periods

$$\begin{aligned} g_3(y) = 0.2 \min[10 + g_2(0); 1 + g_2(y + 1)] \\ + 0.8 \min[10 + g_2(0); y + 1 + g_2(y + 1)]. \quad (19.9) \end{aligned}$$

(a) $y \leqslant 3.56$:

$$g_3(y) = 0.2 \min(12.8; 5.4 + 1.6y) + 0.8 \min(12.8; 5.4 + 2.6y).$$

For $x = 1$, we must choose $y'^* = y + 1$; for $x = y + 1$, we again choose $y + 1$ if $y \leqslant 2.846$, and 0 if $2.846 \leqslant y \leqslant 3.56$. We then have

$$\begin{aligned} g_3(y) &= 5.4 + 2.4y, & y \leqslant 2.846; \\ &= 11.32 + 0.32y, & 2.846 \leqslant y \leqslant 3.56. \end{aligned}$$

(b) $3.56 \leqslant y \leqslant 7$:

$$\begin{aligned} g_3(y) = 0.2 \min(12.8; 10.52 + 0.16y) \\ + 0.8 \min(12.8; 10.52 + 1.16y). \end{aligned}$$

For $x = 1$, we must choose $y'^* = y + 1$; for $x = y + 1$, we must take $y'^* = 0$; and we have

$$g_3(y) = 12.344 + 0.032y.$$

(c) $y \geqslant 7$:

$$g_3(y) = 0.2 \min(12.8; 11.64) + 0.8 \min(12.8; 11.64 + y).$$

For $x = 1$, we must choose $y'^* = y + 1$; for $x = y + 1$, we must select $y'^* = 0$; and we have

$$g_3(y) = 12.568.$$

Summing up, we have

$$g_3(y) = 5.4 + 2.4y, \qquad\qquad y \leqslant 2.846;$$
$$= 11.32 + 0.32y, \qquad 2.846 \leqslant y \leqslant 3.56;$$
$$= 12.344 + 0.032y, \qquad 3.56 \leqslant y \leqslant 7;$$
$$= 12.568 \qquad\qquad y \geqslant 7. \qquad\qquad (19.10)$$

Four periods

$$g_4(y) = 0.2 \min[10 + g_3(0); 1 + g_3(y + 1)]$$
$$+ 0.8 \min[10 + g_3(0); y + 1 + g_3(y + 1)]. \quad (19.11)$$

(a) $y \leqslant 1.846$:

$$g_4(y) = 0.2 \min(15.4; 8.8 + 2.4y) + 0.8 \min(15.6; 8.8 + 3.4y).$$

For $x = 1$, we must take $y'^* = y + 1$; for $x = y + 1$, we must decide $y'^* = y + 1$.
We then have

$$g_4(y) = 8.8 + 3.2y, \qquad y \leqslant 1.846.$$

(b) $1.846 \leqslant y \leqslant 2.56$:

$$g_4(y) = 0.2 \min(15.4; 12.64 + 0.32y) + 0.8 \min(15.4; 12.64 + 1.32y).$$

For $x = 1$, we must take $y'^* = y + 1$; for $x = y + 1$, we must choose $y'^* = y + 1$ if $y \leqslant 2.091$, and $y'^* = 0$ if $y \geqslant 2.091$. We then have

$$g_4(y) = 12.64 + 1.12y \qquad \text{and} \quad 1.846 \leqslant y \leqslant 2.091;$$
$$= 14.848 + 0.064y \qquad \text{and} \quad 2.091 \leqslant y \leqslant 2.56.$$

(c) $2.56 \leqslant y \leqslant 6$:

$$g_4(y) = 0.2 \min(15.4; 13.376 + 0.032y)$$
$$+ 0.8 \min(15.4; 13.376 + 1.032y).$$

For $x = 1$, we decide $y'^* = y + 1$; for $x = y + 1$, we choose $y'^* = 0$. We then have

$$g_4(y) = 14.995 + 0.0064y, \qquad 2.56 \leqslant y \leqslant 6.$$

(d) $y \geqslant 6$:

$$g_4(y) = 0.2 \min(15.4; 13.568) + 0.8 \min(15.4; 13.568 + y).$$

For $x = 1$, we must take $y'^* = y + 1$; for $x = y + 1$, we must choose $y'^* = 0$. We now have

$$g_4(y) = 15.034, \qquad y \geqslant 6.$$

Hence, to sum up, we find

$$
\begin{aligned}
g_4(y) &= 8.8 + 3.2y, & y &\leqslant 1.846; \\
&= 12.64 + 1.12y, & 1.846 &\leqslant y \leqslant 2.091; \\
&= 14.848 + 0.064y, & 2.091 &\leqslant y \leqslant 2.56; \\
&= 14.995 + 0.0064y & 2.56 &\leqslant y \leqslant 6; \\
&= 15.034 & y &\geqslant 6. \qquad (19.12)
\end{aligned}
$$

For the definitive results, the optimal decisions are as follows:

(1) In the first period, repair the machinery if $x = 1$, or if $x = y + 1$ and $y \leqslant 2.091$; replace it if $x = y + 1$ and $y \geqslant 2.091$.

(2) In the second period, repair it if $x = 1$, or if $x = y + 1$ and $y \leqslant 2.846$; replace it if $x = y + 1$ and $y \geqslant 2.846$.

(3) In the third period, repair if $x = 1$, or if $x = y + 1$ and $y \leqslant 4.56$; replace it if $x = y + 1$ and $y \geqslant 4.56$.

(4) In the last period, repair if $x = 1$, or if $x = y + 1$ and $y \leqslant 9$; replace it if $x = y + 1$ and $y \geqslant 9$.

The minimal cost for the year is given by (19.12) and is shown on Fig. 19.1 as a function of the initial age of the machinery.

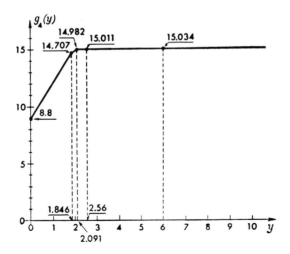

FIG. 19.1

(2)   D.H. DECOMPOSED FORM

This example, which we shall only enunciate, concerns the operation of a "dipole" of electrical production formed by a set of thermal plants and a hydroelectric plant. The dipole has to meet a demand for electric power which varies but is known in advance. The marginal cost of the hydroelectric kilowatt is much less than that of the thermal one which rises as the power required from the thermal complex increases, and older and less efficient plants have to be brought into operation.

Let us take a week as the period, and let us use the following notation:

x_n the quantity of water in the dam at time n;
y_n the quantity of water which would be in the dam at time $(n + 1)$ if no water had been added during period n ($y_n = x_n$ less the amount of water passing through the turbines during period n);
z_n the increase of water in the dam during period n;
M the maximal capacity of the dam;
Q the maximal quantity of water which the turbines can use in a period.

The problem lies in deciding at the beginning of each week the quantity of water that will be used during the week, which amounts to finding y_n. Let us observe that in practice it would also be necessary to apportion this quantity to the different hours of the week, so that we should be in the situation described in Section 7 where a subprogram has to be solved for each period. We shall, however, ignore this suboptimization, and will assume that the quantity of water needed for the week is always used in an optimal manner.

If we prescribe that only the quantity of water in the dam at the beginning of a week can be used in the course of the week, the constraint limiting the field of decision is

$$y_n \in \Delta x_n = \{y_n \mid \max(0, x_n - Q) \leqslant y_n \leqslant x_n\}. \qquad (19.13)$$

This constraint means that the quantity of water used by the turbines is between 0 (and then $y_n = x_n$) and $\min(x_n, Q)$.

Then again, let $J_n(z)$ be the cumulative probability function of z_n; as it is a seasonal phenomenon it will depend on n, so that obviously

$$x_n = \min(y_n + z_n, M), \qquad (19.14)$$

where the second term enters when the dam is full and surplus water must be discharged.

$$H_n(x \mid y_n) = \Pr\{x_n \leqslant x \mid y_n\} = \Pr\{\min(y_n + z_n, M) \leqslant x \mid y_n\}, \quad (19.15)$$

whence

$$H_n(x \mid y_n) = \Pr\{z_n \leqslant x - y_n \mid y_n\} = J_n(x - y_n) \qquad \text{if} \quad x < M,$$
$$= 1 \qquad\qquad\qquad\qquad\qquad\qquad \text{if} \quad x \geqslant M. \quad (19.16)$$

Finally, the present value is of the form

$$v_n(x_{n-1}, y_n, x_n) = a_n(x_{n-1}, y_n). \qquad (19.17)$$

It represents the saving of coal ensured by the use of a quantity of water $(y_n - x_{n-1})$, and to evaluate this saving, we must, on the one hand, calculate the cost of satisfying the weekly demand with the thermal plants only, and, on the other hand, the cost of electrical production when the quantity of water $(y_n - x_{n-1})$ is employed to the best use (see above). As a first approximation the present value (19.17) is a function of $(y_n - x_{n-1})$ only; at the same time, the amount of electricity produced from this quantity of water depends on the level of the dam and hence on x_{n-1}.

Relations (19.13), (19.16), and (19.17) define a nonstationary dynamic program with a decomposed form, and the problem consists in maximizing the total value over a given period such as one year.

CHAPTER 4

DISCRETE DYNAMIC PROGRAMS WITH A RANDOM FUTURE AND UNLIMITED HORIZON (GENERAL CASE)

20. Introduction

When the number of periods N included in a program approaches infinity, the problem of convergence, which arose in cases with a certain future, is also of great importance in cases when the future is random. Our study of convergence will be limited to stationary D. H. programs, which we shall classify as follows.[1]

.

CLASS 1

The expected total value for N periods has a finite limit[2] as $N \to \infty$, and whatever the strategy chosen.

CLASS 2

The expected average value per period calculated for N periods has a finite and nonzero limit as $N \to \infty$, and whatever the strategy chosen.

CLASS 3

Programs which do not belong to either of the above classes.

The inclusion of programs in classes 1 and 2 obviously implies the validity of the theorem of optimality 17.1 for an infinite number of periods

---

[1] Bellman [10] classifies them in three types. The first two, in which the functions v and H must satisfy certain conditions, are included respectively in classes 1 and 2 above. Bellman's type 3 contains programs which are not of either type 1 or 2, and these may belong to any of our three classes.

[2] Nevertheless, with certain strategies, if we maximize the function of value attached to the program, the expected value may approach $(-\infty)$, and in the case of minimization $(+\infty)$.

when we employ the criterion of the expected total value (class 1) or of the average value of a period (class 2).

The above classification makes no reference to the criterion of the total discounted value, but we shall discover that this criterion in fact applies to the first two classes and can also lead to programs of class 3. We may regard the criterion of the nondiscounted total value as a special case of the one where discounting enters; also, we saw in Section 14 that the same applies to the criterion of the average value of a period when the coefficient of discounting approaches 1.

21. Criterion of the Expected Total Value

In Section 13 we examined what is meant by the present (or discounted) value of a policy with a certain future, and a theorem for the convergence of this value was given. We shall now enunciate and prove a more general theorem.

As in Section 13, the value $v_n(x_{n-1}, y_n, x_n)$ is assumed to be known at time n at the end of period n. We shall use r for the coefficient of discounting *per period*; hence the discounted value of v_n at time 0 is

$$r^n v_n(x_{n-1}, y_n, x_n).$$

The recurring equation (17.40) then becomes

$$f_n(x, r) = r \operatorname*{OPT}_{y \in \Delta x} \left[q(x, y) + \int_{x' \in \Omega(x,y)} f_{n-1}(x', r) \cdot dH(x' \mid x, y) \right] \quad (21.1)$$

where $f_n(x, r)$ is the present optimal e.v.[3] of n periods. Equation (21.1) is valid for $n \geqslant 1$ on the condition that we assume

$$f_0(x, r) \equiv 0. \quad (21.2)$$

In order to obtain the solution of

$$f(x, r) = r \operatorname*{OPT}_{y \in \Delta x} \left[q(x, y) + \int_{x' \in \Omega(x,y)} f(x', r) \cdot dH(x' \mid x, y) \right], \quad (21.3)$$

obtained formally by making n approach ∞ in (21.1), we shall proceed as in Section 12. The reader who is pressed for time can omit the following proof and proceed directly to the enunciation of Theorem 21.1.

---

[3] Hereafter we shall often use this abbreviation for expected value.

EXISTENCE

To simplify the notation, we shall assume

$$T(x, r, y, f_{n-1}) = r \left[q(x, y) + \int_{x' \in \Omega(x,y)} f_{n-1}(x', r) \cdot dH(x' \mid x, y) \right]. \quad (21.4)$$

Let us consider a case where the maximum is required; Eq. (21.1) is then expressed

$$f_n(x, r) = \max_{y \in \Delta x} T(x, r, y, f_{n-1}). \quad (21.5)$$

Let $y^{(n-1)}(x)$ be the first decision of an optimal strategy for n periods. In accordance with this definition, we have, for $n \geqslant 0$:

$$f_{n+1}(x, r) = T(x, r, y^{(n)}(x), f_n) \quad (21.6)$$

and

$$f_{n+1}(x, r) \geqslant T(x, r, y^{(n+1)}(x), f_n), \quad (21.7)$$

since $y^{(n+1)}(x) \in \Delta x$. In the same way,

$$f_{n+2}(x, r) = T(x, r, y^{(n+1)}(x), f_{n+1}), \quad (21.8)$$

and

$$f_{n+2}(x, r) \geqslant T(x, r, y^{(n)}(x), f_{n+1}). \quad (21.9)$$

From (21.6) and (21.9) on the one hand, and from (21.7) and (21.8) on the other, we deduce

$$f_{n+1}(x, r) - f_{n+2}(x, r) \leqslant T(x, r, y^{(n)}(x), f_n) - T(x, r, y^n(x), f_{n+1}) = T_1, \quad (21.10)$$

$$f_{n+1}(x, r) - f_{n+2}(x, r) \geqslant T(x, r, y^{(n+1)}(x), f_n)$$
$$- T(x, r, y^{(n+1)}(x), f_{n+1}) = T_2; \quad (21.11)$$

from the property already used to prove (12.16) in Section 12, we then have

$$| f_{n+1}(x, r) - f_{n+2}(x, r) | \leqslant \max(| T_1 |, | T_2 |). \quad (21.12)$$

It is easy to show that this inequality remains unchanged in the case of the minimum, and hereafter we shall treat the two cases simultaneously.

Returning to the definition (21.4) of T, we see that (21.12) becomes

$$| f_{n+1}(x, r) - f_{n+2}(x, r) |$$

$$\leqslant r \max \left\{ \left| \int_{x' \in \Omega[x, y^{(n)}(x)]} [f_n(x', r) - f_{n+1}(x', r)] \cdot dH[x' \mid x, y^{(n)}(x)] \right|, \right.$$

$$\left. \left| \int_{x' \in \Omega[x, y^{(n+1)}(x)]} [f_n(x', r) - f_{n+1}(x', r)] \cdot dH[x' \mid x, y^{(n+1)}(x)] \right| \right\}. \quad (21.13)$$

Let $\mathbf{D}(c)$ be the part of set $\mathbf{X}$ included in the interval $|x| \leqslant c$, where c is any nonnegative number:

$$\mathbf{D}(c) = \{x \mid x \in \mathbf{X}, \mid x \mid \leqslant c\}, \tag{21.14}$$

and let us assume, for every x such that the set $\mathbf{D}(x)$ is not empty,[4]

$$u_n(x, r) = \sup_{z \in \mathbf{D}(x)} |f_n(z, r) - f_{n+1}(z, r)|. \tag{21.15}$$

Lastly, let $z_n(x)$ be a value of z for which the maximum is reached in (21.15):

$$u_n(x, r) = |f_n[z_n(x), r] - f_{n+1}[z_n(x), r]|. \tag{21.16}$$

If the upper bound is never reached in (21.15), we shall take for $z_n(x)$ a quantity such that the difference between the two members of (21.16) is less than a quantity ϵ which can be as small as we wish. The inequalities that follow will be obtained by making ϵ approach zero (see observation 2 in Section 3).

Since $z_n(x) \in \mathbf{D}(x) \subset \mathbf{X}$ for every n, we can replace x by $z_{n+1}(x)$ in (21.13), and the left member is then equal to $u_{n+1}(x, r)$, which gives us

$$u_{n+1}(x, r) \leqslant r \max$$

$$\left\{ \left| \int_{x' \in \Omega[z_{n+1}, y^{(n)}(z_{n+1})]} [f_n(x', r) - f_{n+1}(x', r)] \, dH[x' \mid z_{n+1}, y^{(n)}(z_{n+1})] \right|, \right.$$

$$\left. \left| \int_{x' \in \Omega[z_{n+1}, y^{(n+1)}(z_{n+1})]} [f_n(x', r) - f_{n+1}(x', r)] \, dH[x' \mid z_{n+1}, y^{(n+1)}(z_{n+1})] \right| \right\}, \tag{21.17}$$

where

$$z_{n+1}(x) \in \mathbf{D}(x) \tag{21.18}$$

and

$$y^{(n)}(z_{n+1}), \, y^{(n+1)}(z_{n+1}) \in \Delta z_{n+1}(x). \tag{21.19}$$

Inequality (21.17) is fundamental in studying the sequence $f_n(x, r)$. Indeed, it enables us to establish the conditions needed for the convergence of the series with the general term $u_n(x, r)$.

---

[4] Let $b \geqslant 0$ be the lower bound of $|x|$, in other words, the largest nonnegative number such that $x \in \mathbf{X}$ entails $|x| \geqslant b$.
(a)   If b is a minimum, that is, if $b \in \mathbf{X}$ and/or $(-b) \in \mathbf{X}$, $u_n(x, r)$ is defined for every x such that $|x| \geqslant b$, whether or not x belongs to $\mathbf{X}$.
(b)   If b is not a minimum, $u_n(x, r)$ is defined for every x such that $|x| > b$.

Now, it is easy to prove the inequality

$$| f_N(x, r)| \leqslant \sum_{n=0}^{N-1} u_n(x, r), \tag{21.20}$$

which is similar to (12.30) and which allows us to reach a conclusion as to the behavior of $f_N(x, r)$ when $N \to \infty$.

Let us assume that, for every value of $x \in \mathbf{D}(c)$, the domain Γx of the possible states after a period

$$\Gamma x = \bigcup_{y \in \Delta x} \Omega(x, y), \tag{21.21}$$

is uniformly bounded for its absolute value by a quantity $\theta(c)$, in other words, that $x \in \mathbf{D}(c)$ and $x' \in \Gamma x$ entail $| x' | \leqslant \theta(c)$; that is to say, for every $x \in \mathbf{D}(c)$ and $y \in \Delta x$,

$$\Omega(x, y) \subset \Gamma x \subset \mathbf{D}[\theta(c)]. \tag{21.22}$$

The domain of integration of each of the integrals appearing in (21.17) is then contained in $\mathbf{D}[\theta(x)]$. The expression

$$| f_n(x', r) - f_{n+1}(x', r)| \tag{21.23}$$

is always less than or equal to $u_n[\theta(x), r]$; in consequence, each of the integrals is overvalued by

$$\int u_n[\theta(x), r] \, dH = u_n[\theta(x), r].$$

Hence we have

$$u_{n+1}(x, r) \leqslant r u_n[\theta(x), r]. \tag{21.24}$$

We will consider for the moment the case where discounting actually takes place, in other words, where $| r | < 1$. In accordance with Bellman, we shall distinguish two cases of uniform convergence for $| r | < 1$:

(a) $\theta(x) = x$; in other words, from the definition of $\theta(x)$: $x' \in \Gamma x$ entails $| x' | \leqslant | x |$. Expressed differently, the domain of possible states can never increase. Inequality (21.24) then becomes

$$u_{n+1}(x, r) \leqslant r u_n(x, r), \tag{21.25}$$

whence, progressively,

$$u_n(x, r) \leqslant r^n u_0(x, r). \tag{21.26}$$

This proves the convergence of the series u_n, with the obvious reservation that $u_0(x, r)$ must be finite. Now, by the definition (21.15) of u_n, we have

$$u_0(x, r) = \operatorname*{SUP}_{z \in \mathbf{D}(x)} |f_1(z, r)| = r \operatorname*{SUP}_{z \in \mathbf{D}(x)} |\operatorname*{OPT}_{y \in \Delta z} q(z, y)|. \qquad (21.27)$$

Let us assume, for every c such that $\mathbf{D}(c)$ is not empty,

$$\alpha(c) = \operatorname*{SUP}_{\substack{x \in \mathbf{D}(c) \\ y \in \Delta x}} |q(x, y)| \geqslant \frac{u_0(c, r)}{r}, \qquad (21.28)$$

and let us assume[5] that $\alpha(c) < \infty$ for every $c \geqslant 0$; that is to say, $|q(x, y)|$ is uniformly bounded in every domain $x \in \mathbf{D}(c)$, $y \in \Delta x$. Since $u_0(x, r)$ is by definition a nondecreasing function of x, we have

$$u_n(x, r) \leqslant r^{n+1} \alpha(c). \qquad (21.29)$$

As a result, for any given value $r < 1$, the series $u_n(x, r)$ is *uniformly* convergent in every domain $x \in \mathbf{D}(c)$. Hence, in accordance with (21.20), the sequence $f_N(x, r)$ is absolutely and uniformly convergent in such a domain, and its limit $f(x, r)$ is uniformly bounded:

$$|f(x, r)| \leqslant \frac{r}{1 - r} \cdot \alpha(c). \qquad (21.30)$$

The uniform convergence also shows that $f(x, r)$ is the solution of (21.4).

It will be observed that the condition $\alpha(c) < \infty$ is very open; in fact, one can scarcely conceive of a dynamic program with practical significance which would not satisfy it.

(b) $\forall x \in \mathbf{X}$, $\theta(x) \leqslant c'$, that is to say, the domain of possible states after a certain number of periods is bounded: $\mathbf{X} = \mathbf{D}(c')$ and also $x \in \mathbf{X}$ entails $|x| \leqslant c'$. Inequality (21.24) then implies

$$\forall x, \qquad u_{n+1}(x, r) \leqslant r u_n(c', r), \qquad (21.31)$$

and in particular,

$$u_{n+1}(c', r) \leqslant r u_n(c', r) \leqslant r^{n+1} u_0(c', r), \qquad (21.32)$$

whence

$$\forall x, \qquad u_n(x, r) \leqslant r^{n+1} \alpha(c'), \qquad (21.33)$$

---

[5] It would be sufficient to assume that $u_0(c, r) < \infty$; Theorem 21.1 would then be valid for this less restrictive assumption, but Theorem 23.1 might not apply for certain strategies.

where $\alpha(c)$ is defined by (21.28). Convergence is then assured if $\alpha(c') < \infty$, and we draw the same conclusions as before, including the inequality

$$|f(x, r)| \leqslant \frac{r}{1 - r} \alpha(c'), \qquad \forall x \in \mathbf{X} \quad \text{and} \quad |r| < 1. \tag{21.34}$$

It will be observed that the relations (21.33) and (21.34) are satisfied for every domain $x \in \mathbf{D}(c)$ since, whatever the value of c, we have $\mathbf{D}(c) \subset \mathbf{X}$.

UNIQUENESS

It remains to be considered whether $f(x, r)$ is the sole solution. First, we must notice that if the optimum is actually reached in Eq. (21.3) (see observation 2 in Section 3), there is a function $\mathbf{Y}(x, r)$ which is not usually univocal[6] and which defines the set of optimal decisions. A permanent strategy will be one in which the function of decision is the same in every period. Clearly, if we know all the permanent optimal strategies we can reconstitute all the optimal ones, or otherwise.

A permanent optimal strategy will be designated by a univocal function $y(x, r)$ showing the decision to be taken, whatever the period considered, as a function of the state at the beginning of this period. The expression (17.44) of a permanent optimal strategy now becomes (with the implied dependence in relation to r)

$$\varpi^*(x_0) = \{y(x_0), \varpi^*(x_1)\} = \{y(x_0), y(x_1), y(x_2),..\}. \tag{21.35}$$

The permanent optimal strategy, for a stationary program with an infinite number of periods, is therefore a single function, a fact which is of great practical value in studying such programs.

Let us now return to the question whether $f(x, r)$ is the sole solution[7] and treat it in exactly the same manner as before.

If we assume two given solutions $f(x, r)$ and $g(x, r)$ of (21.3), each uniformly bounded in every domain $x \in \mathbf{D}(c)$, $|r| \leqslant \beta < 1$, and if $y(x, r)$ and $t(x, r)$ are two corresponding optimal strategies, we can easily establish an inequality similar to (21.17):

$$u(x, r) \leqslant r \max \left\{ \left| \int_{x' \in \Omega[z, y(z)]} [f(x', r) - g(x', r)] \cdot dH[x' \mid z, y(z)] \right|, \right.$$

$$\left. \left| \int_{x' \in \Omega[z, t(z)]} [f(x', r) - g(x', r)] \cdot dH[x' \mid z, t(z)] \right| \right\}, \tag{21.36}$$

---

[6] Univocal: a one-by-one correspondence; multivocal: a correspondence which is other than this. [Translator's note.]

[7] This property must not be confused with the uniqueness of the optimal strategy $y(x, r)$, which is only found in much more special cases and is of far less practical interest.

where we have

$$u(x, r) = \sup_{z \in \mathbf{D}(x)} |f(z, r) - g(z, r)|, \tag{21.37}$$

with $u(x, r) < \infty$, in accordance with the assumptions as to f and g.

If the assumption (21.22) is satisfied, we deduce from (21.36) the inequality

$$u(x, r) \leqslant ru[\theta(x), r]. \tag{21.38}$$

In each of the two cases (a) and (b), the inequality (21.38) implies that

$$u(x, r) \equiv 0 \qquad \text{for every} \quad x \in \mathbf{X} \quad \text{and} \quad |r| < 1, \tag{21.39}$$

which proves that $f(x, r)$ is the sole solution.

CONTINUITY IN RELATION TO r

To conclude, we shall show that $f(x, r)$ is continuous in relation to r, still using the same method. To compare the quantities $f_n(x, r)$ and $f_n(x, r')$ corresponding to two different values r and r' of the coefficient of discounting, we look for a bound greater than their difference. To simplify the comparison, we shall take y and y' for the functions $y^{(n-1)}(x, r)$ and $y^{(n-1)}(x, r')$ which respectively lead to the optimum in (21.1), and Ω and Ω' for the domains of integration $\Omega[x, y^{(n-1)}(x, r)]$ and $\Omega[x, y^{(n-1)}(x, r')]$. The inequality we obtain is then expressed,

$$|f_n(x, r) - f_n(x, r')|$$

$$\leqslant \max \left\{ \left| (r - r')q(x, y) + \int_{x' \in \Omega} [f_{n-1}(x', r) - f_{n-1}(x', r')] \, dH(x' \mid x, y) \right|, \right.$$

$$\left. \left| (r - r')q(x, y') + \int_{x' \in \Omega'} [f_{n-1}(x', r) - f_{n-1}(x', r')] \, dH(x' \mid x, y) \right| \right\}. \tag{21.40}$$

Now, it is easy to see that $f_1(x, r)$ is a continuous function of r, while the continuity is also uniform in relation to x in every domain of the form $x \in \mathbf{D}(c)$, since $|q(x, y)|$ is uniformly bounded in it. Inequality (21.40) then enables us to prove that, if $f_{n-1}(x, r)$ has these properties, the same must be true of $f_n(x, r)$. The uniform convergence of f_n towards the solution f of (21.3) enables us to extend these properties equally to the function f. It can be observed further that, if $q(x, y)$ is always nonnegative (or nonpositive), f_1 is a nondecreasing (or nonincreasing) function of r; but the inequalities which establish (21.40), and which have not been given, show that

$$[f_n(x, r) - f_n(x, r')]$$

is included between the quantities for which the absolute values appear
in the second member of (21.40), which enables us to show by recurrence
that $f_n(x, r)$ is a nondecreasing (or nonincreasing) function of r if $q(x, y)$
is always nonnegative (or nonpositive). Since $f_n(x, r)$ converges uniformly
towards $f(x, r)$ for $|r| < 1$, the second function possesses the same
properties.

We have thus proved the following theorem:

THEOREM 21.1.   *Given a stationary program defined for $x \in \mathbf{X}$ by
relations* (17.29) *to* (17.31), *let us consider the semistationary program
obtained by discounting the values of the initial program. Since set $\mathbf{D}(c)$ and
the function $\alpha(c)$ are defined for $c \geqslant 0$ by* (21.14) *and* (21.28) *respectively,
if*:

(1) $\alpha(c) < \infty$ *for every $c \geqslant 0$, that is, $|q(x, y)|$ is uniformly bounded in
every domain $x \in \mathbf{D}(c)$, $y \in \Delta x$;*

(2) $\Gamma x \subset \mathbf{D}(x)$ *for every $x \in \mathbf{X}$, that is, $x' \in \Gamma x$ implies $|x'| \leqslant |x|$ or*[8]
$\mathbf{X} = \mathbf{D}(c')$, *that is, $x \in \mathbf{X}$ implies $|x| \leqslant c'$;*

the function $f_n(x, r)$ defined by (21.1), *in other words, the e.v. of the total
discounted value for n periods is, for $|r| < 1$, the general term of a sequence
absolutely and uniformly convergent in every domain of the form $x \in \mathbf{D}(c)$.
The limit $f(x, r)$ of this sequence is the sole solution of* (21.3) *which is
uniformly bounded in such domain. The upper bound of $f(x, r)$ is given by*
(21.30) *or* (21.34), *depending on whether the first or second part of
assumption* (2) *is satisfied.*

*Finally, $f(x, r)$ is a continuous function of r for $|r| < 1$, and the
continuity is also uniform in relation to x in every domain $x \in \mathbf{D}(c)$. In
addition, it is a nondecreasing (or nonincreasing) function of r if $q(x, y)$ is
always nonnegative (or nonpositive).*

22. Approximation in the Space of the Strategies

The recurring equation (21.1) enables us to calculate by successive
approximations the optimal value over an infinite number of periods,
and each of the terms in this approximation represents the optimal value
for n periods. The initial approximation $f_0(x, r)$ is a zero function, but
we can easily see, by examining the proof of Theorem 21.1, that it is
still valid if this function is replaced by another $g_0(x, r)$, provided that

[8] If we assume $c'' = c$ or c', depending on whether the first or second part of assumption 2
is satisfied, in every case $x' \in \Gamma x$ involves $|x'| \leqslant c''$.

the latter is uniformly bounded in all its domain $x \in \mathbf{D}(c)$, $|r| \leqslant \beta < 1$; further, in accordance with the property of uniqueness which we have proved, we shall obtain the same solution. Hence, to solve a given problem, we can choose an initial approximation which is as good as possible, rather than systematically taking the one we have previously used. As we noticed in Section 12, intuition or experience often enable us to obtain a strategy $y_0(x, r)$ close to the optimal strategy. In this case, we should use as the initial approximation the solution $s^{(0)}(x, r)$ of

$$s^{(0)}(x, r) = r \left[q(x, y_0) + \int_{x' \in \Omega(x, y_0)} s^{(0)}(x', r) \, dH(x' \mid x, y_0) \right], \qquad (22.1)$$

which represents the present total value of the strategy $y_0(x, r)$.

This equation is considerably simpler than (21.3) despite its resemblance to it.

First method. After calculating $s^{(0)}(x, r)$, we successively determine the terms of the sequence $\{s^{(n)}\}$ defined by

$$s^{(n)}(x, r) = r \operatorname*{OPT}_{y \in \Delta x} \left\{ q(x, y) + \int_{x' \in \Omega(x, y)} s^{(n-1)}(x', r) \cdot dH(x' \mid x, y) \right\},$$

$$n = 1, 2, 3, \dots . \quad (22.2)$$

This equation is identical with (21.1), since we have merely replaced f_n by $s^{(n)}$, as the functions we are considering are no longer the optimal values over n periods, but are the values of an infinite number of periods of strategies of the form

$$[y_n, y_{n-1}, \dots, y_1, y_0, y_0, \dots].$$

We shall discover, when we use this method, that the convergence of the sequence $\{s^{(n)}\}$ is monotonic, a very useful property in numerical calculation. To take an example, we shall assume that we are finding the maximal values, in other words, that OPT = MAX. Let us first show that whatever the initial function $s_0(x, r)$ chosen, if the inequality

$$s^{(n)}(x, r) \geqslant s^{(n-1)}(x, r) \qquad (22.3)$$

is satisfied for $n = N$ ($N > 0$), it is equally satisfied for every $n > N$. Let $y^N(x)$ be a function such that

$$s^{(N)}(x, r) = r \left[q(x, y^{(N)}) + \int_{x' \in \Omega(x, y^{(N)})} s^{(N-1)}(x', r) \, dH(x' \mid x, y^{(N)}) \right]. \quad (22.4)$$

By definition, for every $y \in \Delta x$ we have

$$s^{(N+1)}(x, r) \geqslant r \left[q(x, y) + \int_{x' \in \Omega(x, y)} s^{(N)}(x', r) \, dH(x' \mid x, y) \right]. \quad (22.5)$$

By taking $s^{(N)}(x, r)$ from both members and substituting y^N for y, we deduce

$$s^{(N+1)}(x, r) - s^{(N)}(x, r)$$

$$\geqslant r \int_{x' \in \Omega(x, y^{(N)})} \left[[s^{(N)}(x', r) - s^{(N-1)}(x', r)] \, dH(x' \mid x, y^{(N)}) \right]. \quad (22.6)$$

In accordance with the assumption which we made, the second member is nonnegative; hence it is the same with the first member. By repeating the same reasoning, we show that (22.3) is satisfied for every $n > N$.

Now, taking for the initial approximation a function $s^{(0)}(x, r)$ which satisfies (22.1), the function $s^{(1)}(x, r)$ is, as a result of the inequality (22.5) applied for $N = 0$ and $y = y_0$, greater than or equal to $s^{(0)}(x, r)$; hence the sequence $\{s^{(n)}\}$ is monotonically nondecreasing. For programs where OPT = MIN we should show in the same way that it is non-increasing. If we used the initial approximation $s^{(0)}(x, r) = 0$, this property could only be proved with the assumption

$$\underset{y \in \Delta x}{\text{MAX}} \; q(x, y) \geqslant 0$$

(or $\text{MIN}_{y \in \Delta x} \, q(x, y) \leqslant 0$, depending on the case), so that we should have $s^{(i)} \geqslant s^{(0)}$.

Second method.   The first method entails an initial approximation in the permanent strategies' space (or of that of the decision functions), followed by successive approximations in the values' space. But we can also continue the approximations in the former by proceeding in the following way:

Having chosen y_0 and calculated $s^{(0)}$, we utilize (22.2) with $n = 1$ to find a new decision function y_1. Equation (22.1) then enables us to calculate the e.v. of the total[9] value $s^{(1)}$ (over an infinitude of periods) corresponding to the permanent strategy y_1. We then introduce $s^{(1)}$ into the second member of (22.2) to find a new strategy y_2, and so on. Hence we carry out the two following operations alternately:

[9] This value generally differs from the quantity $s^{(1)}$ defined by the first method and corresponding to the strategy $(y_1, y_0, y_0, \ldots)$.

1. Knowing the function $y_n(x)$, find $s^{(n)}(x, r)$ such that

$$s^{(n)}(x, r) = r\left[q(x, y_n) + \int_{x' \in \Omega(x, y_n)} s^{(n)}(x', r) \cdot dH(x' \mid x, y_n)\right]. \quad (22.7)$$

2. Knowing $s^{(n)}(x, r)$, find a function $y_{n+1}(x)$ such that

$$r\left[q(x, y_{n+1}) + \int_{x' \in \Omega(x, y_{n+1})} s^{(n)}(x', r)\, dH(x' \mid x, y_{n+1})\right]$$

$$= r \operatorname*{OPT}_{y \in \Delta x}\left[q(x, y) + \int_{x' \in \Omega(x, y)} s^{(n)}(x', r)\, dH(x' \mid x, y)\right]. \quad (22.8)$$

The process of approximations ends when there is a solution of (22.8) such that

$$y_{n+1}(x, r) \equiv y_n(x, r);$$

the closeness of (22.7) and (22.8) in fact shows that $y_n(x, r)$ and $s^{(n)}(x, r)$ then satisfy (21.3) and hence that they respectively represent a permanent optimal strategy and the corresponding expected value.

We shall also discover that the convergence is monotone,[10] as in the preceding case. If we take $g_{n+1}(x, r)$ for the first member of (22.8), that is, the value of the strategy $[y_{n+1}, y_n, y_n, ...]$,

$$g_{n+1}(x, r) = r\left[q(x, y_{n+1}) + \int_{x' \in \Omega(x, y_{n+1})} s^{(n)}(x', r)\, dH(x' \mid x, y_{n+1})\right]. \quad (22.9)$$

Obviously, if OPT = MAX, we have

$$g_{n+1}(x, r) \geqslant s^{(n)}(x, r), \qquad \forall x, r, \quad (22.10)$$

as we can see by taking $y = y_n$ in the second member of (22.8). We have also by obtaining (22.9) from (22.7) applied for $(n + 1)$:

$$[s^{(n+1)}(x, r) - s^{(n)}(x, r)] - [g_{n+1}(x, r) - s^{(n)}(x, r)]$$

$$= s^{(n+1)}(x, r) - g_{n+1}(x, r)$$

$$= r \int_{x' \in \Omega(x, y_{n+1})} [s^{(n+1)}(x', r) - s^{(n)}(x', r)] \cdot dH(x' \mid x, y_{n+1}), \quad (22.11)$$

[10] The method we are using is a generalization of the one laid down by Howard [36] for programs with Markovian chains (see Chapter 5).

that is, assuming

$$\Delta s^{(n+1)}(x, r) = s^{(n+1)}(x, r) - s^{(n)}(x, r) \qquad (22.12)$$

and

$$r q_{n+1}(x, r) = g_{n+1}(x, r) - s^{(n)}(x, r) \geqslant 0, \qquad (22.13)$$

$$\Delta s^{(n+1)}(x, r) = r \left[q_{n+1}(x, r) + r \int_{x' \in \Omega(x, y_{n+1})} \Delta s^{(n+1)}(x', r) \, dH(x' \mid x, y_{n+1}) \right].$$
$$(22.14)$$

This relation shows that $\Delta s^{(n)}(x, r)$ is the expected present value, over an infinite number of periods, of a stationary dynamic program with the same stochastic structure as the initial program, but in which the expected present value is $q_{n+1}(x, r)$, whatever the period considered. Since this present value is nonnegative, it is clear $\Delta s^{(n)} \geqslant 0$, which constitutes the property we wished to prove. The same procedure could be carried out where OPT = MIN.

23. Convergence of the Total Present Value of an Arbitrary Strategy

When we wrote (22.1) we implicitly assumed that this functional equation has a solution that represents the total present value of the strategy $y_0(x, r)$. It is easy to see that such is the case by the assumptions of Theorem 21.1; in fact, if $s_n(x, r)$ is the present value over n periods of the arbitrary policy y_0 given by the following recurring equation, valid for $n \geqslant 1$, on condition we assume $s_0(x, r) \equiv 0$,

$$s_n(x, r) = r \left[q(x, y_0) + \int_{x' \in \Omega(x, y_0)} s_{n-1}(x', r) \, dH(x' \mid x, y_0) \right]. \qquad (23.1)$$

By rewriting this relation for the value $(n + 1)$, and then finding the difference, we obtain

$$s_{n+1}(x, r) - s_n(x, r) = r \int_{x' \in \Omega(x, y_0)} [s_n(x', r) - s_{n-1}(x', r)] \cdot dH(x' \mid x, y_0), \qquad (23.2)$$

whence

$$n \geqslant 1, \qquad | s_{n+1}(x, r) - s_n(x, r) |$$

$$\leqslant r \int_{x' \in \Omega(x, y_0)} | s_n(x', r) - s_{n-1}(x', r) | \cdot dH(x' \mid x, y_0). \qquad (23.3)$$

.

Beginning with this inequality, which is similar to (21.13), we can use the same reasoning as before, by assuming

$$w_n(x, r) = \underset{z \in \mathbf{D}(x)}{\text{SUP}} \, | \, s_n(z, r) - s_{n+1}(z, r)|, \qquad (23.4)$$

with, in particular,

$$w_0(x, r) = \underset{z \in \mathbf{D}(x)}{\text{SUP}} \, | \, s_1(z, r)| = r \underset{z \in \mathbf{D}(x)}{\text{SUP}} \, | \, q(z, y_0)| \leqslant r\alpha(x), \qquad (23.5)$$

where $\alpha(c)$ is defined by (21.28).

We shall not repeat the proof, which is identical with that of Theorem 21.1 and leads to one of the inequalities,

or
$$\left.\begin{array}{l} w_n(x, r) \leqslant r^{n+1}\alpha(c) \\ w_n(x, r) \leqslant r^{n+1}\alpha(c') \end{array}\right\} \quad \text{for every} \quad x \in \mathbf{D}(c), \qquad \begin{array}{l} (23.6) \\ (23.7) \end{array}$$

depending on which of the second assumptions of Theorem 21.1 is satisfied. From this we deduce the following theorem:

THEOREM 23.1.   *With the same assumptions as in Theorem 21.1, every permanent strategy $y_0(x)$ has, for $|r| < 1$, a present total value $s(x, r)$ uniformly bounded in each domain $x \in \mathbf{D}(c)$, which is the sole solution of*

$$s(x, r) = r \left[q(x, y_0) + \int_{x' \in \Omega(x, y_0)} s(x', r) \, dH(x' \mid x, y_0) \right]. \qquad (23.8)$$

The upper bound of $| \, s(x, r)|$ is the same as that of $| \, f(x, r)|$ (see (21.30) or (21.34), according to the case). The function $s(x, r)$ has the same continuous and (eventually) monotone properties as $f(x, r)$ (see the last paragraph of Theorem 21.1).

24. Influence of the Initial State

Let us assume that the total present value over an infinitude of periods is independent of the initial state $x_0 = x$:

$$f(x, r) = g(r) \qquad \text{for each} \quad x \in \mathbf{X}. \qquad (24.1)$$

If we substitute this solution in (21.3), the integral in the latter becomes

$$\int_{x' \in \Omega(x, y)} g(r) \cdot dH(x' \mid x, y) = g(r), \qquad (24.2)$$

since dH is a density of probability. As this term is independent of the decision y, (21.3) can be expressed

$$g(r) = r[\mathop{\text{OPT}}_{y \in \Delta x} q(x, y) + g(r)], \qquad (24.3)$$

which implies that the quantity

$$\hat{q} = \mathop{\text{OPT}}_{y \in \Delta x} q(x, y) \qquad (24.4)$$

is independent of x. We then have

$$f(x, r) = g(r) = \frac{r}{1 - r}\, \hat{q}. \qquad (24.5)$$

Reciprocally, if (24.4) is independent of x, the expected optimal value for one period is

$$f_1(x, r) = r \mathop{\text{OPT}}_{y \in \Delta x} q(x, y) = r\hat{q}, \qquad (24.6)$$

and the relation (21.1) enables us to prove by recurrence that

$$f_n(x, r) = \hat{q} \sum_{v=1}^{n} r^v = \frac{r(1 - r^n)}{1 - r}\, \hat{q}. \qquad (24.7)$$

When we pass to the limit, we obtain (24.5). Moreover, if $y^*(x)$ is such that

$$q[x, y^*(x)] = \hat{q}, \qquad (24.8)$$

this permanent strategy is optimal over any number of periods, whatever the value of $r(|\,r\,| < 1)$.

THEOREM 24.1. *The necessary and sufficient condition for the total present value to be independent of the initial state x is that the expected optimal value (not discounted) for a period, as defined by (24.4), must itself be independent of x. In this case, every optimal strategy for a period (see (24.8)) is optimal for any number of periods (including an infinite number) whatever the coefficient of discounting $r(|\,r\,| < 1)$ may be; the expected optimal value is given by (24.8).*

It should be observed that the condition given in this theorem is sufficient but not necessary for the existence of a permanent optimal strategy $y^*(x)$ for a given number of periods. Thus, in the example in Section 16, the optimal strategy is always the same, and it would still be so if the costs were discounted, despite the fact that the condition of Theorem 24.1 would not be satisfied.

25. The Criterion of the Expected Total Value without Discounting

As a rule, the expected present optimal value $f(x, r)$ increases indefinitely (in absolute value) as r approaches 1, which amounts to not discounting. However, in certain special cases the nondiscounted total value remains finite, and we shall now prove a theorem which applies to certain of these cases and generalizes that of Section 12.

THEOREM 25.1. *Let us consider a stationary program defined for* $x \in \mathbf{X}$ *by the relations* (17.29) *to* (17.31), *in which the set* $\mathbf{D}(c)$ *and the function* $\alpha(c)$ *are formally defined for* $c \geqslant 0$ *by* (21.14) *and* (21.28) *and where a is a number such that* $0 \leqslant a < 1$. *If*:

(1) *the value* $x = 0$ *is a part[11] of set* $\mathbf{X}$ *and*

$$\sum_{n=0}^{\infty} \alpha(a^n c) < \infty \qquad \text{for every} \quad c \geqslant 0; \tag{25.1}$$

(2) $\Gamma x \subset \mathbf{D}(ax)$ *for every* $x \in \mathbf{X}$, *that is to say,* $x' \in \Gamma x$ *implies* $| x' | \leqslant a | x |$; *then the program belongs to class* 1 (*see Section* 20). *To be more precise, the function* $f_n(x)$ *defined by* (17.40) *and* (17.41) *has a limit* $f(x)$ *which is continuous[12] for* $x = 0$ *and zero at this point; this solution is the only one with these properties among the solutions of*

$$f(x) = \operatorname*{OPT}_{y \in \Delta x} \left[q(x, y) + \int_{x' \in \Omega(x, y)} f(x')\, dH(x' \mid x, y) \right]. \tag{25.2}$$

On the other hand, the expected present optimal value exists, and we have

$$f(x) = \lim_{r \to 1} f(x, r). \tag{25.3}$$

Lastly, Theorem 23.1 *is valid for* $r = 1$.

To prove the convergence of the sequence $\{f_n(x)\}$, we first observe that condition 1 implies that $\alpha(c)$ is defined for every $c \geqslant 0$, that $\alpha(0) = 0$, and that $\alpha(c) \to 0$ when $c \to 0$. The inequalities

$$| f_1(x) | \leqslant \operatorname*{SUP}_{z \in \mathbf{D}(x)} | f_1(z) | \leqslant \alpha(x) \tag{25.4}$$

---

[11] This implies that the lower bound b of $| x |$ defined in the note on p. 139 is zero, and is a minimum.

[12] If $x = 0$ is an isolated point of $\mathbf{X}$, it means that any function $g(x)$ defined in $\mathbf{X}$ is continuous for $x = 0$. If $x \in \mathbf{X}$ implies $x \geqslant 0$, the continuous property of $f(x)$ will extend to the right, and so on.

then show that

$$\lim_{x \to 0} f_1(x) = 0,$$

which implies that $f_1(x)$ is continuous for $x = 0$ and zero at this point. The same property can then be deduced for $f_n(x)$ by recurrence. Then again, the relation (21.24) becomes, in virtue of assumption 2 and by using $u_n(x)$ instead of $u_n(x, 1)$ for simplicity,

$$u_{n+1}(x) \leqslant u_n(ax), \tag{25.5}$$

whence

$$u_n(x) \leqslant u_0(a^n x),$$

with $u_0(x) \leqslant \alpha(x)$. Assumption 1 then involves the uniform convergence of the series $u_n(x)$ and, in consequence, that of the sequence $|f_n(x)|$. As the convergence is uniform, the limit $f(x)$ of this sequence has the same properties as $f_n(x)$, and is the solution of Eq. (25.2). The fact that it is the sole solution is the result of (21.38).

It should be understood that the choice of $x = 0$ in the enunciation is only made to simplify the notation. If the assumptions are satisfied for $x = \theta \in \mathbf{X}$, the variable need only be changed to $\xi = x - \theta$ in order to apply the theorem.

Then again, we observe that the relation $\alpha(0) = 0$ involves

$$q(0, y) = \int_{x' \in \Omega(0, y)} v(0, y, x') \, dH(x' \mid 0, y) = 0. \tag{25.6}$$

Then, by assumption 2, $\Omega(0, y) = \{0\}$, and in consequence (25.6) becomes

$$v(0, y, 0) = 0. \tag{25.7}$$

Hence it follows that the present value of a period, at the beginning of which $x = 0$, must be zero, whatever decision is taken. Finally, a consequence of assumption 1 is that $\alpha(c)$ must be finite, and as a result $q(x, y)$ must be uniformly bounded in every domain $\mathbf{D}(c)$. In consequence, any program that satisfies the assumptions of the above theorem also satisfies those of Theorem 21.1. It is also clear that the criterion of the present total value can be applied for any program of class 1.

Relation (25.3) is obvious. We shall observe that if $y(x, r)$ is an optimal strategy by the criterion of the present total value (for the value r of the coefficient of discounting), and if there is a strategy $y(x)$ such that

$$y(x) = \lim_{r \to 1} y(x, r), \tag{25.8}$$

this strategy is optimal if measured by the criterion of the total non-discounted value.

The assumptions of the above theorem are clearly very restrictive, and although it is not applicable to all the programs of class 1, it can be regarded as applying to the majority of them. From this fact, we conclude that the programs of this class have only a limited practical importance. We shall now see that class 2, on the other hand, has a much more extensive application.

26. The Criterion of the Average Expected Value per Period

We shall now return to the reasoning at the end of Section 14, but as we can now employ a theorem for the convergence of the total discounted value, we shall be able to reach more exact conclusions than those of Theorem 14.2.

Let us examine a stationary program which satisfies the assumptions of Theorem 21.1 (p. 144), and let $y_0(x)$ be an arbitrary permanent strategy for an infinite number of periods. We shall take $q_n(x)$ for the expected present value (not discounted) of the strategy $y_0(x)$ for period n, when the state at time 0 is $x_0 = x$; and $s_N(x, r)$ for the present value, over the first N periods, of this strategy. We thus have

$$s_N(x, r) = \sum_{n=1}^{N} r^n q_n(x), \tag{26.1}$$

$$s(x, r) = \lim_{N \to \infty} s_N(x, r) = \sum_{n=1}^{\infty} r^n q_n(x). \tag{26.2}$$

Then again, let $\sigma_N(x, r)$ be a quantity such that a sequence of N values, each equal to σ_N, defined at times $1, 2, ..., N$, has a discounted value equal to $s_N(x, r)$:

$$\sum_{n=1}^{N} r^n \sigma_N(x, r) = s_N(x, r); \tag{26.3}$$

whence, for $r \neq 1$,

$$\sigma_N(x, r) = \frac{1}{r} \frac{1 - r}{1 - r^N} s_N(x, r) \tag{26.4}$$

and

$$\sigma_N(x, 1) = \frac{1}{N} s_N(x, 1). \tag{26.5}$$

Since $s_N(x, r)$ is a polynomial in r, $\sigma_N(x, r)$ is a continuous function of r; also, as $r \to 1$, (26.5) is the limit of (26.4). This expression (26.5) shows that $\sigma_N(x, 1)$ is the average expected value per period, calculated for the first N periods of the strategy $y_0(x)$ which we are considering; its limit, if it exists, is the value of this strategy measured by the criterion used in this section. To study the existence of this limit, we shall first make r approach 1 in (26.4), then make N approach infinity.

Let us first notice that

$$s_{n+1}(x, r) - s_n(x, r) = r^{n+1}q_{n+1}(x),$$ (26.6)

whence, $\forall x \in \mathbf{D}(c)$:

$$r^{n+1} \mid q_{n+1}(x)\mid \leqslant w_n(c, r) \leqslant r^{n+1}\alpha(c''),$$ (26.7)

in accordance with (23.4) to (23.7), by assuming $c'' = c$ or c', depending on the case. Hence we have

$$\mid q_{n+1}(x)\mid \leqslant \alpha(c''), \qquad n \geqslant 0;$$ (26.8)

which, moreover, is obvious, since $\alpha(c'')$ is the upper bound of $q(x, y)$ and $q_{n+1}(x)$ obtained by weighting $q(x, y_0)$ by the distribution of probability of the state variable x_n, such as it can, calculated at time 0.

Let us assume

$$a_n(x) = \mid q_{n+1}(x)\mid,$$ (26.9)

$$A_N(x, r) = \sum_{n=0}^{N-1} r^n a_n(x),$$ (26.10)

and

$$A(x, r) = \sum_{n=0}^{\infty} r^n a_n(x).$$ (26.11)

The last series is convergent for $\mid r \mid < 1$, in accordance with (26.8),

$$A(x, r) \leqslant \frac{\alpha(c'')}{1 - r}.$$ (26.12)

From a theorem dealing with integral series,[13] the condition

$$\lim_{r \to 1}(1 - r)A(x, r) = \lambda(x) < \infty$$ (26.13)

is necessary and sufficient in order that

$$\lim_{N \to \infty} \frac{1}{N} A_N(x, 1) = \lambda)x).$$ (26.14)

[13] The enunciation of this theorem is given, for example, in G. H. Hardy, *Divergent Series* (Oxford Univ. Press, 1949) in which it is Theorem No. 96.

Now, $A(x, r)$ is, for $|r| < 1$, a continuous function of r, in so much as it is the sum of an integral series of which the radius of convergence is at least equal to 1. As the function $(1 - r)A(x, r)$ is continuous and uniformly bounded [in accordance with (26.12)], the limit (26.13) exists and is at most equal to $\alpha(c'')$. But we have

$$| \sigma_N(x, 1) | = \frac{1}{N} | s_N(x, 1) | \leqslant \frac{1}{N} A_N(x, 1), \qquad (26.15)$$

which shows that $\sigma_N(x, 1)$ has a finite limit when $N \to \infty$; then again,

$$\lim_{N \to \infty} \sigma_N(x, r) = \frac{1 - r}{r} s(x, r), \qquad (26.16)$$

and the expression which appears in the second member has a limit for $r \to 1$, for the same reasons as in the case of

$$(1 - r)A(x, r).$$

Hence we have

$$\lim_{r \to 1} \lim_{N \to \infty} \sigma_N(x, r) = \lim_{r \to 1} \frac{1 - r}{r} s(x, r). \qquad (26.17)$$

Now, we have seen that

$$\lim_{N \to \infty} \lim_{r \to 1} \sigma_N(x, r) = \lim_{N \to \infty} \frac{1}{N} s_N(x, 1). \qquad (26.18)$$

The two limits must be equal:

$$\lim_{N \to \infty} \sigma_N(x, 1) = \lim_{r \to 1} \frac{1 - r}{r} s(x, r), \qquad (26.19)$$

or, taking $\sigma(x)$ for the average value per period,

$$\sigma(x) = \lim_{r \to 1}(1 - r)s(x, r), \qquad (26.20)$$

since the presence of the factor r does not modify the limit. This result may be enunciated as follows:

THEOREM 26.1.   *With the assumptions of Theorem 21.1: The average value for a period $\sigma(x)$ of an arbitrary strategy $y_0(x)$ is the limit, as $r \to 1$, of the expression*

$$(1 - r)s(x, r),$$

where s(x, r) is the total discounted value of the strategy considered, and we have

$$| \sigma(x)| \leqslant \alpha(c''), \tag{26.21}$$

where $c'' = c$ or c', depending on whether the first or second part of assumption 2 in Theorem 21.1 is satisfied.

Let us now consider an optimal strategy $y(x, r)$ by the criterion of the present total value (for the value r of the coefficient of discounting). Taking $f(x, r)$ for the total present value of this strategy, we have, by definition[14]:

$$f(x, r) = \underset{\varpi \in \Pi}{\text{EXT}} \, s(x, r), \tag{26.22}$$

where ϖ represents an arbitrary strategy $y_0(x)$, and Π the set of possible strategies, which is clearly independent of r.

Hence we also have

$$(1 - r)f(x, r) = \underset{\varpi \in \Pi}{\text{EXT}}(1 - r)s(x, r). \tag{26.23}$$

Since the functions in the two members are continuous, we have, by passing to the limit,

$$\varphi(x) = \underset{\varpi \in \Pi}{\text{EXT}} \, \sigma(x), \tag{26.24}$$

assuming

$$\varphi(x) = \lim_{r \to 1}(1 - r)f(x, r) \leqslant \alpha(c''). \tag{26.25}$$

As a result of (26.24) we find that $\varphi(x)$ is the average optimal value of a period.

THEOREM 26.2. *With the assumptions of Theorem 21.1, the average optimal value of a period is given by (26.25).*

We have shown that, using the assumptions of Theorem 21.1, the average value per period of a strategy is always defined, but this does not mean that this criterion is always efficacious. For instance, if the program considered satisfies the assumptions of Theorem 25.1, it is of class 1 and $\sigma(x) \equiv 0$ for every strategy, since the function $s(x, r)$ has a limit (see 26.20). Hence, in this case, the criterion of the average value per period does not enable us to compare the different possible strategies, which is why we say it is not efficacious.

---

[14] The sign EXT designates the upper or lower bound, depending on whether we wish to maximize or minimize the values.

In a case of maximization (OPT = MAX), the criterion will be efficacious if there is a strategy in which the average value of a period is positive for every x. The program then belongs to class 2 for every value of x, and this is the case if

$$\beta(c) = \underset{x \in \mathbf{D}(c)}{\text{INF}} \ \underset{y \in \Delta x}{\text{MAX}} \ q(x, y) > 0 \qquad \text{for every} \quad c \geqslant 0. \qquad (26.26)$$

Indeed, whatever the value of r, if we apply a strategy $y_0(x)$ such that

$$q[x, y_0(x)] = \underset{y \in \Delta x}{\text{MAX}} \ q(x, y), \qquad (26.27)$$

assumption 2 of Theorem 21.1 implies that, for each period, the present nondiscounted value is at least equal to $\beta(c'')$ when the initial state x_0 is such that $x_0 \in \mathbf{D}(c'')$:

$$q[x, y_0(x)] \geqslant \beta(c''). \qquad (26.28)$$

The present total value, for an infinite number of periods, of the strategy will then be

$$s(x, r) \geqslant \sum_{n=1}^{\infty} r^n \beta(c'') = \frac{r}{1-r} \beta(c''). \qquad (26.29)$$

This relation can be expressed,

$$(1 - r)s(x, r) \geqslant r \cdot \beta(c'') > 0; \qquad (26.30)$$

whence, at the limit,

$$\sigma(x) = \lim_{r \to 1}(1 - r)s(x, r) \geqslant \beta(c'') > 0. \qquad (26.31)$$

In the case of OPT = MIN, the property is expressed as:

$$\text{if} \ \beta'(c) = \underset{x \in \mathbf{D}(c)}{\text{SUP}} \ \underset{y \in \Delta x}{\text{MIN}} \ q(x, y) < 0 \qquad \text{for every} \quad c \geqslant 0, \qquad (26.32)$$

the average value for a period $\sigma(x)$ of a strategy $y_0(x)$ such that

$$q[x, y_0(x)] = \underset{y \in \Delta x}{\text{MIN}} \ q(x, y) \qquad (26.33)$$

satisfies the relation

$$\sigma(x) \leqslant \beta'(c'') < 0, \qquad (26.34)$$

and, in consequence, the average optimal value per period is negative. However, this property does not often apply, since the values are frequently defined in such a way as to be nonnegative. The case where (26.33) is always positive is a more useful one to study, and we shall make a rather stronger assumption, similar to (26.26) and (26.32):

$$\beta(c) = \inf_{x \in \mathbf{D}(c)} \min_{y \in \Delta x} q(x, y) > 0 \qquad \text{for every} \quad c \geqslant 0. \tag{26.35}$$

The same reasoning as we have used above shows that the average value per period $\sigma(x)$ of a policy $y_0(x)$ defined by (26.33) is at least equal to $\beta(c'')$ and hence positive. But we can show by more elaborate reasoning that the *optimal* average value per period (which is less than or equal to σ) is itself positive. Indeed, let us consider the relation which corresponds to (21.11), taking into account the change of sign caused by the fact that here OPT = MIN:

$$f_{n+2}(x, r) - f_{n+1}(x, r)$$

$$\geqslant r \int_{x' \in \Omega[x, y^{(n+1)}(x)]} [f_{n+1}(x', r) - f_n(x', r)] \, dH[x' \mid x, y^{(n+1)}(x)]. \tag{26.36}$$

Relation (26.35) shows that

$$f_1(x, r) \geqslant r\beta(c'') \qquad \text{for every} \quad x \in \mathbf{D}(c''). \tag{26.37}$$

By using the same method as in the proof of Theorem 21.1, we then obtain

$$f(x, r) \geqslant \frac{r}{1 - r} \beta(c''), \tag{26.38}$$

whence

$$\varphi(x) = \lim_{r \to 1}(1 - r)f(x, r) \geqslant \beta(c'') > 0. \tag{26.39}$$

In the same way, in the case where OPT = MAX, the condition

$$\beta'(c) = \sup_{x \in \mathbf{D}(c)} \max_{y \in \Delta x} q(x, y) < 0 \tag{26.40}$$

would result in $\varphi(x) < 0$ for every x.

These combined results constitute the following theorem:

THEOREM 26.3. *Given a program which satisfies the assumptions of Theorem* 21.1, *and also such that*

(a) $$\beta(c) = \inf_{x \in \mathbf{D}(c)} \operatorname*{OPT}_{y \in \Delta x} q(x, y) > 0 \qquad \textit{for every} \quad c \geqslant 0, \tag{26.41}$$

or again,

(b) $\beta'(c) = \sup_{x \in \mathbf{D}(c)} \underset{y \in \Delta x}{\text{OPT}}\ q(x, y) < 0 \qquad \textit{for every}\ \ c \geq 0.$

This program belongs to class 2 for all $x \in \mathbf{X}$; the optimal average value of a period $\varphi(x)$ is greater than or equal to $\beta(c'')$ in case (a), and less than or equal to $\beta'(c'')$ in case (b).

27. Optimization of the Average Value per Period

The results obtained in the previous section show that, as with a certain future, the criterion of the average value of a period is, in a certain sense, the limit of the criterion of the total discounted value. We can now ask whether it is not possible to deduce, from the algorithm given in Section 22, a similar one for the optimization of the average value. In fact, R. Howard [36] has given such an algorithm for a case where the number of possible states and decisions in each period is finite (see Sections 33 and 35). For the general case which we are now considering this algorithm, so far as we are aware, has never been used or its convergence proved. We shall now describe it, adding our hope that some mathematician will soon provide a proof of its convergence under certain assumptions, which might well be those of Theorem 21.1.

Let us first observe that for any strategy $y(x)$, we have by definition (see (26.18))

$$\sigma(x) = \lim_{N \to \infty} \frac{1}{N} s_N(x), \qquad (27.1)$$

where $s_N(x) = s_N(x, 1)$ gives the total value for N periods (without discounting). We may therefore surmise that $s_N(x)$ is of the form

$$s_N(x) = N\sigma(x) + \delta(x) + O(N), \qquad (27.2)$$

where $O(N) \to 0$ when $N \to \infty$. By substituting this expression in the recurring equation

$$s_n(x) = q[x, y(x)] + \int_{x' \in \Omega[x, y(x)]} s_{n-1}(x')\, dH[x' \mid x, y(x)], \qquad (27.3)$$

we obtain

$$n\sigma(x) + \delta(x) = q[x, y(x)]$$
$$+ (n-1) \int \sigma(x')\, dH(x' \mid x, y) + \int \delta(x')\, dH(x' \mid x, y) \quad (27.4)$$

by neglecting the terms which approach zero. By indentifying the n terms and the constants, it follows:

$$\sigma(x) = \int_{x' \in \Omega[x, y(x)]} \sigma(x') \, dH[x' \mid x, y(x)], \qquad (27.5)$$

and

$$\delta(x) = q[x, y(x)] - \int \sigma(x') \, dH(x' \mid x, y) + \int \delta(x') \, dH(x' \mid x, y), \quad (27.6)$$

that is to say, taking (27.5) into account,

$$\sigma(x) + \delta(x) = q[x, y(x)] + \int_{x' \in \Omega[x, y(x)]} \delta(x') \, dH[x' \mid x, y(x)]. \quad (27.7)$$

We should observe that relation (27.7) is still satisfied if a constant is added to $\delta(x)$. The system of Eqs. (27.5) and (27.7) does not entirely determine this function $\delta(x)$, but we must agree that it determines $\sigma(x)$.

Using a method similar to the second one in Section 22, we can now visualize the following algorithm, beginning with an arbitrary strategy $y^{(0)}(x)$.

Carry out the two following operations alternately:

(1) Knowing the function $y^{(n)}(x)$, obtain $\sigma^{(n)}(x)$ and a function $\delta^{(n)}(x)$ such that

$$\sigma^{(n)}(x) = \int_{x' \in \Omega^{(n)}(x)} \sigma^{(n)}(x') \, dH^{(n)}(x' \mid x) \qquad (27.8)$$

and

$$\sigma^{(n)}(x) + \delta^{(n)}(x) = q^{(n)}(x) + \int_{x' \in \Omega^{(n)}(x)} \delta^{(n)}(x') \, dH^{(n)}(x' \mid x). \qquad (27.9)$$

(2) Knowing $\sigma^{(n)}(x)$ and $\delta^{(n)}(x)$, determine the set $\mathbf{Y}^{(n+1)}(x)$ such that

$$\forall y^{(n+1)}(x) \in \mathbf{Y}^{(n+1)}(x):$$

$$\int_{x' \in \Omega^{(n+1)}(x)} \sigma^{(n)}(x') \, dH^{(n+1)}(x' \mid x) = \underset{y \in \Delta x}{\mathrm{OPT}} \int_{x' \in \Omega(x, y)} \sigma^{(n)}(x') \, dH(x' \mid x, y), \qquad (27.10)$$

then find a strategy $y^{(n+1)}(x)$ such that

$$q^{(n+1)}(x) + \int_{x' \in \Omega^{(n+1)}(x)} \delta^{(n)}(x') \, dH^{(n+1)}(x' \mid x)$$

$$= \underset{y(x) \in \mathbf{Y}^{(n+1)}(x)}{\mathrm{OPT}} \left[q(x, y) + \int_{x' \in \Omega(x, y)} \delta^{(n)}(x) \, dH(x' \mid x, y) \right]. \qquad (27.11)$$

To simplify the notation, we have assumed

$$q^{(n)}(x) = q[x, y^{(n)}(x)], \qquad (27.12)$$

$$\Omega^{(n)}(x) = \Omega[x, y^{(n)}(x)], \qquad (27.13)$$

$$H^{(n)}(x' \mid x) = H[x' \mid x, y^{(n)}(x)]. \qquad (27.14)$$

As we showed above, we shall surmise that the sequence $\sigma^{(n)}(x)$ converges monotonically towards $\sigma(x)$, with the reservation, for instance, that the assumptions of Theorem 21.1 must be satisfied. The proof is very simple when

$$\forall(n, x): \quad y^{(n)}(x) \in \mathbf{Y}^{(n+1)}(x);$$

in other words, when (27.10) does not ever allow us to eliminate the strategy previously considered. As we shall see in Section 35, this is equivalent to the case where the Markovian chains corresponding to each of the strategies being considered have a single class of closed states (or a single class of recurring states, according to the terminology employed). The proof for the general case is, of course, a much more difficult one.

CHAPTER 5

DISCRETE D.H. DYNAMIC PROGRAMS WITH FINITE MARKOVIAN CHAINS

28. Introduction

In this chapter we shall study *stationary* dynamic programs based on the model[1] in Section 17, in the special case where the set $\mathbf{X}$ of the possible states and the set $\mathbf{Y} = \bigcup_{x \in \mathbf{X}} \varDelta x$ of the possible decisions are both denumerable and finite. It is then always possible, by a suitable alteration of the variables, to define the state variable x and the decision variable y in such a way that

$$\mathbf{X} = \{1, 2, ..., i, ..., M\} \tag{28.1}$$

and

$$\mathbf{Y} = \{1, 2, ..., k, ..., m\} \quad \text{with} \quad \varDelta i \subset \mathbf{Y}, \quad \forall i \in \mathbf{X}. \tag{28.2}$$

Differently expressed, x is an integer between 1 and M, while y is one between 1 and m, belonging to $\varDelta i$.

When at the beginning of a period the system is in state $x = i$ and the decision $y = k$ is taken, the distribution of probability of state x' at the end of the period is given by

$$dH(j \mid i, k) = p_{ij}^{(k)}, \quad j \in \mathbf{X} \tag{28.3}$$

and

$$dH(x' \mid i, k) = 0 \quad \text{for} \quad x' \notin \mathbf{X}. \tag{28.4}$$

We shall also assume that

$$r_{ij}^{(k)} = v(i, k, j). \tag{28.5}$$

---

[1] We shall not repeat the notation given in Section 17, but the reader should, if necessary, refer to it.

Equations (17.40) to (17.42) then become

$$n > 1, \qquad f_n(i) = \operatorname*{OPT}_{k \in \Delta i} \left[q(i, k) + \sum_{j=1}^{M} f_{n-1}(j) \cdot p_{ij}^{(k)} \right], \qquad (28.6)$$

$$f_1(i) = \operatorname*{OPT}_{k \in \Delta i} q(i, k), \qquad (28.7)$$

with

$$q(i, k) = \sum_{j=1}^{M} p_{ij}^{(k)} r_{ij}^{(k)}. \qquad (28.8)$$

For simplicity, we have used $\sum_{j=1}^{M}$ for $\sum_{j \in \Omega(i,k)}$, which does not cause any difficulty, since $p_{ij}^{(k)} = 0$ when j does not belong to $\Omega(i, k)$.

It is clear that

$$0 \leqslant p_{ij}^{(k)} \leqslant 1 \qquad \text{for every} \quad i, j, k; \qquad (28.9)$$

$$\sum_{j=1}^{M} p_{ij}^{(k)} = 1 \qquad \text{for every} \quad i, k, \qquad (28.10)$$

which we can express by saying that for every $i \in \mathbf{X}$, the vectors

$$[p_i^{(k)}] = [p_{i,1}^{(k)} \quad p_{i,2}^{(k)} \cdots p_{i,M}^{(k)}] \qquad (28.11)$$

are stochastic vectors.

The decision functions $y(x)$ defined on p. 119 will be represented here as decision vectors:

$$\{k\} = \begin{Bmatrix} k_1 \\ \vdots \\ k_M \end{Bmatrix}, \qquad (28.12)$$

in which the component k_i shows the decision to be taken when the state at the beginning of the period is i. A strategy will therefore be a sequence of decision vectors.[2]

We have already observed in Section 17 that, for a given strategy, the system is ruled by a random Markovian process $\{x_n\}$; with the assumption of the present chapter, it constitutes a finite Markovian chain.[3] This special random process has been the subject of numerous works of which we shall give a résumé in the following sections, limiting ourselves to points which are of special value in dynamic programming.

---

[2] If the strategy is permanent, all the decisions are equal to $\{k\}$, which may be used for the strategy itself.

[3] The qualification refers to the number of possible states.

The results which we shall explain will enable us to study finite Markovian chains in greater detail. For the moment we shall observe that the programs examined in this chapter satisfy the assumptions of Theorem 21.1. Indeed, the second part of assumption 2 is satisfied for $c' = M$, and assumption 1 follows from the fact that sets **X** and **Y** have a finite number of elements, so that $q(x, y)$ is bounded and at the same time a maximum. Theorems 23.1, 24.1, 26.1, and 26.2, in which the same assumptions are made, are therefore also valid.

Then again, it must be stressed that in practice, the complete *analytical* solution of a random dynamic program is virtually impossible as soon as a certain degree of complexity is reached, which is always the case when we attempt to give a reasonably accurate reproduction of reality. In general, analytical study merely enables us to prove certain properties of the solutions. The invariable method in such a case consists in finding the numerical solution by means of a computer. But to do this, it is essential to restrict the field of variation of the state and decision vectors to a grid of suitably chosen points, and hence to return to the case considered in the present chapter.

29. Structure of Finite Markovian Chains

To study this subject in detail we shall first examine the evolution of the system under the influence of a permanent given strategy $\{k\}$. We say that it is in state E_i at a certain time, when the state variable is equal to i. To simplify the notation, we shall suppress k and take p_{ij} as the probability that the state will be E_j when it was E_i at the beginning.

Hence we possess a system capable at each time n of assuming a finite number of states E_1, E_2,..., E_M. We shall use $p_i(n)$ for the probability of state E_i at time n, when we know the initial distribution of probability $p_1(0)$, $p_2(0)$,..., $p_M(0)$. The Markovian property of this random chain is expressed by the relation

$$p_j(n+1) = \sum_{i=1}^{M} p_i(n) \cdot p_{ij}, \qquad j = 1, 2,..., M. \qquad (29.1)$$

The set of the probabilities of state $p_i(n)$ relative to time n constitutes a state vector.

$$[P(n)] = [p_1(n) \quad p_2(n) \cdots p_M(n)]. \qquad (29.2)$$

Let us recall that a vector of which the sum of the components is equal to 1, and in which each component is real and nonnegative (as is the case here), is a stochastic vector.

Again, the probabilities p_{ij} can be considered as the elements of a matrix, called the "transition matrix" of the Markovian chain:

$$[\mathscr{T}] = \begin{bmatrix} p_{11} & p_{12} & \cdots & p_{1M} \\ p_{21} & p_{22} & \cdots & p_{2M} \\ & & \vdots & \\ p_{M1} & p_{M2} & \cdots & p_{MM} \end{bmatrix}. \tag{29.3}$$

Let us also recall that a stochastic matrix is a square matrix such as (29.3) in which each line is a stochastic vector. Since the matrix $[\mathscr{T}]$ is independent of the time considered, the Markovian chain is said to be stationary.[4]

The set of relations (29.1) can be expressed in the matrical form,

$$[P(n+1)] = [P(n)][\mathscr{T}]. \tag{29.4}$$

By applying this relation successively for $n = 0, 1, 2, 3,...$, we obtain

$$[P(n)] = [P(0)][\mathscr{T}]^n. \tag{29.5}$$

With every stationary Markovian chain we shall associate a graph G, called the "graph of the transitions," containing M vertices corresponding to each of the states, and with two vertices i and j joined by an arc oriented from i towards j if $p_{ij} > 0$. This graph only allows us to distinguish between the transitions that are possible and those that are not. In the theory of graphs we can equally associate with it a boolean matrix $[\mathscr{B}]$ of which the element b_{ij} is equal to 1 if there is an arc from i towards j and is zero in the opposite case (see (4.14)).

Figure 29.1 gives an example of a transition matrix (a); the graph and the associated boolean matrix are shown in (b) and (c).

MATRIX AND DYNAMIC EQUATION

Let

$$[\mathscr{T}] = \begin{bmatrix} p_{11} & p_{12} & p_{13} & \cdots & p_{1M} \\ p_{21} & p_{22} & p_{23} & \cdots & p_{2M} \\ & & & \vdots & \\ p_{M1} & p_{M2} & p_{M3} & \cdots & p_{MM} \end{bmatrix} \tag{29.6}$$

[4] If, in the dynamic program being considered, we adopt a different decision vector in each period, the Markovian chain is no longer stationary. It is the stationary case we are studying in the present section.

	(1)	(2)	(3)	(4)	(5)	(6)	(7)	(8)	(9)
(1)	0	0	0	0	0	0	1	0	0
(2)	0	0	0	0	0	1	0	0	0
(3)	0	0	1	0	0	0	0	0	0
(4)	0	0.1	0.3	0.5	0	0	0	0.1	0
(5)	0	0	0	0	0.7	0.3	0	0	0
(6)	0	0.5	0	0	0.3	0.2	0	0	0
(7)	0.5	0	0	0	0	0	0	0	0.5
(8)	0	0	0.2	0	0	0.3	0.1	0.3	0.1
(9)	0	0	0	0	0	0	1	0	0

$[\mathscr{O}] =$ (rows (1)–(9))

(a)

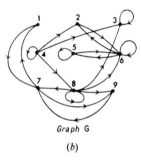

Graph G

(b)

	(1)	(2)	(3)	(4)	(5)	(6)	(7)	(8)	(9)
(1)	0	0	0	0	0	0	1	0	0
(2)	0	0	0	0	0	1	0	0	0
(3)	0	0	1	0	0	0	0	0	0
(4)	0	1	1	1	0	0	0	1	0
(5)	0	0	0	0	1	1	0	0	0
(6)	0	1	0	0	1	1	0	0	0
(7)	1	0	0	0	0	0	0	0	1
(8)	0	0	1	0	0	1	1	1	1
(9)	0	0	0	0	0	0	1	0	0

$[\mathscr{B}] =$ (rows (1)–(9))

(c)

FIG. 29.1

be the transition matrix of a Markovian chain. The matrix

$$[3] = [\mathscr{T}] - [\mathscr{E}_M], \qquad (29.7)$$

where $[\mathscr{E}_M]$ is the unit matrix of order M, Let

$$[3] = \begin{bmatrix} p_{11} - 1 & p_{12} & p_{13} & \cdots & p_{1M} \\ p_{21} & p_{22} - 1 & p_{23} & \cdots & p_{2M} \\ p_{31} & p_{32} & p_{33} - 1 & \cdots & p_{3M} \\ & & & \vdots & \\ p_{M1} & p_{M2} & p_{M3} & \cdots & p_{MM} - 1 \end{bmatrix} \qquad (29.8)$$

be called the "dynamic matrix." If we take z_{ij} for the elements of [3], we have

$$0 \leqslant z_{ij} \leqslant 1, \qquad \forall i \neq j; \tag{29.9}$$

$$-1 \leqslant z_{ii} \leqslant 0, \qquad \forall i; \tag{29.10}$$

$$\sum_{j=1}^{M} z_{ij} = 0, \qquad \forall i. \tag{29.11}$$

It can easily be seen that the determinant | 3 | of the dynamic matrix is always zero. In fact, this determinant does not change if we replace one of its columns by the sum of the M columns, but it then has a column formed of zeros.

By using the dynamic matrix, we can write Eq. (29.4) in the form

$$[P(n + 1)] - [P(n)] = [P(n)][3]. \tag{29.12}$$

Transitions of Order n

Let us assume that at a certain time the system is in state E_i . Since the chain is stationary, we may also assume that this time is the origin, and we then have

$$p_i(0) = 1, \tag{29.13}$$

$$p_j(0) = 0, \qquad \forall j \neq i. \tag{29.14}$$

According to (29.5), the probability of E_j at time n, that is to say, the jth element of the vector $[P(n)]$, is the element (i, j) of matrix $[\mathscr{T}]^n$; we shall take $p_{ij}^{(n)}$ for this probability of transition of order n, with the understanding that $p_{ij}^{(1)} = p_{ij}$. Again, we shall assume $p_{ij}^{(0)} = 0$ if $j \neq 1$, and $p_{ii}^{(0)} = 1$, which enables us to apply (29.5) for $n = 0$.

Decomposition into Equivalence Classes

We shall say that a state E_j is a descendant of a state E_i (whether distinct or not from E_j) if an integer $n \geqslant 0$ exists such that $p_{ij}^{(n)} > 0$, and we shall show this relation as $E_j \geqslant E_i$ or $E_i \leqslant E_j$. As an immediate result of this definition, we always have $E_i \leqslant E_j$. On the other hand, if $E_i \leqslant E_j$ and $E_j \leqslant E_k$, then $E_i \leqslant E_k$, for

$$p_{ik}^{(n_1+n_2)} \geqslant p_{ij}^{(n_1)} \cdot p_{jk}^{(n_2)}.$$

Differently expressed, the relation we have just defined is reflexive and transitive, and is one of preorder.

If we have both $E_i \leqslant E_j$ and $E_j \leqslant E_i$, we say that E_i and E_j possess equivalence, expressed as $E_i \equiv E_j$. This relation is clearly not only reflexive and transitive but also symmetrical, that is, $E_i \equiv E_j$ implies $E_j \equiv E_i$, which is an equivalence relation.

Such a relation enables us to define "equivalence classes" $\mathbf{C}_k$ such that

$$E_i \in \mathbf{C}_k \quad \text{and} \quad E_j \in \mathbf{C}_k \quad \Rightarrow \quad E_i \equiv E_j, \tag{29.15}$$

$$E_i \in \mathbf{C}_k \quad \text{and} \quad E_j \notin \mathbf{C}_k \quad \Rightarrow \quad E_i \not\equiv E_j. \tag{29.16}$$

In the graph associated with the Markovian chain considered, the vertices belonging to the same equivalence class define a subgraph, which[5] is said to be strongly connected: any oriented pair of vertices is joined by at least one route (in each direction).

To find equivalence classes, we can use the method devised by Foulkes:

(1) We consider the associated boolean matrix $[\mathscr{B}]$ and calculate[6]

$$[\mathscr{A}_n] = ([\mathscr{E}_M] + [\mathscr{B}])^{\dot{n}} = [\mathscr{E}_M] + [\mathscr{B}] + [\mathscr{B}]^{\dot{2}} + \cdots + [\mathscr{B}]. \tag{29.17}$$

---

[5] Let us recall that the subgraph defined, in a graph $G = (\mathbf{X}, \Gamma)$, by a subset $\mathbf{A} \subset \mathbf{X}$ of vertices, is the graph obtained by retaining in G only the vertices $x \in \mathbf{A}$, and the arcs $u = (x, y)$ such that $x, y \in \mathbf{A}$.

[6] Let us recall the properties of boolean operations:

$$1 \dot{+} 1 = 0 \dot{+} 1 = 1 \dot{+} 0 = 1, \quad 0 \dot{+} 0 = 0; \quad 1 \cdot 1 = 1, \quad 1 \cdot 0 = 0 \cdot 1 = 0 \cdot 0 = 0.$$

If $[a_{ij}]$ and $[b_{ij}]$ are matrices with binary coefficients,

$$[a_{ij}] \dot{+} [b_{ij}] = [a_{ij} \dot{+} b_{ij}] \quad \text{(boolean matrix sum)},$$

$$[a_{ij}] \cdot [b_{ij}] = [c_{ij}] \quad \text{where} \quad c_{ij} = \underset{k}{\sigma}\, a_{ik} \cdot b_{kj}$$

(boolean matrix product, where σ_k represents a boolean sum).

A boolean power will be shown as $[\sigma_{ij}]^n$:

$$[a_{ij}] = [b_{ij}], \quad [c_{ij}] = [a_{ij}]^{\dot{2}}.$$

A convenient procedure for obtaining a boolean product of two matrices is as follows: let $\mathbf{K}_i$ be the set of the indices of the columns of the matrix $[a_{ij}]$ defined by

$$\mathbf{K}_i = \{k \mid a_{ik} = 1\}.$$

The relation which gives the element c_{ij} of the boolean product of the matrix $[a_{ij}]$ by the matrix $[b_{ij}]$ can then be expressed,

$$c_{ij} = \underset{k \in \mathbf{K}_i}{\sigma}\, b_{kj}.$$

This relation is the same for every value of j and we can directly obtain the vector representing the first line of the matrix product:

$$[c_{i1}\ c_{i2}\ \cdots\ c_{iM}] = \underset{k \in \mathbf{K}_i}{\sigma}\, [b_{k1}\ b_{k2}\ \cdots\ b_{kM}].$$

Expressed differently, line i of this product is the boolean sum of the lines of the matrix

The element (i, j) of this matrix is equal to 1 if there is a route from E_i to E_j of a length at most equal to n, and is 0 in the opposite case.

We successively calculate

$$[\mathscr{A}_2], [\mathscr{A}_4], [\mathscr{A}_8], \ldots$$

until

$$[\mathscr{A}_{2^{K+1}}] = [\mathscr{A}_{2^K}]. \tag{29.18}$$

We can show that this occurs for a value K such that

$$2^{K-1} < M - 1. \tag{29.19}$$

In fact, if there is a route from i to j ($j \neq 1$) of length greater than $M - 1$, there is a vertex k through which it passes at least twice. We can then suppress that portion of the route between the first and second passage through k, and the remaining portion will still connect i and j. By using this procedure for every vertex such as k, we obtain a route from i to j of a length not greater than $M - 1$. Such a route, which never passes twice through the same vertex, is called elementary. Hence, if $E_j \geqslant E_i$, there is an elementary route from E_i to E_j. If K_0 is the greatest integer which satisfies (29.19), we have

$$2^{K_0} \geqslant M - 1, \tag{29.20}$$

and the element (i, j) of $[\mathscr{A}_{2^{k_0}}]$ is equal to 1 if and only if $E_i \leqslant E_j$. The same consideration obviously applies to $[\mathscr{A}_{2^{k_0}} + 1]$, and (29.18) is satisfied for every $K \geqslant K_0$.

(2) Taking the matrix $[\mathscr{A}_{2^k}]$, we look for all the descendants E_j of E_i to which the elements 1 of the first line of this matrix correspond. For each of these descendants, we consider whether $E_j \leqslant E_i$, in other words, whether the element $(j, 1)$ of the matrix is equal to 1. Each state E_j with this property has equivalence with E_i, and we thus obtain all the elements of the equivalence class which contains E_1. We then suppress from the matrix all the lines and columns corresponding to the states of this class. This procedure is then repeated in the matrix obtained, beginning with a chosen state, and so on until all the states are exhausted.

A great advantage of this method is that it can be easily programmed to a computer.

$[b_{ij}]$ of which the number belongs to $\mathbf{K}_i$; for instance, if the second and fifth elements of line i of $[a_{ij}]$ are alone equal to 1, line i of the matrix product is the boolean sum of lines 2 and 5 of $[b_{ij}]$.

Example. Let us consider the Markovian chain defined by the following transition matrix.

$$[\mathcal{T}] = \begin{array}{c} \\ (1) \\ (2) \\ (3) \\ (4) \\ (5) \\ (6) \\ (7) \\ (8) \\ (9) \end{array} \begin{array}{ccccccccc} (1) & (2) & (3) & (4) & (5) & (6) & (7) & (8) & (9) \\ \left[\begin{array}{ccccccccc} 0 & 0 & 0 & 0 & 0.4 & 0.6 & 0 & 0 & 0 \\ 0 & 0.1 & 0 & 0 & 0 & 0 & 0.3 & 0.1 & 0.5 \\ 0 & 0 & 0.1 & 0.8 & 0 & 0 & 0 & 0 & 0.1 \\ 0 & 0 & 1 & 0 & 0 & 0 & 0 & 0 & 0 \\ 0.8 & 0 & 0 & 0 & 0 & 0.2 & 0 & 0 & 0 \\ 1 & 0 & 0 & 0 & 0 & 0 & 0 & 0 & 0 \\ 0 & 0 & 0 & 0 & 0 & 0 & 1 & 0 & 0 \\ 0.1 & 0 & 0.1 & 0 & 0 & 0.1 & 0.1 & 0.6 & 0 \\ 0 & 0 & 1 & 0 & 0 & 0 & 0 & 0 & 0 \end{array}\right] \end{array} . \quad (29.21)$$

$$[\mathcal{B}] = \begin{array}{c} \\ (1) \\ (2) \\ (3) \\ (4) \\ (5) \\ (6) \\ (7) \\ (8) \\ (9) \end{array} \begin{array}{ccccccccc} (1) & (2) & (3) & (4) & (5) & (6) & (7) & (8) & (9) \\ \left[\begin{array}{ccccccccc} 0 & 0 & 0 & 0 & 1 & 1 & 0 & 0 & 0 \\ 0 & 1 & 0 & 0 & 0 & 0 & 1 & 1 & 1 \\ 0 & 0 & 1 & 1 & 0 & 0 & 0 & 0 & 1 \\ 0 & 0 & 1 & 0 & 0 & 0 & 0 & 0 & 0 \\ 1 & 0 & 0 & 0 & 0 & 1 & 0 & 0 & 0 \\ 1 & 0 & 0 & 0 & 0 & 0 & 0 & 0 & 0 \\ 0 & 0 & 0 & 0 & 0 & 0 & 1 & 0 & 0 \\ 1 & 0 & 1 & 0 & 0 & 1 & 1 & 1 & 0 \\ 0 & 0 & 1 & 0 & 0 & 0 & 0 & 0 & 0 \end{array}\right] \end{array} . \quad (29.22)$$

The associated boolean matrix is given by (29.22), while the associated graph is shown in Fig. 29.2. It would not be difficult to find the different

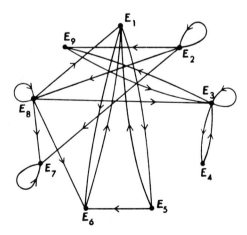

Fig. 29.2

equivalence classes by inspection, but we shall use this easy example to explain the general method.

Let us successively calculate:

$$[\mathscr{A}_1] = \begin{bmatrix} 1 & 0 & 0 & 0 & 1 & 1 & 0 & 0 & 0 \\ 0 & 1 & 0 & 0 & 0 & 0 & 1 & 1 & 1 \\ 0 & 0 & 1 & 1 & 0 & 0 & 0 & 0 & 1 \\ 0 & 0 & 1 & 1 & 0 & 0 & 0 & 0 & 0 \\ 1 & 0 & 0 & 0 & 1 & 1 & 0 & 0 & 0 \\ 1 & 0 & 0 & 0 & 0 & 1 & 0 & 0 & 0 \\ 0 & 0 & 0 & 0 & 0 & 0 & 1 & 0 & 0 \\ 1 & 0 & 1 & 0 & 0 & 1 & 1 & 1 & 0 \\ 0 & 0 & 1 & 0 & 0 & 0 & 0 & 0 & 1 \end{bmatrix}, \quad (29.23)$$

$$[\mathscr{A}_2] = \begin{bmatrix} 1 & 0 & 0 & 0 & 1 & 1 & 0 & 0 & 0 \\ ① & 1 & ① & 0 & 0 & ① & 1 & 1 & 1 \\ 0 & 0 & 1 & 1 & 0 & 0 & 0 & 0 & 1 \\ 0 & 0 & 1 & 1 & 0 & 0 & 0 & 0 & ① \\ 1 & 0 & 0 & 0 & 1 & 1 & 0 & 0 & 0 \\ 1 & 0 & 0 & 0 & ① & 1 & 0 & 0 & 0 \\ 0 & 0 & 0 & 0 & 0 & 0 & 1 & 0 & 0 \\ 1 & 0 & 1 & ① & ① & 1 & 1 & 1 & ① \\ 0 & 0 & 1 & ① & 0 & 0 & 0 & 0 & 1 \end{bmatrix}, \quad (29.24)$$

$$[\mathscr{A}_4] = \begin{bmatrix} 1 & 0 & 0 & 0 & 1 & 1 & 0 & 0 & 0 \\ 1 & 1 & 1 & ① & ① & 1 & 1 & 1 & 1 \\ 0 & 0 & 1 & 1 & 0 & 0 & 0 & 0 & 1 \\ 0 & 0 & 1 & 1 & 0 & 0 & 0 & 0 & 1 \\ 1 & 0 & 0 & 0 & 1 & 1 & 0 & 0 & 0 \\ 1 & 0 & 0 & 0 & 1 & 1 & 0 & 0 & 0 \\ 0 & 0 & 0 & 0 & 0 & 0 & 1 & 0 & 0 \\ 1 & 0 & 1 & 1 & 1 & 1 & 1 & 1 & 1 \\ 0 & 0 & 1 & 1 & 0 & 0 & 0 & 0 & 1 \end{bmatrix}, \quad (29.25)$$

$$
[\mathscr{A}_8] =
\begin{array}{c}
\\ (1) \\ (2) \\ (3) \\ (4) \\ (5) \\ (6) \\ (7) \\ (8) \\ (9)
\end{array}
\begin{array}{c}
\begin{array}{ccccccccc} (1) & (2) & (3) & (4) & (5) & (6) & (7) & (8) & (9) \end{array} \\
\begin{bmatrix} 1 & 0 & 0 & 0 & 1 & 1 & 0 & 0 & 0 \\ 1 & 1 & 1 & 1 & 1 & 1 & 1 & 1 & 1 \\ 0 & 0 & 1 & 1 & 0 & 0 & 0 & 0 & 1 \\ 0 & 0 & 1 & 1 & 0 & 0 & 0 & 0 & 1 \\ 1 & 0 & 0 & 0 & 1 & 1 & 0 & 0 & 0 \\ 1 & 0 & 0 & 0 & 1 & 1 & 0 & 0 & 0 \\ 0 & 0 & 0 & 0 & 0 & 0 & 1 & 0 & 0 \\ 1 & 0 & 1 & 1 & 1 & 1 & 1 & 1 & 1 \\ 0 & 0 & 1 & 1 & 0 & 0 & 0 & 0 & 1 \end{bmatrix}
\end{array}. \quad (29.26)
$$

We have circled the new 1 digits which appear in each elevation of the square. In the end we see that $[\mathscr{A}_4] = [\mathscr{A}_8]$, but even if this had not been the case we should have stopped at $[\mathscr{A}_8]$, for (29.19) shows that $[\mathscr{A}_{16}] = [\mathscr{A}_8]$.

In $[\mathscr{A}_8]$, if we consider line (1) we see that there is a route from E_1 to E_5 and E_6. Again, lines (5) and (6) show that there is a route from E_5 to E_6 and E_1. Hence these vertices belong to the same equivalence class $\mathbf{C}_1$.

Let us now suppress lines and columns (1), (5), and (6), which leaves us matrix (29.28) in which E_2 is an equivalence class of its own. If we now suppress line and column (2), we obtain matrix (28.29) in which E_3, E_4, and E_9 belong to the same class. There remains matrix (29.30) which shows us that E_7 and E_8 do not belong to the same class. Hence there are five classes:

$$\mathbf{C}_1 = \{E_1, E_5, E_6\}, \qquad \mathbf{C}_2 = \{E_2\},$$
$$\mathbf{C}_3 = \{E_3, E_4, E_9\}, \qquad \mathbf{C}_4 = \{7\}, \qquad \mathbf{C}_5 = \{8\}. \tag{29.27}$$

$$
\begin{array}{c}
 \quad (2) \;\; (3) \;\; (4) \;\; (7) \;\; (8) \;\; (9) \\
\begin{array}{c}
(2) \\ (3) \\ (4) \\ (7) \\ (8) \\ (9)
\end{array}
\begin{bmatrix}
1 & 1 & 1 & 1 & 1 & 1 \\
0 & 1 & 1 & 0 & 0 & 1 \\
0 & 1 & 1 & 0 & 0 & 1 \\
0 & 0 & 0 & 1 & 0 & 0 \\
0 & 1 & 1 & 1 & 1 & 1 \\
0 & 1 & 1 & 0 & 0 & 1
\end{bmatrix}
\end{array}
\tag{29.28}
$$

$$
\begin{array}{c}
 \quad (3) \;\; (4) \;\; (7) \;\; (8) \;\; (9) \\
\begin{array}{c}
(3) \\ (4) \\ (7) \\ (8) \\ (9)
\end{array}
\begin{bmatrix}
1 & 1 & 0 & 0 & 1 \\
1 & 1 & 0 & 0 & 1 \\
0 & 0 & 1 & 0 & 0 \\
1 & 1 & 1 & 1 & 1 \\
1 & 1 & 0 & 0 & 1
\end{bmatrix}
\end{array}
\tag{29.29}
$$

$$
\begin{array}{c}
 \quad (7) \;\; (8) \\
\begin{array}{c}
(7) \\ (8)
\end{array}
\begin{bmatrix}
1 & 0 \\
1 & 1
\end{bmatrix}
\end{array}
\tag{29.30}
$$

We thus obtain the graph of Fig. 29.3 in which the five equivalence classes are shown.

The procedure can be shortened by first eliminating the lines formed by 1 elements only (the class which precedes all the others) or the lines composed only of 0's except for the 1 on the main diagonal; it is then a case of a class which follows all the others.

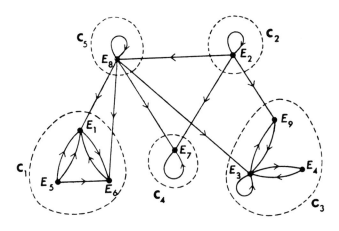

FIG. 29.3

CLOSED SET OF STATES. PERSISTENT STATES. TRANSITORY STATES

We say that an equivalence class $\mathbf{C}_k$ forms a closed set of states when there is no oriented pair (i, j) such that $E_i \in \mathbf{C}_k$, $E_j \notin \mathbf{C}_k$, and $E_i \leqslant E_j$. Expressed differently, the system can never emerge from set $\mathbf{C}_k$ once it has entered it. The states of a set of this kind are called persistent. For instance, in Fig. 29.3 it will be seen that classes $\mathbf{C}_1$, $\mathbf{C}_3$, and $\mathbf{C}_4$ form closed sets of states and that the states contained in them are persistent.

If set $\mathbf{C}_k$ is closed, we have by definition $p_{ij}^{(n)} = 0$, whatever the value of $n > 0$, for $E_i \in \mathbf{C}_k$ and $E_j \notin \mathbf{C}_k$; in particular,

$$p_{ij} = p_{ij}^{(1)} = 0.$$

Reciprocally, if $p_{ij} = 0$, $\mathbf{C}_k$ is obviously closed.

If a set is not closed, its states are termed *transitory*, as, for example, E_2 and E_8 in Fig. 29.3.

It can easily be seen that in an arbitrary stochastic matrix $[\mathscr{T}]$, there is at least one closed set $\mathbf{C}_k$, and in consequence at least one persistent state in the chain.

NORMAL FORM

We say that the chain or stochastic matrix is irreducible if all the states belong to the same equivalence class, in other words, if the associated graph is strongly connected. The result of this is that in an irreducible chain any state can be reached from any other.

When the matrix is not irreducible there are at least two equivalence classes, and it is termed *reducible*. Let us consider a reducible matrix $[\mathscr{T}]$ and assume that the equivalence classes $\mathbf{C}_1$, $\mathbf{C}_2$,..., $\mathbf{C}_h$ are closed. Let us also change the numbering of the sets, assigning the index numbers 1, 2,..., M, first to the states of class $\mathbf{C}_1$, then to those of $\mathbf{C}_2$,..., $\mathbf{C}_h$, and finally to those of classes $\mathbf{C}_k$ if there are any which are not closed. The new matrix $[\mathscr{T}]$, which is obtained by a suitable permutation of the lines and columns, then has the following form, called the normal form:

$$[\mathscr{T}] = \begin{bmatrix} \mathscr{T}_1 & 0 & \cdots & 0 & 0 \\ 0 & \mathscr{T}_2 & \cdots & 0 & 0 \\ \vdots & \vdots & & \vdots & \vdots \\ 0 & 0 & & \mathscr{T}_h & 0 \\ \mathscr{R}_1 & \mathscr{R}_2 & \cdots & \mathscr{R}_h & \mathscr{T}_T \end{bmatrix}, \tag{29.31}$$

where $[\mathscr{T}_1]$, $[\mathscr{T}_2]$,..., $[\mathscr{T}_h]$ are irreducible square stochastic matrices, and $[\mathscr{T}_T]$ a square matrix which is not stochastic. If there are no transitory states, the normal form is

$$[\mathscr{T}] = \begin{bmatrix} \mathscr{T}_1 & 0 & \cdots & 0 \\ 0 & \mathscr{T}_2 & \cdots & 0 \\ & & \vdots & \\ 0 & 0 & \cdots & \mathscr{T}_h \end{bmatrix}. \tag{29.32}$$

A matrix which contains a single closed set is called unireducible (see Section 32), and all the persistent states in it belong to the same equivalence class $(h = 1)$.

For instance, if we arrange the lines and columns in matrix (29.21) in such a way that we successively find the states of $\mathbf{C}_1$, $\mathbf{C}_3$, $\mathbf{C}_4$, and then of $\mathbf{C}_2$ and $\mathbf{C}_5$, we obtain

	(1)	(5)	(6)	(7)	(3)	(4)	(9)	(2)	(8)
(1)	0	0.4	0.6	0	0	0	0	0	0
(5)	0.8	0	0.2	0	0	0	0	0	0
(6)	1	0	0	0	0	0	0	0	0
(7)	0	0	0	1	0	0	0	0	0
(3)	0	0	0	0	0.1	0.8	0.1	0	0
(4)	0	0	0	0	1	0	0	0	0
(9)	0	0	0	0	1	0	0	0	0
(2)	0	0	0	0.3	0	0	0.5	0.1	0.1
(8)	0.1	0	0.1	0.1	0.1	0	0	0	0.6

$$[\mathscr{T}] = \qquad \tag{29.33}$$

States E_2 and E_8 are transitory, while the others are persistent and form three irreducible subchains. The matrix is neither reducible nor unireducible.

When $[\mathscr{T}]$ is put in the normal form (29.31), we can easily find the asymptotes of the $p_{ij}^{(n)}$ terms, at least for certain oriented pairs (i, j):

(a) We have seen that if $E_i \in \mathbf{C}_k$ with $1 \leqslant k \leqslant h$ (in other words, if $\mathbf{C}_k$ is closed, or if E_i is persistent., we have

$$p_{ij}^{(n)} = 0, \qquad \forall n > 0 \quad \text{and} \quad \forall j \qquad \text{such that} \quad E_j \notin C_k . \qquad (29.34)$$

(a) If

$$E_i \in \mathbf{T} \qquad \text{where} \quad \mathbf{T} = \bigcup_{k > h} \mathbf{C}_k \qquad (29.35)$$

is the set of transitory states, we have

$$\lim_{n \to \infty} p_{ij}^{(n)} = 0, \qquad \forall j \quad \text{such that} \quad E_j \in \mathbf{T}. \qquad (29.36)$$

Indeed, since E_i is transitory, $p_{ii} > 1$ (otherwise E_i would form a closed equivalence class), and the probability of the system remaining indefinitely in state E_i is equal to

$$\lim_{n \to \infty} p_{ii}^n ,$$

and is therefore zero. As this is true for every transitory state, and as these are finite in number (since the number of states is finite), the system cannot remain indefinitely in state $\mathbf{T}$, that is to say,

$$\lim_{n \to \infty} \sum_{E_j \in \mathbf{T}} p_{ij}^{(n)} = 0, \qquad (29.37)$$

whence we obtain (29.36). It now only remains for us to study the probabilities $p_{ij}^{(n)}$.

(a) For states $E_i , E_j \in \mathbf{C}_k$ $(1 \leqslant k \leqslant h)$, these probabilities clearly only depend on the irreducible matrix $[\mathscr{T}_k]$, so that we can make a separate study of the random chain of which it is the matrix. The corresponding graph will be a strongly connected subgraph of the initial graph, obtained by suppressing all the vertices (states) which do not belong to $\mathbf{C}_k$ and all the arcs joining them to $\mathbf{C}_k$. Hence we are led to examine in particular the irreducible chains, as we shall do further on.

(b) The probabilities for $E_i \in \mathbf{T}$ and $E_j \notin \mathbf{T}$ will be considered in Section 32.

30. Irreducible Finite Markovian Chain[7]

Let us assume that the chain which has $[\mathscr{T}]$ for its matrix is irreducible. Let us recall that all the states of an irreducible chain belong to the same equivalence class, in other words, for every oriented pair (i, j) there is a route from E_i to E_j and one from E_j to E_i, a property expressed by saying that the graph is strongly connected.

PERIODIC STATE

A state E_i is called periodic and has a period t $(t > 1)$ when the following conditions are satisfied:

(a) $p_{ii}^{(n)} = 0$ except for $n = 0$ and perhaps for $n = t, 2t, 3t,...$; or, alternatively, $p_{ii}^{(n)} > 0 \Rightarrow n$ multiple of t.

(b) t is the largest integer for which this is true.

If there is no integer $t > 1$ which satisfies these conditions, state E_i is called aperiodic. Such is the case, in particular, if $p_{ii} > 0$, and the graph is then said to have a loop in E_i.

A circuit of the graph associated with a Markovian chain is a route which begins and ends at the same vertex. If we bear this in mind, the conditions "$p_{ii}^{(l)} > 0$" and "there is a circuit of length l" are clearly equivalent.[8] Let us now consider the set $\mathbf{L}_i$ of the lengths of the circuits of the graph passing through i.

$$\mathbf{L}_i = \{l \mid p_{ii}^{(l)} > 0\}. \tag{30.1}$$

The above conditions (a) and (b) can then be expressed: the highest common factor of the elements of $\mathbf{L}_i$ is equal to t.

Given a periodic state E_i and its period $t > 1$, with $b_{ij}^{(n)}$ the elements of the boolean matrix associated with $[\mathscr{T}]$,

$$b_{ij}^{(n)} = 1 \quad \text{if} \quad p_{ij}^{(n)} > 0,$$
$$= 0 \quad \text{if} \quad p_{ij}^{(n)} = 0. \tag{30.2}$$

We then have $b_{11}^{(n)} = 0$, except for $n = 0$, and perhaps $n = t, 2t, 3t,...$. If we now consider an arbitrary state E_i $(i \neq 1)$, with α and β the respective lengths of a route from E_1 to E_i and one from E_i to E_i, since

---

[7] See W. Feller, *An Introduction to Probability Theory and Its Applications*, Vol. I, 2nd ed. John Wiley, 1957, p. 360.
[8] The length of a route is the number of arcs contained in it.

E_1 has the period t, $\alpha + \beta = kt$, where k is a positive integer. Further, we shall prove that

$$b_{11}^{(n+kt)} \geq b_{ii}^{(n)}, \qquad \forall n. \tag{30.3}$$

This inequality is obvious if $b_{ii}^{(n)} = 0$; if it is equal to 1, the circuit obtained by adding the routes $E_1 \to E_i$ and $E_i \to E_1$ to a circuit of length n passing through E_i, passes through E_1 and has the length

$$n + \alpha + \beta = n + kt.$$

But this is only possible if $n + kt$, and hence n, is a multiple of t. Thus

$$b_{ii}^{(n)} = 1 \qquad \Rightarrow \qquad n \text{ multiple of } t. \tag{30.4}$$

This shows that E_i has a period less than or equal to t. But the same reasoning, carried out with E_1 and E_i interchanged, would show that t is less than or equal to the period of E_1, which implies that the period of E_i is equal to 1.

Since this is valid for i, all the states of the chain are periodic and have the same period t. The result is that if there are two routes from E_i to E_j respectively n_1 and n_2 in length, their difference $|n_1 - n_2|$ is a multiple of t, or each has the same remainder when divided by t. It is therefore possible, if we take as our base a certain state E_i, to distribute the states in t groups[9] $\mathbf{G}_0, \mathbf{G}_1 ,..., \mathbf{G}_{t-1}$ such that an arbitrary state E_j belongs to $\mathbf{G}_r$ $(0 \leq r < t)$ if the length of a route from E_i to E_j is equal to $(kt + r)$. If, at a given time, the system is in one of the states of $\mathbf{G}_r$, it must be in one of those of $\mathbf{G}_{r+1}$ (or of $\mathbf{G}_0$ if $r = t - 1$) at the following time. In other words, the system traverses the groups in a cyclic manner.

Examples

(1) The matrix

$$[\mathscr{T}] = \begin{bmatrix} 0 & 0.5 & 0.5 \\ 1 & 0 & 0 \\ 1 & 0 & 0 \end{bmatrix} \tag{30.5}$$

is that of an irreducible periodic chain with a period 2. Of the two groups $\mathbf{G}_0$ and $\mathbf{G}_1$, the first is formed by E_1 and the second by E_2 and E_3. Every circuit in the corresponding graph (Fig. 30.1) has a length which is a multiple of 2.

---

[9] The word "group" is not used here with the meaning it customarily possesses in the theory of sets, but to distinguish subsets.

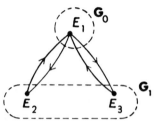

FIG. 30.1

(2) The matrix

$$[\mathscr{T}] = \begin{bmatrix} 0 & 1 & 0 & 0 & 0 & 0 \\ 0 & 0 & 1 & 0 & 0 & 0 \\ * & 0 & 0 & * & 0 & 0 \\ 0 & 0 & 0 & 0 & 1 & 0 \\ 0 & 0 & 0 & 0 & 0 & 1 \\ 1 & 0 & 0 & 0 & 0 & 0 \end{bmatrix},$$

(30.6)

where the asterisks in the third line represent nonzero elements with a sum of unity, is periodic with a period $t = 3$, as can easily be seen in Fig. 30.2.

It should be observed that there is no circuit with a length of 3 passing through E_4, E_5, and E_6, but only circuits of length 6, 9, 12,... . On the other hand, there is a vertex in each group $\mathbf{G}$ through which there passes a circuit of length 3.

At the same time, there may be no circuit of length t in the graph, as is the case in Fig. 30.3 where $t = 2$.

This partition of the set of states into t groups enables us to put the matrix $[\mathscr{T})$ into a simple form. To do so, we change the numbering of the states, giving the index numbers 1, 2,..., M in succession, first to the

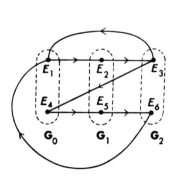

FIG. 30.2

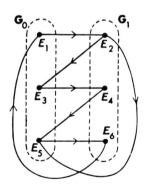

FIG. 30.3

states of $\mathbf{G}_0$ (for example), then to those of $\mathbf{G}_1$,..., and finally to those of $\mathbf{G}_{t-1}$. After this permutation, the new matrix acquires the cyclic form

$$[\mathscr{T}] = \begin{bmatrix} 0 & \mathscr{G}_0 & 0 & \cdots & 0 \\ 0 & 0 & \mathscr{G}_1 & \cdots & 0 \\ & & & \vdots & \\ 0 & 0 & 0 & \cdots & \mathscr{G}_{t-2} \\ \mathscr{G}_{t-1} & 0 & 0 & \cdots & 0 \end{bmatrix}, \tag{30.7}$$

where the zeros on the main diagonal represent square matrices in which all the elements are zero. The order of each of these matrices is equal to the number of states $|\mathbf{G}_r|$ of the corresponding group $\mathbf{G}_r$. The $[\mathscr{G}_r]$ matrices can be rectangular since $[\mathscr{G}_r]$ is of the order $|\mathbf{G}_r| \times |\mathbf{G}_{r+1}|$, or $|\mathbf{G}_{t-1}| \times |\mathbf{G}_0|$ if $r = t - 1$, but the sum of the elements of each line is equal to 1.

Examples

(1) In (30.5) above, the transition matrix is already in the cyclic form

$$[\mathscr{T}] = \begin{bmatrix} 0 & 0.5 & 0.5 \\ 1 & 0 & 0 \\ 1 & 0 & 0 \end{bmatrix}. \tag{30.8}$$

(2) In (30.6), a suitable permutation of the numbers of the states gives

$$[\mathscr{T}] = \begin{array}{c} \\ (1) \\ (4) \\ \\ (2) \\ (5) \\ \\ (3) \\ (6) \end{array} \begin{array}{cc} \overset{(1)\,(4)}{} & \overset{(2)\,(5)}{} & \overset{(3)\,(6)}{} \\ \begin{bmatrix} 0 & 0 & 1 & 0 & 0 & 0 \\ 0 & 0 & 0 & 1 & 0 & 0 \\ 0 & 0 & 0 & 0 & 1 & 0 \\ 0 & 0 & 0 & 0 & 0 & 1 \\ * & * & 0 & 0 & 0 & 0 \\ 1 & 0 & 0 & 0 & 0 & 0 \end{bmatrix}. \end{array} \tag{30.9}$$

If we consider the system only at times $n, n + t, n + 2t,...$, we obtain a new chain the transition matrix of which has the elements $p_{ij}^{(t)}$ and is therefore equal to $[\mathscr{T}]^t$. Since $p_{ij}^{(t)}$ can only differ from zero if E_i and E_j

belong to the same group, in which case at least one of the $p_{ij}^{(kt)}$ elements is not zero, this new chain contains t closed equivalence classes, and its matrix has the form

$$[\mathscr{T}]^t = \begin{bmatrix} \mathscr{A}_0 & 0 & \cdots & 0 \\ 0 & \mathscr{A}_1 & \cdots & 0 \\ & & \vdots & \\ 0 & 0 & \cdots & \mathscr{A}_{t-1} \end{bmatrix} \qquad \text{(order of } [\mathscr{A}_r] = |\, \mathbf{G}_r\,|). \quad (30.10)$$

Then again, let us assume a state E_i is periodic in this new chain, in other words, that there is an integer $t' > 1$ such that the probability of a return to E_i in k transitions satisfies

$$p_{ii}^{(kt)} > 0 \qquad \Rightarrow \qquad k \text{ multiple of } t'. \qquad (30.11)$$

The probability $p_{ii}^{(n)}$ could then only be positive when n is a multiple of tt', and in the initial chain E_i would have the period $tt' > t$, which is contrary to the assumption. Hence all the states are aperiodic in the chain of matrix $[\mathscr{T}]^t$.

PERIODIC CHAIN

We call an irreducible Markovian chain periodic if all its states are periodic, and in this case the period t is the same for all of them. The only other possible case is where they are all aperiodic, and this term is then applied to the chain itself.

In a periodic chain with a period t, the probabilities of transition of order n are zero when n is not a multiple of t. Also, we have seen that the $p_{ij}^{(kt)}$ elements are the transition probabilities of order k of a reducible chain composed of t closed classes which are irreducible and aperiodic. It therefore only remains for us to study the case of an irreducible aperiodic chain, which we shall do in Section 32.

METHOD FOR FINDING WHETHER AN IRREDUCIBLE MATRIX IS PERIODIC

A graph with a loop has an aperiodic matrix and can at once be eliminated.

The method we shall use is similar to that described in Section 29 for decomposing into equivalence classes, but we shall now be calculating the successive boolean powers of the associated boolean matrix $[\mathscr{B}]$. We shall assume

$$[\mathscr{B}_n] = [\mathscr{B}]^n. \qquad (30.12)$$

The element (i, j) of (30.12) is 1 if and only if there is a route of length n from E_i to E_j ; if $j = i$, this route is a circuit.

Also, as we have seen, the chain is periodic if the H.C.F. of the elements of the set $\mathbf{L}_i$, defined by (30.1) for an arbitrary vertex, is greater than 1. The calculation of the matrices (30.12) in theory enables us to form the sets $\mathbf{L}_i$, but these, unfortunately, are infinite, since we can obtain a circuit of any length we wish by repeating a given circuit the requisite number of times or by associating with it circuits having a common vertex. Nevertheless, as we shall now see, a method exists for obtaining a finite set.

An "elementary" circuit is one which does not pass through the same vertex twice and may be regarded as the sum of other elementary circuits, so that the H.C.F. of $\mathbf{L}$ defined by

$$\mathbf{L} = \bigcup_{i=1}^{M} \mathbf{L}_i = \{l \mid \text{there is a circuit of length } l\}. \tag{30.13}$$

is the same as that of the following set $\mathbf{L}'$:

$$\mathbf{L}' = \{l \mid \text{there is an } elementary \text{ circuit of length } l\}. \tag{30.14}$$

In more general terms, the H.C.F. is the same for any set $\mathbf{L}''$ such that

$$\mathbf{L}' \subset \mathbf{L}'' \subset \mathbf{L}. \tag{30.15}$$

But, on the other hand, all the sets $\mathbf{L}_i$ have the same H.C.F., and in consequence $\mathbf{L}$ also has it. Hence, a necessary and sufficient condition for the chain to possess the period t is that the H.C.F. of $\mathbf{L}'$ must be t.

To form a set $\mathbf{L}''$ which satisfies (30.15), we calculate the sequence $[\mathscr{B}_1], [\mathscr{B}_2],..., [\mathscr{B}_M]$, and as an elementary circuit cannot have a length greater than M, we thus find all of them.[10] The term *boolean trace* is used for the boolean sum[11] of the elements on the main diagonal of $[\mathscr{B}]$.

$$\text{tr}[\mathscr{B}] = \sigma_i b_{ii} . \tag{30.16}$$

We then consider the set

$$\mathbf{L}'' = \{l \mid 0 < l \leqslant M \quad \text{and} \quad \text{tr}[\mathscr{B}_l] = 1\}. \tag{30.17}$$

If the H.C.F. of this set is greater than 1, the matrix is periodic with a period equal to the H.C.F.; if it is 1, the matrix is aperiodic.

---

[10] The reader might also consult the article by A. Kaufmann and Y. Malgrange "Recherche des chemins et circuits hamiltoniens d'un graphe," *Revue Française de Recherche Opérationnelle* **26**, 61–73 (1963).

[11] See the note on boolean operations on p. 168.

Example. Given the chain of which the graph was shown in Fig. 30.3,

$$
[\mathscr{B}] = \begin{array}{c}
\\
(1)\\(2)\\(3)\\(4)\\(5)\\(6)
\end{array}
\begin{array}{cccccc}
(1) & (2) & (3) & (4) & (5) & (6)
\end{array}
\begin{bmatrix}
0 & 1 & 0 & 0 & 0 & 0\\
0 & 0 & 1 & 0 & 1 & 0\\
0 & 0 & 0 & 1 & 0 & 0\\
0 & 0 & 0 & 0 & 1 & 0\\
0 & 0 & 0 & 0 & 0 & 1\\
1 & 0 & 0 & 0 & 0 & 0
\end{bmatrix}. \tag{30.18}
$$

This graph has no loops, since there is no 1 on the main diagonal. The successive boolean powers of this matrix are:

$$
[\mathscr{B}_2] = \begin{bmatrix}
0 & 0 & 1 & 0 & 1 & 0\\
0 & 0 & 0 & 1 & 0 & 1\\
0 & 0 & 0 & 0 & 1 & 0\\
0 & 0 & 0 & 0 & 0 & 1\\
1 & 0 & 0 & 0 & 0 & 0\\
0 & 1 & 0 & 0 & 0 & 0
\end{bmatrix}, \tag{30.19}
$$

$$
[\mathscr{B}_3] = \begin{bmatrix}
0 & 0 & 0 & 1 & 0 & 1\\
1 & 0 & 0 & 0 & 1 & 0\\
0 & 0 & 0 & 0 & 0 & 1\\
1 & 0 & 0 & 0 & 0 & 0\\
0 & 1 & 0 & 0 & 0 & 0\\
0 & 0 & 1 & 0 & 1 & 0
\end{bmatrix}, \tag{30.20}
$$

$$
[\mathscr{B}_4] = \begin{bmatrix}
1 & 0 & 0 & 0 & 1 & 0\\
0 & 1 & 0 & 0 & 0 & 1\\
1 & 0 & 0 & 0 & 0 & 0\\
0 & 1 & 0 & 0 & 0 & 0\\
0 & 0 & 1 & 0 & 1 & 0\\
0 & 0 & 0 & 1 & 0 & 1
\end{bmatrix}, \tag{30.21}
$$

$$
[\mathscr{B}_5] = \begin{bmatrix}
0 & 1 & 0 & 0 & 0 & 1\\
1 & 0 & 1 & 0 & 1 & 0\\
0 & 1 & 0 & 0 & 0 & 0\\
0 & 0 & 1 & 0 & 1 & 0\\
0 & 0 & 0 & 1 & 0 & 1\\
1 & 0 & 0 & 0 & 1 & 0
\end{bmatrix}, \tag{30.22}
$$

$$[\mathscr{B}_6] = \begin{bmatrix} 1 & 0 & 1 & 0 & 1 & 0 \\ 0 & 1 & 0 & 1 & 0 & 1 \\ 0 & 0 & 1 & 0 & 1 & 0 \\ 0 & 0 & 0 & 1 & 0 & 1 \\ 1 & 0 & 0 & 0 & 1 & 0 \\ 0 & 1 & 0 & 0 & 0 & 1 \end{bmatrix}. \tag{30.23}$$

Their traces are

$$\mathrm{tr}[\mathscr{B}_1] = 0; \quad \mathrm{tr}[\mathscr{B}_2] = 0; \quad \mathrm{tr}[\mathscr{B}_3] = 0;$$
$$\mathrm{tr}[\mathscr{B}_4] = 1; \quad \mathrm{tr}[\mathscr{B}_5] = 0; \quad \mathrm{tr}[\mathscr{B}_6] = 1. \tag{30.24}$$

Thus the set to be considered is

$$\mathbf{L}'' = \{4, 6\}, \tag{30.25}$$

of which the H.C.F. is 2. Hence the matrix has a period of 2.

31. The Generating Function (z-Transform)

In order to prove the principal properties of stationary Markovian chains and to study the permanent systems in various problems, the generating function can be extremely useful. In the form in which we shall use it, it will be a biunivocal[12] functional transform known as the z transform.

Let us consider a sequence or function $f(n)$ defined and univocal for integral nonnegative values of n ($n = 1, 2, 3,...$), and assume that there exists an $a \geqslant 0$ such that, whatever the value of n, the function satisfies the condition

$$|f(n)| \leqslant a^n. \tag{31.1}$$

The series[13]

$$f^*(z) = \sum_{n=0}^{\infty} f(n) \cdot z^n, \tag{31.2}$$

____

[12] A reciprocal one-by-one correspondence [translator's note].
[13] The transform

$$f^*(z) = (1 - z) \sum_{n=0}^{\infty} f(n) \cdot z^n$$

has the advantage over (31.2) of giving 1 for the z transform of (31.3), and proves more convenient in certain cases.

called the "generating function" of $f(n)$, is then uniformly convergent, at least for

$$| z | < \frac{1}{a} .$$

As a result it is holomorphic in this domain.

If the above conditions are satisfied there is a reciprocal correspondence between $f^*(z)$ and $f(n)$. Indeed, to every function $f(n)$ there corresponds one and only one function $f^*(z)$; reciprocally, every function $f^*(z)$ holomorphic for $| z | < 1/a$, can be expanded, in one way only, into an integral series in this domain, and the coefficients of this expansion define a single function $f(n)$. The function $f^*(z)$ is the z transform of $f(n)$.

First example (Fig. 31.2).   Let

$$f(n) = 0, \qquad n < 0;$$
$$= 1, \qquad n = 0, 1, 2, 3,.... \qquad (31.3)$$

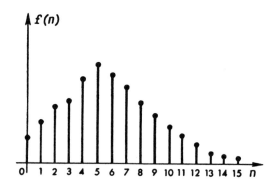

Fig. 31.1

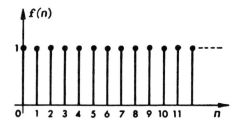

Fig. 31.2

The prescribed conditions are satisfied for every $a \geqslant 1$, and we have

$$f^*(z) = \sum_{n=0}^{\infty} f(n) \cdot z^n = \sum_{n=0}^{\infty} z^n$$

$$= 1 + z + z^2 + z^3 + \cdots + z^n + \cdots \qquad (31.4)$$

$$= \frac{1}{1-z}.$$

Hence, the z-transform of $f(n)$ is

$$f^*(z) = \frac{1}{1-z}.$$

Second example (Fig. 31.3).   Let

$$f(n) = 0, \qquad n < 0;$$
$$= n, \qquad n = 0, 1, 2,\ldots. \qquad (31.5)$$

Then

$$f^*(z) = \sum_{n=0}^{\infty} nz^n = z \frac{d}{dz}\left(\sum_{n=0}^{\infty} z^n\right), \qquad (31.6)$$

whence

$$f^*(z) = \frac{z}{(1-z)^2}. \qquad (31.7)$$

PRINCIPAL PROPERTIES OF THE z-TRANSFORM

(1)   If $f(n) = f_1(n) + f_2(n)$ then $f^*(z) = f_1{}^*(z) + f_2{}^*(z);$ (31.8)

(2)   If $F(n) = kf(n)$ then $F^*(z) = kf^*(z);$ (31.9)

(3)   If $F(n) = f(n-1)$ then $F^*(z) = zf^*(z);$ (31.10)

(4)   If $F(n) = f(n+1)$ then $F^*(z) = \dfrac{f^*(z) - f(0)}{z};$ (31.11)

(5)   If $F(n) = \alpha^n f(n)$ then $F^*(z) = f^*(\alpha z).$ (31.12)

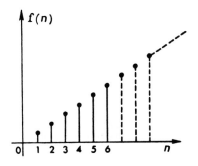

FIG. 31.3

(6)   If $F(n) = \sum\limits_{i=0}^{n} f(i)$ (31.13)

and $f^*(z)$ is the z-transform of $f(n)$, then

$$F^*(z) = \frac{f^*(z)}{1-z}.$$

(7) $\lim\limits_{N \to \infty} \frac{1}{N} \sum\limits_{n=0}^{N-1} f(n) = \lim\limits_{z \to 1}(1-z)f^*(z)$ (31.14)

in the sense that if one of these limits exists, the other also exists and is
equal to it. This relation is the direct result of the theorem referred to
in Section 26, p. 155. The first member represents the "limit in the
sense of Cesaro" of $f(n)$; we know that if $f(n)$ has a limit in the strict
sense, Cesaro's limit must also exist and is equal to it. Hence we also
have:

If $f(n)$ has a limit when $n \to \infty$,

(8) $\lim\limits_{n \to \infty} f(n) = \lim\limits_{z \to 1}(1-z) \cdot f^*(z).$ (31.15)

TABLE OF THE PRINCIPAL z-TRANSFORMS[a]

$f(n)$		$f^*(z)$	
$f(n) = 0,$	$n \neq 0$	1	
$\quad = 1,$	$n = 0$		(31.16)
$f(n) = 0,$	$n \neq \alpha$	z^α	
$\quad = 1,$	$n = \alpha$		(31.17)
	α complete		
$f(n) = 0,$	$n < 0$	$\dfrac{1}{1-z}$	(31.18)
$\quad = 1,$	$n = 0, 1, 2,...$		
$f(n) = 0,$	$n < 0$	$\dfrac{1}{1-\alpha z}$	(31.19)
$\quad = \alpha^n,$	$n = 0, 1, 2,...$ $\mid \alpha \mid \leqslant 1,$		
$f(n) = 0,$	$n < 0$	$\dfrac{\alpha z}{(1-\alpha z)^2}$	(31.20)
$\quad = n\alpha^n,$	$n = 0, 1, 2,...$ $\mid \alpha \mid \leqslant 1,$		
$f(n) = 0,$	$n < 0$	$\dfrac{\alpha z}{(1-z)^2}$	(31.21)
$\quad = \alpha n,$	$n = 0, 1, 2,...$		
$f(n) = 0$	$n < 0$ $\mid \alpha \mid \leqslant 1,$	$\dfrac{1}{(1-\alpha z)^p}$	(31.22)
$\quad = C^n_{n+p-1} \cdot \alpha^n,$	$n = 0, 1, 2,...$ $p = 1, 2, 3,...$		
$f(n) = 0,$	$n < 0$ $\mid \alpha \mid \leqslant 1,$	$\dfrac{\alpha z}{(1-\alpha z)^p}$	(31.23)
$\quad = C^{n-1}_{n+p-2} \cdot \alpha^n,$	$n = 0, 1, 2,...$ $p = 1, 2, 3,...$		

[a] A more complete table will be found in [4].

INVERSE TRANSFORM OF A RATIONAL FRACTION WITH MODULUS POLES $\geqslant 1$.

Let

$$f^*(z) = U(z)/V(z) \tag{31.24}$$

be a rational fraction, where $U(z)$ and $V(z)$ are polynomials without a common root. We shall assume that the degree of U is less than that of V (in the opposite case this condition could be obtained by dividing U by V for the decreasing powers of z), and that the roots $1/\alpha_1$, $1/\alpha_2$,..., $1/\alpha_L$ of $V(z)$ have a modulus $\geqslant 1$, that is to say, $|\alpha_l| \geqslant 1$, $l = 1, 2,..., L$. We know that such a fraction is decomposable into simple elements, in other words, that it can be put into the form

$$f^*(z) = \sum_{l=1}^{L} \sum_{p=1}^{P_l} \frac{A_{p,l}}{(1 - \alpha_l z)^p}, \tag{31.25}$$

where p_l is the degree of multiplicity of the root $1/\alpha_l$.

Let us take the inverse transform of (31.25), making use of (31.8), (31.9), and (31.22):

$$f(n) = 0, \qquad n < 0 = \sum_{l=1}^{L} \sum_{p=1}^{P_l} C_{n+p-1}^{n} \cdot A_{p,l}\alpha_l^{n} = \sum_{l=1}^{L} B_l(n)\alpha_l^{n},$$

$$n = 0, 1, 2,..., \tag{31.26}$$

where

$$B_l(n) = \sum_{p=1}^{P_l} C_{n+p-1}^{n} \cdot A_{p,l}. \tag{31.27}$$

The expression of the coefficients $B_l(n)$ as a function of the polynomials U and V is usually a complicated one; nevertheless, if α_1 , for instance, is a simple root of V, that is, if $p_1 = 1$, we have

$$B_1(n) = C_n^{n}A_{1,1} = A_{1,1}. \tag{31.28}$$

In addition, if we assume

$$V(z) = (1 - \alpha_1 z)W(z), \tag{31.29}$$

the comparison of (31.24) and (31.25) enables us to show that

$$B_1(n) = A_{1,1} = \frac{U(1/\alpha_1)}{W(1/\alpha_1)} = -\alpha_1 \frac{U(1/\alpha_1)}{V'(1/\alpha_1)} = \lim_{z \to 1/\alpha_1} (1 - \alpha_1 z) \cdot f^*(z), \tag{31.30}$$

where $V'(z)$ represents the derivative of $V(z)$ in relation to z.

32. Quantitative Study of Finite Markovian Chains

We shall now make use of the z-transform to calculate the probabilities of transition of order n.

We use the term *generating matrix* for the matrix

$$[\mathscr{T}^*(z)] = \sum_{n=0}^{\infty} z^n \cdot [\mathscr{T}]^n, \qquad (32.1)$$

that is, the transform of $[\mathscr{T}]^n$ defined for $|z| < 1$ (see footnote 15 of this chapter), of which the elements are

$$p_{ij}^*(z) = \sum_{n=0}^{\infty} z^n \cdot p_{ij}^{(n)}. \qquad (32.2)$$

Let us assume

$$[\mathscr{C}(z)] = [\mathscr{E}_M] - z[\mathscr{T}] = \begin{bmatrix} 1 - zp_{11} & -zp_{12} & \cdots & -zp_{1M} \\ -zp_{21} & 1 - zp_{22} & \cdots & -zp_{2M} \\ & & \vdots & \\ -zp_{M1} & -zp_{M2} & \cdots & 1 - zp_{MM} \end{bmatrix}, \qquad (32.3)$$

where $[\mathscr{E}_M]$ is the matrix unit of order M. We then have

$$[\mathscr{C}(z)][\mathscr{T}^*(z)] = ([\mathscr{E}_M] - z[\mathscr{T}]) \cdot \sum_{n=0}^{\infty} z^n \cdot [\mathscr{T}]^n$$

$$= \sum_{n=0}^{\infty} z^n [\mathscr{T}]^n - \sum_{n=1}^{\infty} z^n [\mathscr{T}]^n$$

$$= [\mathscr{T}]^0 = [\mathscr{E}_M]; \qquad (32.4)$$

whence

$$[\mathscr{T}^*(z)] = [\mathscr{C}(z)]^{-1}. \qquad (32.5)$$

In accordance with matrical theory, we know that

$$[\mathscr{C}(z)]^{-1} = \frac{[\tilde{\mathscr{C}}(z)]}{|\mathscr{C}(z)|}, \qquad (32.6)$$

where $[\tilde{\mathscr{C}}(z)]$ is the associated matrix of $[\mathscr{C}(z)]$, in other words, the matrix obtained by transposing the matrix of the cofactors of the determinant $|\mathscr{C}(z)|$. If we take $c_{ij}(z)$ and $\tilde{c}_{ij}(z)$ respectively for the elements of $[\mathscr{C}(z)]$ and $[\tilde{\mathscr{C}}(z)]$, we have

$$\tilde{c}_{ij}(z) = (-1)^{i+j} \cdot M_{ji}(z), \qquad (32.7)$$

where $M_{ij}(z)$ is the determinant obtained by suppressing line i and column j in the determinant $|\mathscr{C}(z)|$.

As a result, each element of the generating matrix is a rational fraction

$$p_{ij}^*(z) = \sum_{n=0}^{\infty} z^n p_{ii}^{(n)} = \frac{\tilde{c}_{ij}(z)}{|\mathscr{C}(z)|}. \tag{32.8}$$

We discovered in Section 31 that the inverse transform of an expression such as (32.8) is a sum of terms in $\alpha_l^{(n)}$, where the α_l terms are the reciprocals of the roots of the denominator, in other words, that the roots of the equation

$$\lambda^n \,|\, \mathscr{C}(1/\lambda)| = 0, \tag{32.9}$$

which is called the "characteristic equation" of matrix $[\mathscr{T}]$; the roots α_1 of (32.9) are called the "proper values" of this matrix.

Let us consider any roots $1/\alpha_l$ of $|\mathscr{C}(z)| = 0$, and let $\{U\}$ be a vector column of components u_i, $i = 1, 2,..., M$. The system of linear and homogeneous equations

$$[\mathscr{C}(1/\alpha_l)]\{U\} = \{0\}, \tag{32.10}$$

where the unknowns are the u_i values, has a zero determinant by assumption. Hence there is at least one vector $\{U\}$ which is not zero and satisfies (32.10), and, in accordance with the definition of $[\mathscr{C}(z)]$, this equation can be expressed

$$[\mathscr{T}]\{U\} = \alpha_l\{U\}. \tag{32.11}$$

A solution of this equation is called a "proper vector" of $[\mathscr{T}]$.

If $\{U\}$ is such a vector, every vector $k\{U\}$ is also one with the same direction, called the "proper direction" of $[\mathscr{T}]$.

We can prove that:

(1) In a square matrix $[\mathscr{M}]$ of order M in which the elements m_{ij} satisfy the relations

$$0 \leqslant m_{ij} \leqslant 1, \tag{32.12}$$

$$s_i = \sum_{j=1}^{M} m_{ij} \leqslant 1, \tag{32.13}$$

every proper value has a modulus not greater[14] than 1, and l is such a value if and only if $[\mathscr{M}]$ is stochastic ($s_i = 1$, $i = 1, 2,..., M$) or contains

---

[14] This property gives validity to our use of the z-transform, for it ensures that (32.1) is convergent for $|z| < 1$, since the roots $1/\alpha_l$ of the denominator of (32.5) have a modulus at least equal to 1.

a stochastic matrix. We say that $[\mathcal{M}]$ contains one if such a matrix can be obtained by simultaneously suppressing m lines and m columns $(m > 0)$ with the same index in $[\mathcal{M}]$.

(2) In an irreducible stochastic matrix, the proper values of modulus 1 are simple and are the roots of an equation of the form

$$\alpha^t = 1, \tag{32.14}$$

where t is a positive integer.[15]

CASE OF AN IRREDUCIBLE CHAIN

Let us first consider an irreducible stochastic matrix $[\mathcal{T}]$ where α_0, α_1,..., α_{t-1} are the proper values with modulus 1, with $\alpha_0 = 1$, and where the other proper values have a modulus less than 1. The generating matrix can then be decomposed into simple elements and put in the form

$$[\mathcal{T}*(z)] = \frac{[\Pi]}{1-z} + \sum_{l=1}^{t-1} \frac{[\mathcal{M}_l]}{1-\alpha_l z} + \sum_{l=t}^{L} \sum_{p=1}^{P_l} \frac{[A_{p,l}]}{(1-\alpha_l z)^p}. \tag{32.15}$$

The inverse transform is then

$$[\mathcal{T}]^n = [\Pi] + \sum_{l=1}^{t-1} \alpha_l{}^n [\mathcal{M}_l] + \sum_{l=t}^{L} \alpha_l{}^n [\mathcal{M}_l(n)], \tag{32.16}$$

where $[\Pi]$ and $[\mathcal{M}_l]$ are independent of n and are obtained, in accordance with (31.30) by the relations

$$[\Pi] = \lim_{z \to 1}(1 - z)[\mathcal{T}*(z)], \tag{32 17}$$

$$[\mathcal{M}_l] = \lim_{z \to 1/\alpha_l} (1 - \alpha_l z)[\mathcal{T}*(z)], \qquad l = 1, 2, ..., t-1. \tag{32.18}$$

The matrix $[\Pi]$ is called the "matrix limit" of the Markovian chain. Let us assume

$$c = \lim_{z \to 1} \frac{1}{1-z} \mid \mathcal{C}(z) \mid. \tag{32.19}$$

Taking (32.6) into account, (32.17) can now be expressed

$$[\Pi] = \frac{[\tilde{\mathcal{C}}(1)]}{c}. \tag{32.20}$$

---

[15] This property is derived from a theorem of G. Frobenius.

Further, if we add all the other columns to column i of $[\mathscr{C}(z)]$, and if we develop the determinant in relation to the elements of this new column, which are all equal to $(1 - z)$ as shown by (32.3), we obtain[16]

$$| \mathscr{C}(z)| \equiv (1 - z) \sum_{j=1}^{M} \tilde{c}_{ij}(z), \qquad i = 1, 2,..., M. \tag{32.21}$$

The fact that 1 is a simple root implies that at least one of the $\tilde{c}_{ij}(1)$ elements is not zero; and (32.10) is of rank $(M - 1)$ for $l = 0$. Now, this system is satisfied when all the elements of $\{U\}$ are equal to 1; hence this is the sole solution, except for one factor. If we now multiply the two members of (32.16) by $[\mathscr{T}]$, we obtain $[\mathscr{T}]^{n+1}$ in the first member, and since this matrix must have a form similar to (32.16), we have

$$[\mathscr{T}][\Pi] = [\Pi], \tag{32.22}$$

which shows that each column of the matrix limit is a proper vector of $[\mathscr{T}]$, a property which is valid, moreover, even if $[\mathscr{T}]$ is not irreducible. Thus the elements of $[\Pi]$ satisfy the relations

$$\varpi_{1j} = \varpi_{2j} = \cdots = \varpi_{Mj} = \varpi_j, \qquad j = 1, 2,..., M, \tag{32.23}$$

where ϖ_j is, by definition, the common value of the elements of column j of $[\Pi]$. We shall observe that $\varpi_j > 0$, for in the contrary case a complete column of $[\Pi]$ would be composed of zeros and (32.20) and (32.21) would imply that root 1 is double.

Let us now consider the second term of (32.16). If the value t which appears in (32.14) is >1, the term

$$\sum_{l=1}^{t-1} \alpha_l{}^n [\mathscr{M}_l]$$

is periodic. Indeed, if we assume $n = kt + r$ with $0 \leqslant r < t$, we have

$$\sum_{l=1}^{t-1} \alpha_l{}^n [\mathscr{M}_l] = (\alpha_l{}^t)^k \sum_{l=1}^{t-1} \alpha_l{}^r [\mathscr{M}_l] = \sum_{l=1}^{t-1} \alpha_l{}^r [\mathscr{M}_l], \tag{32.24}$$

and this expression does not depend on k. By referring to the results in Section 30 we find that this is impossible if the chain has the period t. We know that the states can then be distributed into t groups G_0, G_1 ,...,

---

[16] It must not be forgotten that the $\tilde{c}_{ij}(z)$ values are the cofactors of the *transposed* determinant of $[\tilde{\mathscr{C}}(z)]$.

G_{l-1}, such that, if $E_i \in G_{r'}$ and $E_j = G_{r''}$, if r is the remainder when $|r'' - r'|$ is divided by t, we have

$$p_{ij}^{(kt+s)} = 0 \qquad \text{for} \quad 0 \leqslant s < t \quad \text{and} \quad s \neq r. \tag{32.25}$$

But, for $0 \leqslant s < t$, and taking (32.24) into account, (32.16) involves

$$\lim_{k \to \infty}[\mathscr{T}]^{(kt+s)} = [\varPi] + \sum_{l=1}^{t-1} \alpha_l^s[\mathscr{M}_l], \tag{32.26}$$

since the terms corresponding to $1 \geqslant t$ approach zero.

By adding the t relations (32.26) corresponding to $s = 0, 1, 2,..., t-1$, and taking the relation[17] $\sum_{s=0}^{t-1} \alpha_l^s = 0$ into account, we obtain

$$\lim_{k \to \infty} \sum_{s=0}^{t-1} [\mathscr{T}]^{(kt+s)} = t[\varPi] \tag{32.27}$$

or

$$\lim_{k \to \infty} \sum_{s=0}^{t-1} p_{ij}^{(kt+s)} = t\varpi_j . \tag{32.28}$$

The case where $t = 1$ clearly corresponds to an aperiodic chain, since the second term of (32.16) then disappears. To sum up:

(a) If the chain is aperiodic,

$$\lim_{n \to \infty} p_{ij}^{(n)} = \varpi_j > 0, \tag{32.29}$$

and we then say the chain is ergodic.

(b) If the chain is periodic, the matrix $[\mathscr{T}]^n$ is asymptotically periodic with

$$\lim_{k \to \infty} p_{ij}^{(kt+s)} = 0 \qquad \text{for} \quad 0 \leqslant s < t \quad \text{and} \quad s \neq r,$$
$$= t\varpi_j \qquad \text{for} \qquad s = r. \tag{32.30}$$

As a result,

$$\sum_{n=1}^{N} p_{ij}^{(n)} \approx \frac{N}{t} \cdot t\varpi_j = N\varpi_j , \tag{32.31}$$

---

[17] This relation is derived from the identity

$$1 - \alpha_l^t = (1 - \alpha_l)(1 + \alpha_l + \alpha_l^2 + \cdots + \alpha_l^{t-1}),$$

if α_l is a tth root of the unit, other than 1, the first number is zero, and the first term of the second member is other than 0; hence the second is zero.

whence

$$\lim_{N \to \infty} \frac{1}{N} \sum_{n=1}^{N} p_{ij}^{(n)} = \varpi_j > 0, \tag{32.32}$$

that is to say, $p_{ij}^{(n)}$ has a limit in the sense of Cesaro.

Hence in every case we can write

$$\lim_{N \to \infty} \frac{1}{N} \sum_{n=1}^{N} [\mathcal{T}]^n = [\Pi]. \tag{32.33}$$

Relations (32.29) and (32.30) show that the asymptotic behavior of the chain depends only on the vector

$$[\varpi] = [\varpi_1 \quad \varpi_2 \cdots \varpi_j \cdots \varpi_M]. \tag{32.34}$$

To calculate this vector, we shall use the relation

$$[\Pi][\mathcal{T}] = [\Pi], \tag{32.35}$$

which is obtained by multiplying (32.16) by $[\mathcal{T}]$. This relation can be expressed more simply,

$$[\varpi][\mathcal{T}] = [\varpi], \tag{32.36}$$

or again,

$$[\varpi][\mathfrak{Z}] = [0], \tag{32.37}$$

by using the dynamic matrix defined by (29.7).

We thus have a system of M linear and homogeneous equations of rank $M - 1$; this enables us to calculate the ϖ_j values, taking into account the norm,

$$\sum_{j=1}^{M} \varpi_j = 1. \tag{32.38}$$

The vector $[\varpi]$ is called the "permanent state vector" (see what is stated further on about nonreducible chains).

Examples

First example (Fig. 32.1). Aperiodic Matrix. Let

$$[\mathcal{T}] = \begin{bmatrix} 0.2 & 0.5 & 0.3 \\ 1 & 0 & 0 \\ 0.3 & 0 & 0.7 \end{bmatrix}. \tag{32.39}$$

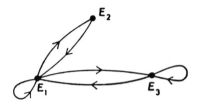

FIG. 32.1

The matrix $[\mathscr{C}(z)]$ then becomes

$$[\mathscr{C}(z)] = \begin{bmatrix} 1 - 0.2z & -0.5z & -0.3z \\ -z & 1 & 0 \\ -0.3z & 0 & 1 - 0.7z \end{bmatrix}. \quad (32.40)$$

The generating matrix is the inverse of this (see 32.5). To calculate it we successively determine

$$|\mathscr{C}(z)| = (1 - 0.2z)(1 - 0.7z) - 0.09z^2 - 0.5z^2(1 - 0.7z)$$
$$= (1 - z)(1 + 0.1z - 0.35z^2), \quad (32.41)$$

$$[\tilde{\mathscr{C}}(z)] = \begin{bmatrix} 1 - 0.7z & 0.5z(1 - 0.7z) & 0.3z \\ z(1 - 0.7z) & 1 - 0.9z + 0.05z^2 & 0.3z^2 \\ 0.3z & 0.15z^2 & 1 - 0.2z - 0.5z^2 \end{bmatrix}, \quad (32.42)$$

whence

$$[\mathscr{T}^*(z)] = \frac{[\tilde{\mathscr{C}}(z)]}{|\mathscr{C}(z)|}. \quad (32.43)$$

We must verify that the sum of the elements of any line of (32.43) is, in fact, equal to $1/(1 - z)$. It will be observed that $|\mathscr{C}(z)|/(1 - z)$ has no roots with modulus 1, which corresponds to the aperiodic property of the chain.

The asymptotic behavior is given by matrix $[\Pi]$ defined by (32.17):

$$[\Pi] = \lim_{z \to 1}(1 - z)[\mathscr{T}^*(z)]$$

$$= \frac{[\tilde{\mathscr{C}}(1)]}{c}, \qquad \text{where} \qquad c = \lim_{z \to 1} \frac{|\mathscr{C}(z)|}{1 - z},$$

$$= \frac{\begin{bmatrix} 0 3 & 0.15 & 0.3 \\ 0.3 & 0.15 & 0.3 \\ 0.3 & 0.15 & 0.3 \end{bmatrix}}{\lim_{z \to 1}(1 + 0.1z - 0.35z^2)}$$

$$= \begin{bmatrix} 0.4 & 0.2 & 0.4 \\ 0.4 & 0.2 & 0.4 \\ 0.4 & 0.2 & 0.4 \end{bmatrix}. \quad (32.44)$$

Second example (Fig. 32.2). Periodic Matrix.   Let

$$[\mathscr{T}] = \begin{bmatrix} 0 & 0.5 & 0.5 \\ 1 & 0 & 0 \\ 1 & 0 & 0 \end{bmatrix}. \tag{32.45}$$

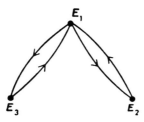

$$E_1$$

$$E_3 \qquad E_2$$

Fig. 32.2

We use the same method of calculation as in the first example[18]:

$$[\mathscr{C}(z)] = \begin{bmatrix} 1 & -0.5z & -0.5z \\ -z & 1 & 0 \\ -z & 0 & 1 \end{bmatrix}. \tag{32.46}$$

$$|\mathscr{C}(z)| = (1 - z)(1 + z). \tag{32.47}$$

$$[\tilde{\mathscr{C}}(z)] = \begin{bmatrix} 1 & 0.5z & 0.5z \\ z & 1 - 0.5z^2 & 0.5z^2 \\ z & 0.5z^2 & 1 - 0.5z^2 \end{bmatrix}. \tag{32.48}$$

$$[\mathscr{T}^*(z)] = \frac{[\tilde{\mathscr{C}}(z)]}{|\mathscr{C}(z)|}. \tag{32.49}$$

$$[\Pi] = \begin{bmatrix} 0.5 & 0.25 & 0.25 \\ 0.5 & 0.25 & 0.25 \\ 0.5 & 0.25 & 0.25 \end{bmatrix}. \tag{32.50}$$

GENERAL CASE

We shall first calculate the generating matrix $[\mathscr{T}^*(z)]$ by inverting $[\mathscr{C}(z)]$ defined by (32.3). We know that such calculations can be very laborious as soon as the order M becomes at all large. It is therefore useful to study the special structure of the generating matrix when $[\mathscr{T}]$ is reducible, and we are then led to the inversion of matrices of an order

---

[18] We find that $|\mathscr{C}(z)|$ is of the second degree instead of the third, which is due to the special structure of the transition graph, sometimes known as a "rose."

less than M. We shall assume the transition matrix is put into the normal form (29.31), and $[\mathscr{C}(z)]$ will then appear as follows:

$$[\mathscr{C}(z)] = \begin{bmatrix} \mathscr{C}_1(z) & \cdots & 0 & 0 \\ \vdots & \ddots & \vdots & \vdots \\ 0 & \cdots & \mathscr{C}_h(z) & 0 \\ -z\mathscr{A}_1 & \cdots & -z\mathscr{A}_h & \mathscr{C}_T(z) \end{bmatrix}, \qquad (32.51)$$

where

$$[\mathscr{C}_k(z)] = [\mathscr{E}_{|\mathbf{C}_k|}] - z[\mathscr{T}_k], \qquad k = 1, 2,..., h, \qquad (32.52)$$

where $| \mathbf{C}_k |$ represents the number of states in the kth closed class (a similar expression could be used for $[\mathscr{C}_T(z)]$).

For $E_i \in \mathbf{C}_k$ and $E_j \in \mathbf{C}_k$, the probabilities $p_{ij}^{(n)}$ depend only on $[\mathscr{T}_k]$. The generating submatrix $[\mathscr{T}_k{}^*(z)]$ corresponding to it is therefore the generating matrix of a Markovian chain of transition matrix $[\mathscr{T}_k]$, and in accordance with (32.5) we have

$$[\mathscr{T}_k{}^*(z)] = [\mathscr{C}_k(z)]^{-1}. \qquad (32.53)$$

Then again, we discovered in Section 29 that for $E_i \in \mathbf{C}_k$ and $E_j \notin \mathbf{C}_k$, $p_{ij} = 0$, and in consequence $p_{ij}^*(z) \equiv 0$. Hence the generating matrix has the form

$$[\mathscr{T}^*(z)] = \begin{bmatrix} \mathscr{T}_1{}^*(z) & \cdots & 0 & 0 \\ \vdots & \ddots & \vdots & \vdots \\ 0 & \cdots & \mathscr{T}_h{}^*(z) & 0 \\ \mathscr{B}_1(z) & \cdots & \mathscr{B}_h(z) & \mathscr{B}_T(z) \end{bmatrix}, \qquad (32.54)$$

where the matrices $[\mathscr{B}_k(z)]$, $k = 1, 2,..., h$, are rectangular and of order $| \mathbf{T} | \times | \mathbf{C}_k |$ and $[\mathscr{B}_T(z)]$ is a square matrix of order $| T |$.

If we substitute (32.51) and (32.54) in (32.4), it will be found that

$$[\mathscr{C}_T(z)][\mathscr{B}_T(z)] = [\mathscr{E}_{|\mathbf{T}|}] \qquad (32.55)$$

and

$$-z[\mathscr{A}_k][\mathscr{T}_k{}^*(z)] + [\mathscr{C}_T(z)][\mathscr{B}_k(z)] = [0], \qquad k = 1, 2,..., h, \quad (32.56)$$

whence

$$[\mathscr{B}_T(z)] = [\mathscr{C}_T(z)]^{-1} = [\mathscr{T}_T{}^*(z)] \qquad (32.57)$$

and

$$[\mathscr{B}_k(z)] = z[\mathscr{T}_T{}^*(z)][\mathscr{A}_k][\mathscr{T}_k{}^*(z)], \qquad k = 1, 2,..., h. \qquad (32.58)$$

The final calculation consists in inverting $(k + 1)$ matrices of which the sum of the respective orders is equal to M, then in carrying out the $2h$ matricial multiplications indicated by (32.58).

The above expressions enable us to find the asymptotic expression of $[\mathscr{T}]^n$. Indeed, in accordance with (31.14) we have

$$\lim_{N \to \infty} \frac{1}{N} \sum_{n=1}^{N} [\mathscr{T}]^n = \lim_{z \to 1}(1 - z)[\mathscr{T}^*(z)]$$

$$= [\Pi] = \begin{bmatrix} \Pi_1 & \cdots & 0 & 0 \\ \vdots & \ddots & \vdots & \vdots \\ 0 & \cdots & \Pi_h & 0 \\ \mathscr{B}_1' & \cdots & \mathscr{B}_h' & \mathscr{B}_T' \end{bmatrix}, \qquad (32.59)$$

with

$$[\mathscr{B}_T'] = \lim_{z \to 1}(1 - z)[\mathscr{B}_T(z)] = [0], \qquad (32.60)$$

since the matrix $[\mathscr{T}_T]$ has no proper value equal to 1, a result already obtained in Section 29, and

$$[\mathscr{B}_k'] = \lim_{z \to 1}(1 - z)[\mathscr{B}_k(z)] = [\mathscr{T}_T^*(1)][\mathscr{A}_k][\Pi_k], \qquad k = 1. \quad (32.61)$$

Here again, $[\Pi]$ defined by (32.59) is called the "matrix limit."

Let us observe that if we postmultiply (32.61) by $[\mathscr{T}_k]$, the last member does not change, whence

$$[\mathscr{B}_k'][\mathscr{T}_k] = [\mathscr{B}_k']. \qquad (32.62)$$

In comparing this equation with the equation similar to (32.35), expressed for the kth irreducible subchain, we find that each line of $[\mathscr{B}_k']$ is proportional to a line of $[\Pi_k]$. If we now call the elements of the matrix limit ϖ_{ij} with ϖ_j their common value such that E_i, $E_j \in \mathbf{C}_k$, this property can be expressed as

$$\varpi_{ij} = x_{ik} \cdot \varpi_j \qquad \text{for} \quad E_i \in \mathbf{T}, \quad E_j \notin \mathbf{T}. \qquad (32.63)$$

The factor x_{ik} is easily interpreted as the probability that the system will finally enter $\mathbf{C}_k$ if it starts from the transitory state E_i. Moreover, the relation (32.63) implies that

$$\sum_{k=1}^{h} x_{ik} = 1. \qquad (32.64)$$

If we wish to calculate the ϖ_{ij} elements directly without finding the generating matrix, this expression can be used to advantage. We can show[19] that beginning with (32.61), for each value of k, the x_{ik} values ($E_i \in \mathbf{T}$) are the solutions of the system of $|\mathbf{T}|$ equations:

$$x_{ik} = \sum_{E_j \in \mathbf{C}_k} p_{ij} + \sum_{E_j \in \mathbf{T}} p_{ij} x_{jk} \,. \tag{32.65}$$

Having calculated the x_{ik} values, we obtain the elements of the matrices $[\mathscr{B}_k{}']$ by means of (32.63).

PERMANENT RULE

The matrix limit defined by (32.59) satisfies the relation

$$[\Pi][\mathscr{T}] = [\Pi], \tag{32.66}$$

which can be proved starting with (32.59), and sums up the similar relations corresponding to the irreducible subchains, as well as the relations (32.60) and (32.61). If we take a line of $[\Pi]$ as the initial state vector $[P(0)]$ of the chain, we find, by considering the corresponding line of the matrices appearing in both members of (32.66), that

$$[P(1)] = [P(0)][\mathscr{T}] = [P(0)], \tag{32.67}$$

whence, by recurrence,

$$[P(n)] = [P(0)], \qquad \forall n. \tag{32.68}$$

A state vector which satisfies (32.68) is called permanent. Naturally, this does not mean that the system will never change its state, since we know, on the contrary, that it will pass in a sufficiently long interval through each of the states of which the initial probability is positive (these are persistent states). Consideration of the expression (32.59) of $[\Pi]$ shows that for each closed equivalence class $\mathbf{C}_k$ there is a corresponding permanent state vector ϖ_k, of which all the components are zero except for those corresponding to the states of this class, which are equal to the ϖ_j ($E_j \in \mathbf{C}_k$) values. These h vectors are linearly independent, whereas the vectors corresponding to the transitory states are linear combinations of the preceding ones, as shown in (32.63). It is clear that the h vectors ϖ_k constitute a base in the space of the permanent state vectors.

Let us now consider an initial vector $P[(0)]$. The state vector at time n is then

$$[P(n)] = [P(0)][\mathscr{T}]^n. \tag{32.69}$$

---

[19] Feller has given a direct proof of this expression on p. 363 of the work referred to in an earlier note.

In accordance with (32.59) we have

$$\lim_{N\to\infty} \frac{1}{N}[P(n)] = [P(0)][\Pi]. \qquad (32.70)$$

The limit of $[P(n)]$ in Cesaro's sense, which is clearly a permanent vector, is therefore a linear combination of h permanent vectors with base

$$\lim_{N\to\infty} \frac{1}{N}[P(n)] = \sum_{k=1}^{h} \lambda_k[\varpi_k], \qquad (32.71)$$

where

$$\lambda_k = \sum_{E_i \in C_k} p_i(0) + \sum_{E_i \in T} x_{ik}p_i(0). \qquad (32.72)$$

The coefficient λ_k represents the probability that the system will, after a large number of transitions, be in class C_k.

If all the irreducible subchains are aperiodic, expressions (32.59) and (32.70) represent limits both in Cesaro's and in a strict sense, and we then say that the chain is aperiodic. In the contrary case, the chain has a period equal to the least common multiple t of the periods t_1, t_2,..., t_h of the irreducible subchains with $t_k = 1$ if the subchain k is aperiodic. Vector (32.71) can then be taken as the approximate expression of $[P(n)]$ on condition that n is sufficiently large and *that it is random*, with a distribution such that the remainder, when n is divided by t, will have an equiprobable distribution among the numbers $0, 1, 2,..., t - 1$.

Example. Let us consider the Markovian chain defined by matrix (32.7) of which the associated graph is shown in Fig. 32.3. For instruc-

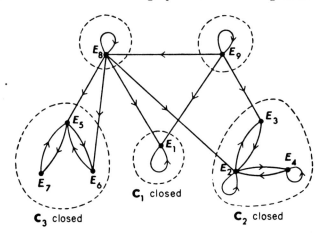

FIG. 32.3

tional purposes this example differs from that given by (29.21) and Fig. 29.3. We have assumed that the given matrix was in the normal form; we have already learned in Section 29 how to obtain this form.

$$[\mathscr{T}] = \begin{array}{c} \\ (1) \\ (2) \\ (3) \\ (4) \\ (5) \\ (6) \\ (7) \\ (8) \\ (9) \end{array} \begin{array}{ccccccccc} (1) & (2) & (3) & (4) & (5) & (6) & (7) & (8) & (9) \\ \left[\begin{array}{c|ccc|ccc|cc} 1 & 0 & 0 & 0 & 0 & 0 & 0 & 0 & 0 \\ \hline 0 & 0.2 & 0.5 & 0.3 & 0 & 0 & 0 & 0 & 0 \\ 0 & 1 & 0 & 0 & 0 & 0 & 0 & 0 & 0 \\ 0 & 0.3 & 0 & 0.7 & 0 & 0 & 0 & 0 & 0 \\ \hline 0 & 0 & 0 & 0 & 0 & 0.5 & 0.5 & 0 & 0 \\ 0 & 0 & 0 & 0 & 1 & 0 & 0 & 0 & 0 \\ 0 & 0 & 0 & 0 & 1 & 0 & 0 & 0 & 0 \\ \hline 0.2 & 0.3 & 0 & 0 & 0.1 & 0.1 & 0 & 0.3 & 0 \\ 0.3 & 0 & 0.1 & 0 & 0 & 0 & 0 & 0.1 & 0.5 \end{array}\right] \end{array} . \quad (32.73)$$

The matrix $[\mathscr{C}(z)]$ is then expressed,

$$[\mathscr{C}(z)] =$$

$$\begin{array}{c} \\ (1) \\ (2) \\ (3) \\ (4) \\ (5) \\ (6) \\ (7) \\ (8) \\ (9) \end{array} \begin{array}{ccccccccc} (1) & (2) & (3) & (4) & (5) & (6) & (7) & (8) & (9) \\ \left[\begin{array}{c|ccc|ccc|cc} 1-z & 0 & 0 & 0 & 0 & 0 & 0 & 0 & 0 \\ \hline 0 & 1-0.5z & -0.5z & -0.3z & 0 & 0 & 0 & 0 & 0 \\ 0 & -z & 1 & 0 & 0 & 0 & 0 & 0 & 0 \\ 0 & -0.3z & 0 & 1-0.7z & 0 & 0 & 0 & 0 & 0 \\ \hline 0 & 0 & 0 & 0 & 1 & -0.5z & -0.5z & 0 & 0 \\ 0 & 0 & 0 & 0 & -z & 1 & 0 & 0 & 0 \\ 0 & 0 & 0 & 0 & -z & 0 & 1 & 0 & 0 \\ \hline -0.2z & -0.3z & 0 & 0 & -0.1z & -0.1z & 0 & 1-0.3z & 0 \\ -0.3z & 0 & -0.1z & 0 & 0 & 0 & 0 & -0.1z & 1-0.5z \end{array}\right] \end{array}$$

$$(32.74)$$

We shall calculate the generating matrix (32.54), using (32.53), (32.57), and (32.58); in so doing, we must not forget that $[\tilde{\mathscr{C}}_k(z)]$ is the *transposed* matrix of the matrix of the cofactors of $|\mathscr{C}_k(z)|$.

We first have

$$| \mathscr{C}_1(z) | = 1 - z, \tag{32.75}$$

$$[\tilde{\mathscr{C}}_1(z)] = [1], \tag{32.76}$$

$$[\mathscr{T}_1^*(z)] = \left[\frac{1}{1-z} \right]. \tag{32.77}$$

For the subchains with index 2 and 3, the calculations have been given in (32.39) to (32.50). Let us recall these results, taking into account the changed numbering of the states:

$$| \mathscr{C}_2(z) | = (1 - 0.2z)(1 - 0.7z) - 0.09z^2 - 0.5z^2(1 - 0.7z)$$

$$= (1 - z)(1 + 0.1z - 0.35z^2); \tag{32.78}$$

$$[\tilde{\mathscr{C}}_2(z)] = \begin{matrix} (2) \\ (3) \\ (4) \end{matrix} \begin{bmatrix} \overset{(2)}{1 - 0.7z} & \overset{(3)}{0.5z(1 - 0.7z)} & \overset{(4)}{0.3z} \\ z(1 - 0.7z) & 1 - 0.9z + 0.05z^2 & 0.3z^2 \\ 0.3z & 0.15z^2 & 1 - 0.2z - 0.5z^2 \end{bmatrix}; \tag{32.79}$$

$$[\mathscr{T}_2^*(z)] = \frac{[\tilde{\mathscr{C}}_2(z)]}{| \mathscr{C}_2(z) |}; \tag{32.80}$$

$$| \mathscr{C}_3(z) | = 1 - z^2 = (1 - z)(1 + z); \tag{32.81}$$

$$[\tilde{\mathscr{C}}_3(z)] = \begin{matrix} (5) \\ (6) \\ (7) \end{matrix} \begin{bmatrix} \overset{(5)}{1} & \overset{(6)}{0.5z} & \overset{(7)}{0.5z} \\ z & 1 - 0.5z^2 & 0.5z^2 \\ z & 0.5z^2 & 1 - 0.5z^2 \end{bmatrix}; \tag{32.82}$$

$$[\mathscr{T}_3^*(z)] = \frac{[\tilde{\mathscr{C}}_3(z)]}{| \mathscr{C}_3(z) |}. \tag{32.83}$$

As a check, it is useful, to remember that the sum of the elements of any line of $[\mathscr{T}^*(z)]$ must equal $1/(1 - z)$, so that the similar sum in $[\tilde{\mathscr{C}}_k(z)]$ must be equal to the coefficient of $(1 - z)$ in $| \mathscr{C}_k(z) |$. Then again, all the elements of $[\mathscr{T}_k^*(z)]$ must be positive if z is real and $| z | < 1$.

$$| \mathscr{C}_T(z) | = (1 - 0.3z)(1 - 0.5z), \tag{32.84}$$

$$[\mathscr{B}_T(z)] = [\mathscr{T}_T^*(z)] = \frac{[\tilde{\mathscr{C}}_T(z)]}{| \mathscr{C}_T(z) |}, \tag{32.85}$$

$$[\tilde{\mathscr{C}}_T(z)] = \begin{matrix} (8) \\ (9) \end{matrix} \begin{bmatrix} \overset{(8)}{1 - 0.5z} & \overset{(9)}{0} \\ 0.1z & 1 - 0.3z \end{bmatrix}. \tag{32.86}$$

Then again, we obtain

$$[\mathscr{B}_1(z)] = \frac{z[\tilde{\mathscr{C}}_T(z)] \cdot [\mathscr{A}_1] \cdot [\tilde{\mathscr{C}}_1(z)]}{|\mathscr{C}_T(z)| \cdot |\mathscr{C}_1(z)|} \tag{32.87}$$

with

$$[\mathscr{A}_1] = \begin{bmatrix} 0.2 \\ 0.3 \end{bmatrix}, \tag{32.88}$$

whence

$$[\mathscr{B}_1(z)] = \frac{z}{(1-z)(1-0.3z)(1-0.5z)} \begin{matrix} (1) \\ (8) \\ (9) \end{matrix} \begin{bmatrix} 0.2(1-0.5z) \\ 0.3-0\,07z \end{bmatrix}; \tag{32.89}$$

and in the same way,[20]

$$[\mathscr{B}_2(z)] = \frac{z}{(1-z)(1+0.1z-0.35z^2)(1-0.3z)(1-0.5z)}$$

$$\times \begin{bmatrix} 0.3(1-0.5z)(1-0.7z) \\ 0.1z(1-0.7z)(1.3-0.3z) \end{bmatrix}$$

$$\begin{bmatrix} 0.15z(1-0.5z)(1-0.7z) & 0.09z(1-0.5z) \\ 0.1(1-1.2z+0.47z^2-0.12z^3) & 0.03z^2(1.3-0.3z) \end{bmatrix} \tag{32.90}$$

$$[\mathscr{B}_3(z)] = \frac{z}{(1-z)(1+z)(1-0.3z)(1-0.5z)}$$

$$\times \begin{bmatrix} 0.1\underline{(1+z)}(1-0.5z) \\ 0.01z\underline{(1+z)} \end{bmatrix}$$

$$\begin{bmatrix} 0.1(1-0.5z)^2\underline{(1+z)} & 0.05z\underline{(1+z)}(1-0.5z) \\ 0.01z\underline{(1+z)}(1-0.5z) & 0.005z^2\underline{(1+z)} \end{bmatrix}. \tag{32.91}$$

Here again, we must check that the sum of the elements of each line of the generating matrix corresponding to a transitory state is equal to $1/(1-z)$.

When we have thus obtained all the elements of $[\mathscr{T}^*(z)]$, we can calculate all the transition probabilities. For instance,

$$p_{9.6}^*(z) \equiv \frac{0.01z^2}{(1-z)(1-0.3z)} \equiv \frac{0.1}{3} + \frac{0.1}{7(1-z)} - \frac{1}{21(1-0.3z)}, \tag{32.92}$$

[20] The $\underline{(1+z)}$ terms which appear in (32.91) disappear.

whence, by taking the inverse transform,

$$p_{9.6}^{(n)} = \frac{0.1}{7} - \frac{1}{21} \cdot (0.3)^n, \qquad n > 0, \tag{32.93}$$

$$p_{9.6}^{(0)} = \frac{0.1}{3} + \frac{0.1}{7} - \frac{1}{21} = 0. \tag{32.94}$$

The matrix limit is obtained, in accordance with (32.59), by suppressing the factor $(1 - z)$ which appears in the denominator of $p_{ij}^*(z)$, then by substituting 1 for z. In this way we obtain

$$[\Pi] = \begin{array}{c} \\ (1) \\ (2) \\ (3) \\ (4) \\ (5) \\ (6) \\ (7) \\ (8) \\ (9) \end{array}
\begin{bmatrix}
1 & 0 & 0 & 0 & 0 & 0 & 0 & 0 & 0 \\
0 & 0.4 & 0.2 & 0.4 & 0 & 0 & 0 & 0 & 0 \\
0 & 0.4 & 0.2 & 0.4 & 0 & 0 & 0 & 0 & 0 \\
0 & 0.4 & 0.2 & 0.4 & 0 & 0 & 0 & 0 & 0 \\
0 & 0 & 0 & 0 & 0.5 & 0.25 & 0.25 & 0 & 0 \\
0 & 0 & 0 & 0 & 0.5 & 0.25 & 0.25 & 0 & 0 \\
0 & 0 & 0 & 0 & 0.5 & 0.25 & 0.25 & 0 & 0 \\
0.286 & 0.171 & 0.086 & 0.171 & 0.143 & 0.071 & 0.071 & 0 & 0 \\
0.657 & 0.114 & 0.057 & 0.114 & 0.029 & 0.014 & 0.014 & 0 & 0
\end{bmatrix}. \tag{32.95}$$

with column headings (1) (2) (3) (4) (5) (6) (7) (8) (9).

This example shows that even if the order of the irreducible submatrices does not exceed 3, the calculation of the generating matrix is a lengthy process. If we are only interested in the asymptotic behavior, it is obviously preferable to calculate the matrix limit directly, using (32.36) and (32.38) for each of the irreducible submatrices, and (32.63), (32.64) and (32.65) for the transitory states. We suggest the reader should perform this calculation for the above example.

UNIREDUCIBLE CHAIN

We say that $[\mathcal{T}]$ is unireducible when there is only one closed equivalence class $(k = 1)$. If all the states belong to this class, the matrix is irreducible; if not, the states which do not belong to the closed class are transitory. In both cases, there is a single permanent vector and the proper value 1 is simple.

Let us consider a unireducible but not irreducible chain; the probability x_{i1} that the system will end in the closed class, when it starts from a transitory state E_i, is equal to 1 in accordance with (32.64). All the lines of $[\Pi]$ are then the same, and the regime is *independent of the initial state vector* ($\lambda = 1$ in (32.72)), which is also clear from the fact that this is the only regime.

Example (Fig. 32.4).   Let

$$[\mathcal{I}] = \begin{bmatrix} 0.4 & 0.6 & \vdots & 0 & 0 \\ 1 & 0 & \vdots & 0 & 0 \\ \hline 0 & 0.4 & \vdots & 0 & 0.6 \\ 0 & 0.7 & \vdots & 0 & 0.3 \end{bmatrix}. \tag{32.96}$$

We shall only calculate $[\Pi]$, using the direct method suggested above. For the irreducible subchain $\mathbf{C}_1$, we use (32.36) and (32.38), which are expressed here as

$$[\varpi_1 \quad \varpi_2] \begin{bmatrix} 0.4 & 0.6 \\ 1 & 0 \end{bmatrix} = [\varpi_1 \quad \varpi_2] \tag{32.97}$$

and

$$\varpi_1 + \varpi_2 = 1. \tag{32.98}$$

The solution of this system gives

$$\varpi_1 = 0.625 \quad \text{and} \quad \varpi_2 = 0.375. \tag{32.99}$$

Then again, (32.63) and (32.64) can be expressed

$$\varpi_{ij} = x_{ik} \cdot \varpi_j \quad \text{for} \quad E_i \in \{E_3, E_4\}, \\ E_j \notin \{E_3, E_4\}, \tag{32.100}$$

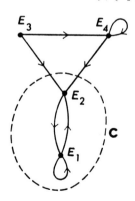

FIG. 32.4

and

$$x_{i1} = 1; \tag{32.101}$$

whence

$$\varpi_{ij} = \varpi_j . \tag{32.102}$$

Finally, let

$$[\Pi] = \begin{bmatrix} 0.625 & 0.375 & 0 & 0 \\ 0.625 & 0.375 & 0 & 0 \\ 0.625 & 0.375 & 0 & 0 \\ 0.625 & 0.375 & 0 & 0 \end{bmatrix}. \tag{32.103}$$

33. Value of a Permanent Strategy

In a stationary dynamic program as defined in Section 28, for each decision vector $\{k\}$ there is a corresponding transition matrix $[\mathscr{T}] = [p_{ij}]$, and also a matrix of the present values $[\mathscr{R}] = [r_{ij}]$, where r_{ij} is given by (28.5) and the index k is understood as in Sections 29 to 32. We take $\{q\}$ for the vector of the probable present values, with components

$$q_i = \sum_{j=1}^{M} p_{ij} r_{ij} , \qquad i = 1, 2,..., M. \tag{33.1}$$

Let us consider a strategy such that whatever the value of time n, the decision vector is always the same, in other words, a permanent strategy (see Section 21, p. 142). We shall begin by studying the discounted value of such a strategy over an infinitude of periods.

TOTAL PRESENT VALUE

The present value $s_n(i, r)$ of this strategy, for the first n periods and an initial state i, is given by the recurring equation

$$s_n(i, r) = rq_i + r \sum_{j=1}^{M} p_{ij} s_{n-1}(j, r); \tag{33.2}$$

or, if we take $\{s_n(r)\}$ for the vector of the present values over n periods,

$$\{s_n(r)\} = r\{q\} + r[\mathscr{T}]\{s_{n-1}(r)\}. \tag{33.2'}$$

If we take the z transform, it follows:

$$\{s^*(z, r)\} = \sum_{n=0}^{\infty} z^n \{s_n(r)\} = \frac{rz}{1-z}[\mathscr{T}^*(rz)]\{q\}, \tag{33.3}$$

whence, for $|r| < 1$,

$$\lim_{z \to 1}(1 - z)\{s^*(z, r)\} = r[\mathscr{T}^*(r)]\{q\}. \tag{33.4}$$

This expression has a meaning, since $[\mathscr{T}^*(z)]$ is finite for $|z| < 1$, from its definition (32.1). Moreover, we know from Theorem 23.1 that $\{s_n(r)\}$ has a limit for $n \to \infty$. By using property (31.14) of the z transform, we obtain

$$\{s(r)\} = \lim_{n \to \infty}\{s_n(r)\} = r[\mathscr{T}^*(r)]\{q\}. \tag{33.5}$$

In addition, Theorem 23.1 shows that $\{s(r)\}$ is a nondecreasing (or nonincreasing) function of r if $\{q\}$ is nonnegative (or nonpositive).

Expression (33.5) enables us to find this value for each initial state E_i when we find the generating matrix $[\mathscr{T}^*(r)]$, which is obtained by the methods explained in the previous section.

Example. Let us assume that in the example of Section 32, p. 193, each period represents a year, and that the coefficient of discounting is $r = 0.9$, which corresponds to a rate of interest of 11.11%. In accordance with the results obtained in Section 32, the generating matrix is then

$$[\mathscr{T}^*(0.9)] = \begin{array}{c} \\ 1 \\ 2 \\ 3 \\ 4 \\ 5 \\ 6 \\ 7 \\ 8 \\ 9 \end{array} \begin{array}{|ccccccccc|} 1 & 2 & 3 & 4 & 5 & 6 & 7 & 8 & 9 \\ 10 & 0 & 0 & 0 & 0 & 0 & 0 & 0 & 0 \\ 0 & 4.59 & 2.06 & 3.35 & 0 & 0 & 0 & 0 & 0 \\ 0 & 4.13 & 2.86 & 3.01 & 0 & 0 & 0 & 0 & 0 \\ 0 & 3.35 & 1.51 & 5.14 & 0 & 0 & 0 & 0 & 0 \\ 0 & 0 & 0 & 0 & 5.26 & 2.37 & 2.37 & 0 & 0 \\ 0 & 0 & 0 & 0 & 4.74 & 3.13 & 2.13 & 0 & 0 \\ 0 & 0 & 0 & 0 & 4.74 & 2.13 & 3.13 & 0 & 0 \\ 2.46 & 1.70 & 0.85 & 1.24 & 1.24 & 0.68 & 0.55 & 1.38 & 0 \\ 5.23 & 0.95 & 0.57 & 0.70 & 0.20 & 0.11 & 0.09 & 0.22 & 1.82 \end{array}$$

$$\tag{33.6}$$

We check that the sum of the elements of each of the lines is equal to $1/(1 - 0.9) = 10$. From (33.5), the present value $s_i(r)$ corresponding to the initial state E_i, where $E_i \in \mathbf{C}_k$, depends only on the components q_j ($E_j \in \mathbf{C}_k$) of $\{q\}$. For example, if

$$
r\{q\} = \begin{Bmatrix} 1 \\ \vdots \\ 2 \\ -1 \\ 3 \\ \vdots \\ 0 \\ 1 \\ -2 \\ \vdots \\ 2 \\ 3 \end{Bmatrix},
\tag{33.7}
$$

we have

$$
s(r) = \begin{Bmatrix} 10 \\ \vdots \\ 17.17 \\ 14.43 \\ 20.61 \\ \vdots \\ -2.37 \\ -1.13 \\ -4.13 \\ \vdots \\ 11.07 \\ 14.56 \end{Bmatrix}.
\tag{33.8}
$$

Average Value of a Period

From Theorem 26.1, the vector $\{\sigma\}$ of the average value of a period (for an infinitude of periods) is given by the relation

$$
\{\sigma\} = \lim_{r \to 1}(1 - r)\{s(r)\},
\tag{33.9}
$$

whence

$$
\{\sigma\} = [\Pi]\{q\},
\tag{33.10}
$$

where $[\Pi]$ is the matrix limit defined by (32.59). In particular, if the chain is *unireducible*, all the lines of $[\Pi]$ are the same, so that the average value of a period is *independent of the initial state*, and is given by

$$\sigma = [\varpi]\{q\} = \sum_{i=1}^{M} \varpi_i q_i \, , \qquad (33.11)$$

where $[\varpi]$ is any line of $[\Pi]$. If there are transitory states forming a set **T**, $\varpi_i = 0$ for every $E_i \in$ **T**, so that the components of the vector $\{q\}$ corresponding to the transitory states do not enter into the calculation of the average value. In a general way, the relation

$$\{\sigma\} = [\mathscr{T}]\{\sigma\}, \qquad (33.12)$$

obtained by premultiplying (33.10) by $[\mathscr{T}]$, shows that $\{\sigma\}$ is a proper vector of the transition matrix corresponding to the value 1 (see 32.11).

This property enables us to show that the vector $\{\sigma\}$ has a very special structure, which can also be seen by referring to the expression (32.59) of $[\Pi]$ and using it in (33.10). As a result of these expressions, the components of $\{\sigma\}$ corresponding to initial states, which are part of the same irreducible subchain $\mathbf{C}_k$, are equal:

$$\sigma_i = \sigma_j \qquad \text{if} \quad E_i, E_j \in \mathbf{C}_k, \qquad (k = 1, 2, ..., h). \qquad (33.13)$$

Taking $\sigma \mathbf{C}_k$ for this common value, we have

$$\sigma_{\mathbf{C}_k} = \sum_{E_j \in \mathbf{C}_k} \varpi_j q_j \, . \qquad (33.14)$$

Further, if the initial state E_i is transitory $(E_i \in$ **T**$)$, we have, in accordance with (32.63),

$$\sigma_i = \sum_{E_j \notin \mathbf{T}} \varpi_{ij} q_j = \sum_{E_j \notin \mathbf{T}} x_{ik} \varpi_j q_j \, , \qquad (33.15)$$

whence

$$\sigma_i = \sum_{k=1}^{h} x_{ik} \sigma_{\mathbf{C}_k} \, , \qquad E_i \in \mathbf{T}, \qquad (33.15')$$

a relation that could well have been anticipated.

TOTAL VALUE WITHOUT DISCOUNTING

We discovered in Section 25 that the total value is usually infinite. By intuition, it is clear that this will not be the case if r_{ij} only differs from zero when E_i is transitory; but it is not clear that this is a necessary condition. In fact, it can easily be shown that the necessary and sufficient condition for the total value to be finite, irrespective of the initial state, is that

$$[\Pi]\{q\} = \{0\}. \tag{33.16}$$

Indeed, the condition is necessary since, if it is not satisfied, at least one of the components $\{\sigma\}$ of the average value per period is other than zero, and the component corresponding to the total value is infinite. To show that the condition is sufficient, let us first examine the case of an irreducible chain. From (33.5) and (32.15), the total discounted value is

$$\{s(r)\} = \frac{r}{1-r} [\Pi]\{q\} + r \sum_{l=1}^{t-1} \frac{1}{1 - \alpha_l r} [\mathscr{M}_l]\{q\}$$

$$+ r \sum_{l=t}^{L} \sum_{p=1}^{P_l} \frac{1}{(1 - \alpha_l r)_p} [\mathscr{A}_{p,l}]\{q\}. \tag{33.17}$$

Since the first term of the second member is zero, it follows that

$$\{s(1)\} = \sum_{l=1}^{t-1} \frac{1}{1 - \alpha_l} [\mathscr{M}_l]\{q\} + \sum_{l=t}^{L} \sum_{p=1}^{P_l} \frac{1}{(1 - \alpha_l)_p} [\mathscr{A}_{p,l}]\{q\} < \infty. \tag{33.18}$$

In the general case, the expression (32.54) of the generating matrix shows that $[\mathscr{T}^*(z)]$ has the form

$$[\mathscr{T}^*(z)] = \frac{1}{1-z} [\Pi] + [\mathscr{M}(z)], \tag{33.19}$$

where $[\mathscr{M}(1)] < \infty$, which completes the proof.

When the condition (33.16) is satisfied,[21] the total value is

$$\{s\} = [\mathscr{M}]\{q\}. \tag{33.19'}$$

FINDING THE AVERAGE VALUE OF A PERIOD BY HOWARD'S METHOD

Howard [36] has suggested a method for finding the average value of a period, in which the formula (33.10), which requires us to find the matrix limit, is replaced by a system of linear equations. The length of the calculations is much the same, but direct use of the results can be made to improve the strategy. We shall see in the following section the value of the algorithm of optimization to which it gives rise.

---

[21] Let us observe that it implies that the q_i terms must not all have the same sign, since the components of $[\pi]$ are nonnegative.

For the moment, we shall proceed with the problem of finding the value of a permanent given strategy, and shall explain Howard's method when we come to consider the total present value.

In accordance with the expression (33.19) of the generating matrix, and with (33.5) and (33.10), we have

$$\frac{1-r}{r}\{s(r)\} - \{\sigma\} = (1-r)[\mathscr{T}^*(r)]\{q\} - [\Pi]\{q\}$$

$$= (1-r)\left([\mathscr{T}^*(r)] - \frac{[\Pi]}{1-r}\right)\{q\}$$

$$= (1-r)[\mathscr{M}(r)]\{q\}. \tag{33.20}$$

Let us assume

$$\{\delta(r)\} = [\mathscr{M}(r)]\{q\}. \tag{33.21}$$

The relation (33.20) can then be expressed

$$\{s(r)\} = \frac{r}{1-r}\{\sigma\} + r\{\delta(r)\}. \tag{33.22}$$

It will be observed that if E_i and E_j belong to the same irreducible subchain $\mathbf{C}_k$,

$$s_i(r) - s_j(r) = r[\delta_i(r) - \delta_j(r)]. \tag{33.23}$$

The term $\delta_i(r)$ can therefore be interpreted as taking account of the initial state, inside the same equivalence class. For any two states E_i and E_j, we have

$$s_i(r) - s_j(r) = \frac{r}{1-r}(\sigma_i - \sigma_j) + r(\delta_i(r) - \delta_j(r)). \tag{33.24}$$

The influence of the initial state is then expressed by two terms, the first resulting from the variation of the average value per period from one equivalence class to another (eventually), and the second, the one mentioned above.

Again, (33.5) can also be expressed

$$\{s(r)\} = r\{q\} + r[\mathscr{T}]\{s(r)\}. \tag{33.25}$$

This equation is none other than the recurring equation (33.2) used when n is infinite.

Substituting (33.22) in (33.25), we obtain

$$\frac{r}{1-r}\{\sigma\} + r\{\delta(r)\} = r\{q\} + \frac{r^2}{1-r}[\mathscr{T}]\{\sigma\} + r^2[\mathscr{T}]\{\delta(r)\}, \tag{33.25'}$$

whence, taking (33.12) into account,

$$\{\sigma\} + \{\delta(r)\} = \{q\} + r[\mathscr{T}]\{\delta(r)\}. \tag{33.26}$$

Finally, as $r \to 1$, $\{\delta(r)\}$ has a limit $\{\delta\}$; in fact, the matrix that appears in the second member of (33.21) is defined by (33.19), and we have seen that

$$\lim_{z \to 1}[\mathscr{M}(z)] = [\mathscr{M}] < \infty, \tag{33.27}$$

whence

$$\{\delta\} = [\mathscr{M}]\{q\}. \tag{33.28}$$

At its limit, relation (33.26) gives

$$\{\sigma\} + \{\delta\} = \{q\} + [\mathscr{T}]\{\delta\}, \tag{33.29}$$

or alternatively,

$$[3]\{\delta\} = \{\sigma\} - \{q\}, \tag{33.30}$$

where $[3]$ is the dynamic matrix defined in Section 29.

(1) Let us first examine the case of a *unireducible chain*, taking σ for the common value of the components of the vector $\{\sigma\}$. If we provisionally treat σ as a parameter, the M scalar equations of (33.30) will then constitute a linear system with M unknowns which are the δ_i values. In Section 32, we discovered that the matrix $[3]$ of the coefficients has the rank $(M - 1)$ when the proper value 1 is simple, which constitutes the definition of an unireducible chain. As a result, the linear system that is being considered has a solution only when a certain condition of compatibility between the M equations is satisfied. To find this condition, let us refer to (33.26) and express it in a form similar to (33.30):

$$[\mathscr{C}(r)]\{\delta(r)\} = \{q\} - \{\sigma\}, \tag{33.30'}$$

or, from (32.5),

$$\{\delta(r)\} = [\mathscr{T}^*(r)](\{q\} - \{\sigma\}). \tag{33.31}$$

The sum of the elements of any line of the generating matrix $[\mathscr{T}^*(r)]$ is equal to $1/(1 - r)$; also, all the components of $\{\sigma\}$ are equal. Hence the above relation can be expressed

$$\{\delta(r)\} = [\mathscr{T}^*(r)]\{q\} - \frac{1}{1 - r}\{\sigma\}. \tag{33.32}$$

By multiplying the two members by $(1 - r)$ and by making r approach 1, we obtain (33.10):

$$\{\sigma\} = \lim_{r \to 1}(1 - r)[\mathcal{T}^*(r)]\{q\} = [\Pi]\{q\}. \tag{33.33}$$

The matricial equation (33.30) therefore has a solution only when the parameter in the second member truly represents the average value per period, and the solution gives us the value of σ. Once the condition of compatibility is satisfied, the system has an infinite number of solutions $\{\delta'\}$; besides, it can be seen that by adding to all the components of one of the solutions the same quantity a, we obtain a further solution. Hence we can arbitrarily choose one of the components (for example, take $\delta' = 0$) and deduce the others from it; the vector $\{\delta'\}$ thus obtained will usually differ from the vector $\{\delta\}$ defined by (33.28), but we shall always have

$$\delta_i' - \delta_j' = \delta_i - \delta_j, \qquad \forall i, j. \tag{33.34}$$

Referring to (33.23), we see that

$$\lim_{r \to 1}\{s_i(r) - s_j(r)\} = \delta_i - \delta_j. \tag{33.35}$$

Although, as a rule, the two terms in the first member increase indefinitely, their difference remains finite, and in order to calculate it we need only have found a vector $\{\delta'\}$. Any such vector which is a solution of (33.30) will be called the "vector of the relative values."

We shall now give an explicit solution of (33.30), which may facilitate the numerical calculation.

Let us arbitrarily choose $\delta' = 0$, which defines a vector of the relative values $\{\delta'\}$ (we assume that state E_1 is not transitory). Since $\delta_1' = 0$, the elements of the first column of $[3]$ do not enter, and we assume

$$l_{ij} = -z_{ij}, \qquad j \neq 1, \quad \forall i; \tag{33.36}$$

$$l_{i1} = 1, \qquad \forall i, \tag{33.37}$$

where the z_{ij} values are the elements of $[3]$.

This matrix can be replaced in (33.30) by $-[\mathcal{L}]$, where $[\mathcal{L}]$ is the matrix with elements l_{ij}, and $\{\delta\}$ can be replaced by $\{\delta'\}$, whence

$$\mathcal{L}[\{\delta'\} + \{\sigma\} = \{q\}. \tag{33.38}$$

Let us now assume

$$\tilde{\delta}_1 = \sigma, \tag{33.39}$$

$$\tilde{\delta}_i = \delta_i', \qquad i \neq 1. \tag{33.40}$$

It can easily be seen that the equation

$$[\mathscr{L}]\{\overset{\circ}{\delta}\} = \{q\} \tag{33.41}$$

is equivalent to (33.38).

We deduce from this that

$$\{\overset{\circ}{\delta}\} = [\mathscr{L}]^{-1}\{q\}. \tag{33.42}$$

Hence, to obtain both σ and $\{\delta'\}$, all we need do is premultiply $\{q\}$ by the inverse of the matrix of which the elements are defined by (33.36) and (33.37).

We may find (unless all the q_i terms have the same sign) that the solution of (33.30) or (33.42) leads to $\sigma = 0$, which shows that the vector of the total values (without discounting) is finite. This vector is then the same as $\{\delta\}$, as is shown by the closeness of (33.19') and (33.28). Besides, the relation (33.29) can be reduced, when $\sigma = 0$, to the recurring relation which gives the total value. It would be useful, in this special case, to calculate $\{\delta\}$ as well as a vector $\{\delta'\}$ which differs from it by a constant. To do so, we must calculate a line of the matrix $[\mathscr{M}]$ so as to obtain a component of $\{\delta\}$, the others being deduced from it when we know $\{\delta'\}$.

(2) Let us now consider *any chain*, using the decomposition into equivalence classes explained in Section 29. From (33.29) and (33.30) we find that the scalar equation

$$\sigma_i + \delta_i = q_i + \sum_{j=1}^{M} p_{ij}\,\delta_j \tag{33.43}$$

corresponding to a persistent state i only introduces the values of δ_j for which the state E_j belongs to the same equivalence class as E_i.

The equations corresponding to the states E_i, which belong to the same irreducible subchain $\mathbf{C}_k$ ($k = 1, 2,..., h$), therefore form an independent system to which the considerations explained above will apply. For the h irreducible subchains, we must arbitrarily choose h quantities δ_i, and we shall then obtain h values σ_i, one for each subchain. We are left with the $|\mathbf{T}|$ equations, corresponding to the transitory states, which contain two $|\mathbf{T}|$ unknowns, namely, the σ_i and δ_i values for $E_i \in \mathbf{T}$. To eliminate the indetermination, we must have recourse to Eq. (33.12), which we repeat:

$$\{\sigma\} = [\mathscr{T}]\{\sigma\} \tag{33.44}$$

or

$$[3]\{\sigma\} = \{0\}. \tag{33.45}$$

We have not explicitly used this relation in the case of a unireducible chain, for in that case it would merely have implied that all the components of $\{\sigma\}$ are equal. In the general case, the relation implies that this is true for the components relative to the same subchain, and also enables us to calculate the σ_i terms for $E_i = \mathbf{T}$ as a function of the σ_j values for $E_j \notin \mathbf{T}$. To do so, we use the $|\mathbf{T}|$ scalar equations corresponding to the transitory states.

To sum up, the set of Eqs. (33.45) and (33.30) or (33.42) enables us to calculate $\{\sigma\}$ and $\{\delta'\}$ after we have given an arbitrary value (for instance 0) to h of the components δ_i' suitably chosen. We observe that it is useful, when making this calculation, to work the decomposition into equivalence classes by using the procedure explained in Section 29, a method that allows us to take advantage of the particular structure of the systems of equations to be solved.

To conclude, let us note that it is possible to obtain $\sigma_i = 0$ for certain values of i; for this case, the reader should refer to what was stated earlier on the subject.

Example. Given the transition matrix,

$$[\mathscr{T}] = \begin{bmatrix} 0.5 & 0.5 \\ 0.7 & 0.3 \end{bmatrix}, \tag{33.46}$$

and the matrix of the returns,

$$[\mathscr{R}] = \begin{bmatrix} 500 & 150 \\ 200 & -400 \end{bmatrix}. \tag{33.47}$$

Using (33.1), let us calculate

$$q_i = \sum_{j=1}^{M} p_{ij} r_{ij} \; ; \tag{33.48}$$

that is,

$$q_1 = (0.5)(500) + (0.5)(150) \quad = 325, \tag{33.49}$$

$$q_2 = (0.7)(200) + (0.3)(-400) = 20. \tag{33.50}$$

The dynamic matrix of the process is

$$[3] = \begin{bmatrix} -0.5 & 0.5 \\ 0.7 & -0.7 \end{bmatrix}. \tag{33.51}$$

Thence, in accordance with (33.36) and (33.37),

$$[\mathscr{L}] = \begin{bmatrix} 1 & -0.5 \\ 1 & 0.7 \end{bmatrix}. \tag{33.52}$$

$$[\mathscr{L}]^{-1} = \frac{1}{1.2} \begin{bmatrix} 0.7 & 0.5 \\ -1 & 1 \end{bmatrix}. \tag{33.53}$$

$$\{\delta\} = [\mathscr{L}]^{-1}\{q\} = \frac{1}{1.2} \begin{bmatrix} 0.7 & 0.5 \\ -1 & 1 \end{bmatrix} \begin{Bmatrix} 325 \\ 20 \end{Bmatrix} = \begin{Bmatrix} 197.92 \\ -254.17 \end{Bmatrix}. \tag{33.54}$$

Hence we have

$$\tilde{\delta}_1 = \sigma = 197.92 \tag{33.55}$$

and

$$\tilde{\delta}_2 = \delta_2' = -254.17. \tag{33.56}$$

34. Optimization of the Total Present Value

Let us resume our study of dynamic programs, taking $[\mathscr{T}^{(k)}]$ and $[\mathscr{R}^{(k)}]$ for the matrices of transition and of the present values corresponding to the decision vector $\{k\}$. In accordance with the theorem of optimality 17.1, the vector of the present optimal value for n periods is given, for $n > 1$, by the recurring relation,

$$\{f_n(r)\} = r \cdot \underset{k \in \mathbf{K}}{\mathrm{OPT}}[\{q^{(k)}\} + [\mathscr{T}^{(k)}]\{f_{n-1}(r)\}], \tag{34.1}$$

where **K** represents the set of possible decision vectors. This relation is a special form of (21.1).

The optimal value for a period will clearly be

$$\{f_1(r)\} = r \underset{k \in \mathbf{K}}{\mathrm{OPT}}\{q^{(k)}\}. \tag{34.2}$$

This same relation can also be obtained by using (34.1) for $n = 1$ and assuming $f_0(r) = 0$.

We shall not dwell on the case where n remains finite, and will merely recall that an optimal strategy for it usually involves decision vectors $\{k_1\}, \{k_2\}, \ldots, \{k_n\}$, which differ from one period to the next.

To find optimal strategies where n is infinite, we must solve the equation

$$\{f(r)\} = r \underset{k \in \mathbf{K}}{\mathrm{OPT}}(\{q^{(k)}\} + [\mathscr{T}^{(k)}]\{f(r)\}). \tag{34.3}$$

This matricial equation, in fact, represents a system of M scalar equations, and by Theorem 21.1 there is a single vector $\{f(r)\}$ which satisfies all of them. On the other hand, there may be several vectors $\{k^*\}$ which provide the optimum, since they satisfy the matricial equation[22]

$$\{f(r)\} = r(\{q^{(k)}\} + [\mathscr{T}^{(k)}]\{f(r)\}), \tag{34.4}$$

where $\{f(r)\}$ is assumed to be known. We shall use $\mathbf{K}^*$ for the set of optimal decision vectors. In point of fact, none of the corresponding scalar equations,

$$f(i, r) = r \left[q_i^{(k_i^*)} + \sum_{j=1}^{M} p_{ij}^{(k_i^*)} \cdot f(j, r) \right], \qquad i = 1, 2, ..., M, \tag{34.5}$$

introduces more than one component k_i^* of the vector $\{k^*\}$, and they are therefore mutually independent. If we take $\mathbf{K}_i^*$ for the set of solutions of (34.5), and $|\mathbf{K}_i^*|$ for their number, we can form an optimal decision vector $\{k^*\}$ by choosing the first component in the set $\mathbf{K}_1^*$, the second in $\mathbf{K}_2^*$, and so on, until we have obtained a number of optimal decision vectors equal to

$$|\mathbf{K}^*| = |\mathbf{K}_1^*| \cdot |\mathbf{K}_2^*| \cdot \cdots \cdot |\mathbf{K}_M^*|. \tag{34.6}$$

In accordance with (34.3), we obtain an optimal strategy by placing before any optimal strategy a decision vector $\{k^*\}$ itself arbitrarily chosen from the set[23] $\mathbf{K}^*$. Since this procedure can be repeated as often as we wish, it follows that an optimal strategy is a sequence of vectors, each arbitrarily chosen in this set. In practice, however, we nearly always use the permanent strategies composed of a sequence of identical vectors with a finite number equal to $|\mathbf{K}^*|$. In any case, the set of optimal strategies (which is infinite if $|\mathbf{K}^*| > 1$) is determined by the set $\mathbf{K}^*$, and our problem is how to calculate simultaneously this set and the vector $\{f(r)\}$, which form the solutions of (34.3).

TEMPORAL APPROXIMATION

One method is to use the recurring equations (34.1) and (34.2) to find the optimal strategies and the present value for n periods. We know that these quantities respectively approach the corresponding quantities where n is infinite; but since the number of possible states and the

---

[22] It can easily be seen that this equation is formally equivalent to (33.5), where, however, it is the decision vector which is given and the total present value which is unknown.

[23] This is, in fact, only a form of the theorem of optimality.

number of possible decision vectors are both finite, there is a finite value N of n beginning with which every decision vector $\{k^*\}$ (which satisfies (34.1)) belongs to $\mathbf{K}^*$. On the other hand, the vector of values $\{f_n(r)\}$ usually differs from $\{f(r)\}$, even for $n > N$. It would obviously be useful to have at our disposal a criterion enabling us to recognize the value N of n beginning with which the set of optimal decision vectors for the Nth period is identical with $\mathbf{K}^*$. One of the advantages of the second method, which we shall now explain, is that it provides us with this very criterion.

APPROXIMATION IN THE SPACE OF THE STRATEGIES

This method was described on p. 144 of Section 22 for the case of random programs, and we shall only recall the second method of Section 22 (using the notation of the present chapter), which consists in performing the two following operations alternately:

(1) Given a permanent strategy $\{k^{(l)}\}$, we determine the vector of the total present value from the equation

$$\{s^{(l)}(r)\} = r(\{q^{(l)}\} + [\mathscr{T}^{(l)}]\{s^{(l)}(r)\}), \tag{34.7}$$

or from the equivalent equation (33.5).

(2) Given the same permanent strategy of which the vector of the total present values is $\{s^{(l)}(r)\}$, we seek a strategy $\{k^{(l+1)}\}$ such that

$$\{q^{(l+1)}\} + [\mathscr{T}^{(l+1)}]\{s^{(l)}(r)\} = \operatorname*{OPT}_{k \in \mathbf{K}}[\{q^{(k)}\} + [\mathscr{T}^{(k)}]\{s^{(l)}(r)\}], \tag{34.8}$$

where the index $(l + 1)$ in the first member is relative to the strategy $\{k^{(l+1)}\}$.

The optimization process normally begins with the choice of as good as possible a strategy $\{k^{(0)}\}$ whose value is obtained by using (34.7). If we lack any information enabling us to choose this strategy, we can make $n = 0$ and $\{s^{(0)}(r)\} = \{0\}$ in (34.8), which allows us to obtain an initial strategy optimizing the present value. The optimum is reached when (34.8) is satisfied for $\{k^{(l+1)}\} = \{k^{(l)}\}$, which must take place for a certain value of l, since the number of permanent strategies is finite. Also, as we proved in Section 22, we have

$$\{s^{(l+1)}(r)\} \geqslant \{s^{(l)}(r)\}, \tag{34.9}$$

in the sense that each of the components of the first member is at least equal to the corresponding component of the second member. Hence the equality is only satisfied for all the components when the optimum is reached and the common value of the two members is $\{f(r)\}$.

Example. Using the notation of Section 28, we shall take an example of dynamic programming in which the set of possible states is $\mathbf{X} = \{1, 2\}$ and the set of decisions $\mathbf{Y} = \{1, 2\}$ with $\Delta 1 = \{1, 2\}$ and $\Delta 2 = \{1, 2\}$; that is to say, in each state either of the decisions 1 or 2 can be taken.
We shall assume that the probabilities of transition are

$$p_{11}^{(1)} = 0.5, \qquad p_{12}^{(1)} = 0.5, \qquad p_{21}^{(1)} = 0.7, \qquad p_{22}^{(1)} = 0.3,$$

$$p_{11}^{(2)} = 0.6, \qquad p_{12}^{(2)} = 0.4, \qquad p_{21}^{(2)} = 0.8, \qquad p_{22}^{(2)} = 0.2, \qquad (34.10)$$

to which the following present values correspond:

$$r_{11}^{(1)} = 500, \qquad r_{12}^{(1)} = 150, \qquad r_{21}^{(1)} = 200, \qquad r_{22}^{(1)} = -400,$$

$$r_{11}^{(2)} = 400, \qquad r_{12}^{(2)} = 200, \qquad r_{21}^{(2)} = 100, \qquad r_{22}^{(2)} = -800. \qquad (34.11)$$

Hence there are four possible decision vectors:

$$k_1 = \begin{Bmatrix}1\\1\end{Bmatrix}, \qquad k_2 = \begin{Bmatrix}1\\2\end{Bmatrix}, \qquad k_3 = \begin{Bmatrix}2\\1\end{Bmatrix}, \qquad k_4 = \begin{Bmatrix}2\\2\end{Bmatrix}, \qquad (34.12)$$

to which the following transition matrices correspond:

$$[\mathscr{T}_1] = \begin{bmatrix}0.5 & 0.5\\0.7 & 0.3\end{bmatrix}, \qquad [\mathscr{T}_2] = \begin{bmatrix}0.5 & 0.5\\0.8 & 0.2\end{bmatrix},$$

$$[\mathscr{T}_3] = \begin{bmatrix}0.6 & 0.4\\0.7 & 0.3\end{bmatrix}, \qquad [\mathscr{T}_4] = \begin{bmatrix}0.6 & 0.4\\0.8 & 0.2\end{bmatrix}, \qquad (34.13)$$

and the matrices of values:

$$[\mathscr{R}_1] = \begin{bmatrix}500 & 150\\200 & -400\end{bmatrix}, \qquad [\mathscr{R}_2] = \begin{bmatrix}500 & 150\\100 & -800\end{bmatrix},$$

$$[\mathscr{R}_3] = \begin{bmatrix}400 & 200\\300 & -400\end{bmatrix}, \qquad [\mathscr{R}_4] = \begin{bmatrix}400 & 200\\100 & -800\end{bmatrix}. \qquad (34.14)$$

The probable value $q(i, k)$ when the decision k is taken in the state i is given by (28.8), which we now repeat:

$$q(i, k) = \sum_{j=1}^{M} p_{ij}^{(k)} r_{ij}^{(k)}. \qquad (34.15)$$

Whence

$$q(1,1) = 325, \qquad q(2,1) = 20, \qquad q(1,2) = 320, \qquad q(2,2) = -80. \quad (34.16)$$

To find the optimal strategy, we shall use the method of approximation in the strategies' space which we have just described, assuming that we are maximizing the values, and that $r = 0.9$.

We shall arbitrarily select as a permanent initial strategy the strategy defined by the decision vector $\{k_1\}$.

First iteration

(1) We assume

$$\{k^{(0)}\} = \{k_1\} = \begin{Bmatrix} 1 \\ 1 \end{Bmatrix}. \quad (34.17)$$

The vector of the total present values is given by (34.7):

$$\{s^{(0)}(r)\} = r(\{q^0\} + [\mathscr{T}^{(0)}]\{s^{(0)}(r)\}), \quad (34.18)$$

that is,

$$s_1^{(0)}(r) = r \times 325 + 0.5r[s_1^{(0)}(r) + s_2^{(0)}(r)]$$
$$= 292.5 + 0.45[s_1^{(0)}(0.9) + s_2^{(0)}(0.9)], \quad (34.19)$$

$$s_2^{(0)}(r) = r \times 20 + 0.7rs_1^{(0)}(r) + 0.3rs_2^{(0)}(r)$$
$$= 18 + 0.63rs_1^{(0)}(0.9) + 0.27s_2^{(0)}(0.9). \quad (34.20)$$

To simplify what follows, we shall assume

$$s_1^{(l)} = s_1^{(l)}(0.9) \qquad \text{and} \qquad s_2^{(l)} = s_2^{(l)}(0.9), \qquad l = 0, 1, 2,\dots . \quad (34.21)$$

From (34.19) and (34.20) we obtain

$$\{s^{(0)}\} = \begin{Bmatrix} 1,878.17 \\ 1,645.54 \end{Bmatrix}. \quad (34.22)$$

We might equally have used (33.5) instead of (34.7), and we shall do so in the second iteration in order to show the two methods.

(2) We now seek the maximum of

$$\{z^{(k)}\} = \{q^{(k)}\} + [\mathscr{T}^{(k)}]\{s^{(0)}\}. \quad (34.23)$$

We can choose the two lines of the second member separately.

First line:

$$z_1^{(k)} = q(1, k) + p_{11}^{(k)} \cdot s_1^{(0)} + p_{12}^{(k)} \cdot s_2^{(0)}. \tag{34.24}$$

That is, for $k_1 = 1$:

$$z_1^{(1)} = 325 + (0.5)(1{,}878.17) + (0.5)(1{,}645.54)$$
$$= 2{,}086.86; \tag{34.25}$$

and for $k_1 = 2$:

$$z_1^{(2)} = 320 + (0.6)(1{,}878.17) + (0.4)(1{,}645.54)$$
$$= 2{,}105.12. \tag{34.26}$$

Whence

$$\max(z_1^{(1)}, z_1^{(2)}) = z_1^{(2)} = 2{,}105.12, \tag{34.27}$$

and we take $k_1^{(1)} = 2$.

Second line:

$$z_2^{(k)} = q(2, k) + p_{21}^{(k)} \cdot s_1^{(0)} + p_{22}^{(k)} \cdot s_2^{(0)}; \tag{34.28}$$

that is, for $k_2 = 1$:

$$z_2^{(1)} = 20 + (0.7)(1{,}878.17) + (0.3)(1{,}645.54),$$
$$= 1{,}828.38; \tag{34.29}$$

and for $k_2 = 2$:

$$z_2^{(2)} = -80 + (0.8)(1{,}878.17) + (0.2)(1{,}645.54)$$
$$= 1{,}751.64. \tag{34.30}$$

Whence

$$\max(z_2^{(1)}, z_2^{(2)}) = z_2^{(1)} = 1{,}828.38, \tag{34.31}$$

and we take $k_2^{(1)} = 1$.

Second iteration

(1) We have

$$\{k^{(1)}\} = \begin{Bmatrix} 2 \\ 1 \end{Bmatrix}. \tag{34.32}$$

This time, we shall, as we mentioned above, calculate the vector of the total present values by using (33.5).

$$\{s^{(1)}\} = 0.9[\mathcal{T}^{*(1)}(0.9)]\{q^{(1)}\}$$

$$= 0.9 \begin{bmatrix} 1 - 0.6r & -0.4r \\ -0.7r & 1 - 0.3r \end{bmatrix}^{-1} \begin{Bmatrix} 320 \\ 20 \end{Bmatrix}$$

$$= 0.9 \begin{bmatrix} 0.46 & -0.36 \\ -0.63 & 0.73 \end{bmatrix}^{-1} \begin{Bmatrix} 320 \\ 20 \end{Bmatrix}$$

$$= \begin{bmatrix} 6.028 & 2.973 \\ 5.202 & 3.799 \end{bmatrix} \begin{Bmatrix} 320 \\ 20 \end{Bmatrix} = \begin{Bmatrix} 1,988.42 \\ 1,740.62 \end{Bmatrix}. \tag{34.33}$$

(2) We seek the maximum of

$$\{z^{(k)}\} = \{q^{(k)}\} + [\mathcal{T}^{(k)}]\{s^{(1)}\}.$$

First line:

$$z_1^{(k)} = q(1, k) + p_{11}^{(k)}s_1^{(1)} + p_{12}^{(k)}s_2^{(1)}; \tag{34.34}$$

that is, for $k_1 = 1$:

$$z_1^{(1)} = 325 + (0.5)(1,988.42) + (0.4)(1,740.62)$$
$$= 2,189.52; \tag{34.35}$$

and for $k_1 = 2$:

$$z_1^{(2)} = 320 + (0.6)(1,988.42) + (0.4)(1,740.62)$$
$$= 2,209.30, \tag{34.36}$$

whence

$$\max(z_1^{(1)}, z_1^{(2)}) = z_1^{(2)} = 2,209.30, \tag{34.37}$$

and we take $k_1^{(2)} = 2$.

Second line:

$$z_2^{(k)} = q(2, k) + p_{21}^{(k)}s_1^{(1)} + p_{22}^{(k)}s_2^{(1)}; \tag{34.38}$$

that is, for $k_2 = 1$:

$$z_2^{(1)} = 20 + (0.7)(1,988.42) + (0.3)(1,740.62)$$
$$= 1,934.08; \tag{34.39}$$

and for $k_2 = 2$:

$$z_2^{(2)} = -80 + (0.8)(1,988.42) + (0.2)(1,740.62)$$
$$= 1,858.86, \tag{34.40}$$

whence

$$\max(z_2^{(1)}, z_2^{(2)}) = z_2^{(1)} = 1,934.08, \tag{34.41}$$

and we take $k_2^{(2)} = 1$.
Since we find

$$\{k^{(2)}\} = \{k^{(1)}\} = \begin{Bmatrix} 2 \\ 1 \end{Bmatrix}, \tag{34.42}$$

the strategy $\begin{Bmatrix} 2 \\ 1 \end{Bmatrix}$ is optimal, and to it correspond the total values given by (34.33), namely,

$$\{f(0.9)\} = \begin{Bmatrix} 1,988.42 \\ 1,740.62 \end{Bmatrix}. \tag{34.43}$$

It is interesting to discover in what interval of values of r this strategy remains optimal; to save space we shall only give the results, which are set out in the following table:

r	0	0.179		0.9	1
$k_1{}^*$		$\vdots$		2	
$k_2{}^*$			1		
$f_1(r)$	0	65.0		1.988	∞
$f_2(r)$	0	12.3		1.741	∞

Thus, the strategy remains optimal in the interval $0.79 \leqslant r < 1$.

35. Optimization of the Average Value per Period (or of the Total Value)

The introduction of the vector of the relative values made it possible for Howard (see Section 33) to develop an algorithm for optimizing the average value of a period, similar to the one given in Section 34 under the heading Approximation in the Space of the Strategies.[24] We shall, more-

---

[24] A generalization of this algorithm was suggested in Section 27, p. 159.

over, extend the latter by considering what occurs when the coefficient of discounting, in other words, the rate of interest $(1 - r)/r$, approaches 0. We saw at the end of Section 33 that Eq. (33.5) or (34.7), which enables us to calculate the vector of the total values $\{s^{(k)}(r)\}$ corresponding to a permanent strategy $\{k\}$, was replaced at the limit by Eqs. (33.30) or (33.42), and (33.45). Let us now consider Eq. (34.8), which allows us to obtain, starting with a strategy $\{k^{(l)}\}$, a strategy $\{k^{(l+1)}\}$ of which the total discounted value is nearer to the optimum. Proceeding as in Section 33, we shall replace $\{s(r)\}$ by its expression (33.22) in this equation, and it then follows:

$$\{q^{(l+1)}\} + \frac{r}{1-r}[\mathscr{T}^{(l+1)}]\{\sigma^{(l)}\} + r[\mathscr{T}^{(l+1)}]\{\delta^{(l)}(r)\}$$
$$= \underset{k \in \mathbf{K}}{\mathrm{OPT}}\left(\{q^{(k)}\} + \frac{r}{1-r}[\mathscr{T}^{(k)}]\{\sigma^{(l)}\} + r[\mathscr{T}^{(k)}]\{\delta^{(l)}(r)\}\right), \quad (35.1)$$

where, as we recall, the index (l) is relative to the strategy $\{k^{(l)}\}$. If we multiply both members by $(1 - r)$ and make r approach 1, we obtain

$$[\mathscr{T}^{(l+1)}]\{\sigma^{(l)}\} = \underset{k \in \mathbf{K}}{\mathrm{OPT}}[\mathscr{T}^{(k)}]\{\sigma^{(l)}\}. \quad (35.2)$$

This equation only introduces the transition matrix relative to each strategy $\{k\}$, and not the matrix of the corresponding present values. We therefore deduce that it is generally not sufficient to determine a strategy $\{k^{(l+1)}\}$ better than $\{k^{(l)}\}$, and we shall return later to this question. For the present, we shall proceed by observing that if r is sufficiently close to 1, it seems logical to replace $\mathbf{K}$ by $\mathbf{K}'$ in (35.1), where the latter is the set of decision vectors $\{k^{(l+1)}\}$ which satisfy (35.2); at the limit, this restriction of the domain of optimization cannot have any influence. But then, the term in $r/(1 - r)$ which appears in the second member is independent of $\{k\}$, for $\{k\} \in \mathbf{K}'$, and equal to the corresponding term of the first member. Thus the equation is reduced to

$$\{q^{(l+1)}\} + r[\mathscr{T}^{(l+1)}]\{\delta^{(l)}(r)\} = \underset{k \in \mathbf{K}'}{\mathrm{OPT}}(\{q^{(k)}\} + r[\mathscr{T}^{(k)}]\{\delta^{(l)}(r)\}), \quad (35.3)$$

whence, for $r \to 1$,

$$\{q^{(l+1)}\} + [\mathscr{T}^{(l+1)}]\{\delta^{(l)}\} = \underset{k \in \mathbf{K}'}{\mathrm{OPT}}(\{q^{(k)}\} + [\mathscr{T}^{(k)}]\{\delta^{(l)}\}). \quad (35.4)$$

It is clear that no difficulty will arise if in this equation we replace the vector $\{\delta^{(l)}\}$ by a vector $\{\delta'^{(l)}\}$ obtained by adding a quantity a to all the components of the first vector, a procedure enabling us to use the results of Section 33.

Hence we are led to the following.

ALGORITHM OF OPTIMIZATION

(1) Given a permanent strategy $\{k^{(l)}\}$, we find the vectors $\{\delta^{(l)}\}$ and $\{\delta'^{(l)}\}$ by the use of (33.42) or (33.30), and (33.45) if the transition matrix is not unireducible.

(2) Given the same permanent strategy, of which the vector of the average value per period is $\{\sigma^{(l)}\}$, and of which a vector of the relative values is $\{\delta'^{(l)}\}$, we find a strategy $\{k^{(l+1)}\}$ by the successive use of (35.2) and (35.4).

Howard [36] has given a direct justification of this algorithm, showing that it leads to the optimum in a finite number of iterations, and, moreover, that the successive vectors of the average values per period are such that

$$\{\sigma^{(n+1)}\} \geqslant \{\sigma^{(n)}\}. \tag{35.5}$$

Then again, we shall discover that when the transition matrix $[\mathscr{T}^{(n)}]$ is unireducible, $\mathbf{K}' = \mathbf{K}$, with the result that it is unnecessary to consider Eq. (35.2) and we can proceed directly to (35.4).

In fact, we know that then all the components of the vector $\{\sigma^{(n)}\}$ of the average values per period are equal (see Section 33), so that

$$[\mathscr{T}^{(k)}]\{\sigma^{(n)}\} = \{\sigma^{(n)}\} \tag{35.6}$$

for every stochastic matrix $[\mathscr{T}^{(k)}]$ of order M. Equation (35.2) is then satisfied for every strategy $\{k^{(n+1)}\}$, that is to say, $\mathbf{K}' = \mathbf{K}$.

In the case of a nonunireducible matrix, the eventuality that $\mathbf{K}' = \mathbf{K}$ cannot be excluded, but is very unlikely. Let us consider one of the scalar equations corresponding to (35.2):

$$\sum_{j=1}^{M} p_{ij}^{(n+1)}\sigma_j^{(n)} = \underset{k \in \mathbf{K}}{\mathrm{OPT}} \sum_{j=1}^{M} p_{ij}^{(k)}\sigma_j^{(n)}. \tag{35.7}$$

This equation will be satisfied for every possible decision $k_i^{(n+1)}$ if:

(a) the state E_i is, in the chain $[\mathscr{T}^{(n)}]$, a persistent state, in other words if $E_i \notin \mathbf{T}^{(n)}$;

(b) taking $\mathbf{C}^{(k)}$ for the equivalence class of E_i in the chain $[\mathscr{T}^{(k)}]$, we have

$$\left[\bigcup_{k \in \mathbf{K}} \mathbf{C}^{(k)} \right] \subset \mathbf{C}^{(n)}, \qquad \forall k \in \mathbf{K}. \tag{35.8}$$

In fact, $p_{ij}^{(k)}$ can only then differ from zero if $E_j \in \mathbf{C}^{(n)}$, and the second member of (35.7) is equal to the average value per period common to all the states of $\mathbf{C}^{(n)}$ in the chain $[\mathscr{T}^{(n)}]$.

The algorithm given above can be used even if, for certain strategies, the vector of the average values per period has some zero components. All the same, if the average optimal value per period (for a certain initial state) is zero, the algorithm does not necessarily enable us to find the optimal strategy by the criterion of the total value (any more than, in the general case, it allows us to choose between two strategies with the same vector of average values per period but with different vectors of relative values). It is then necessary to calculate the total values as explained in Section 33 and to compare them directly.

Example.   Let us use the example given in Section 34 (p. 218), with the same initial strategy.

First iteration

(1) We have

$$\{k^{(0)}\} = \begin{Bmatrix} 1 \\ 1 \end{Bmatrix}. \tag{35.9}$$

Since the corresponding transition matrix is irreducible [as are all the matrices (34.13)], we find the average value per period by using (33.30) or (33.42). The calculations were performed in Section 33, where [from (33.55) and (33.56)] we obtained

$$\sigma^{(0)} = 197.92 \tag{35.10}$$

and

$$\delta_2'^{(0)} = -254.17, \quad \text{with} \quad \delta_1'^{(0)} = 0. \tag{35.11}$$

(2) We seek a new strategy $\{k^{(1)}\}$ which maximizes

$$\{z^{(k)}\} = \{q^{(k)}\} + [\mathcal{T}^{(k)}]\{\delta'^{(0)}\}. \tag{35.12}$$

First line:

$$z_1^{(k)} = q(1, k) + p_{11}^{(k)} \cdot \delta_1'^{(0)} + p_{12}^{(k)} \cdot \delta_2'^{(0)}; \tag{35.13}$$

that is, for $k_1 = 1$:

$$\begin{aligned} z_1^{(1)} &= 325 + (0.5)(0) + (0.5)(-254.17) \\ &= 197.92; \end{aligned}$$

and for $k_1 = 2$:

$$\begin{aligned} z_1^{(2)} &= 320 + (0.6)(0) + (0.4)(-254.17) \\ &= 218.33, \end{aligned} \tag{35.14}$$

whence

$$\max(z_1^{(1)}, z_1^{(2)}) = z_1^{(2)} = 218.33 \qquad (35.15)$$

and we take $k_1^{(1)} = 2$.

Second line:

$$z_2^{(k)} = q(2, k) + p_{21}^{(k)} \cdot \delta'^{(0)}_1 + p_{22}^{(k)} \cdot \delta'^{(0)}_2; \qquad (35.16)$$

that is, for $k_2 = 1$:

$$\begin{aligned} z_2^{(1)} &= 20 + (0.7)(0) + (0.3)(-254.17) \\ &= -56.25; \end{aligned} \qquad (35.17)$$

and for $k_2 = 2$:

$$\begin{aligned} z_2^{(2)} &= -80 + (0.8)(0) + (0.2)(-254.17) \\ &= -130.83, \end{aligned} \qquad (35.18)$$

whence

$$\max(z_2^{(1)}, z_2^{(2)}) = z_2^{(1)} = -56.25 \qquad (35.19)$$

and we take $k_2^{(1)} = 1$.

Second iteration

(1) We have

$$\{k^{(1)}\} = \begin{Bmatrix} 2 \\ 1 \end{Bmatrix}. \qquad (35.20)$$

We shall calculate the average value per period, this time from (33.30), that is,

$$[3]\{\delta'\} = \{\sigma\} - \{q\}, \qquad (35.21)$$

which gives

$$\begin{bmatrix} -0.4 & 0.4 \\ 0.3 & -0.3 \end{bmatrix} \begin{Bmatrix} \delta_1' \\ \delta_2' \end{Bmatrix} = \begin{Bmatrix} \sigma \\ \sigma \end{Bmatrix} - \begin{Bmatrix} 320 \\ 20 \end{Bmatrix}. \qquad (35.22)$$

If we treat (35.22) as a system of two equations whose unknowns are δ_1' and δ_2', the determinant of the coefficients of these unknowns is zero (since [3] is always single); the system can only be solved for a particular value of σ, which is found by equating with zero the determinant obtained by replacing one of the columns of the determinant of the coefficients by the column of the second members of the equations

$$\begin{vmatrix} -0.4 & \sigma - 320 \\ 0.3 & \sigma - 20 \end{vmatrix} = 0, \qquad (35.23)$$

whence

$$\sigma = 148.57. \tag{35.24}$$

The system is now indeterminate, but we can obtain a special solution by making, for instance,

$$\delta_1' = 0, \tag{35.25}$$

whence

$$\delta_2' = -428.57. \tag{35.26}$$

(2) We seek a new strategy $\{k^{(2)}\}$ which maximizes

$$\{z^{(k)}\} = \{q^{(k)}\} + [\mathcal{T}^{(k)}]\{\delta'^{(1)}\}. \tag{35.27}$$

First line:

$$z_1^{(k)} = q(1, k) + p_{11}^{(k)} \cdot \delta_1'^{(1)} + p_{12}^{(k)} \cdot \delta_2'^{(1)}, \tag{35.28}$$

that is, for $k_1 = 1$:

$$z_1^{(1)} = 325 + (0.5)(0) + (0.5)(-428.57)$$
$$= 110.72; \tag{35.29}$$

and for $k_1 = 2$:

$$z_1^{(2)} = 320 + (0.6)(0) + (0.4)(-428.57)$$
$$= 148.57, \tag{35.30}$$

whence

$$\max(z_1^{(1)}, z_1^{(2)}) = z_1^{(2)} = 148.57, \tag{35.31}$$

and we take $k_1^{(2)} = 2$.

Second line:

$$z_2^{(k)} = q(2, k) + p_{21}^{(k)} \cdot \delta_1'^{(1)} + p_{22}^{(k)} \cdot \delta_2'^{(1)}; \tag{35.32}$$

that is, for $k_2 = 1$:

$$z_2^{(1)} = 20 + (0.7)(0) + (0.3)(-428.57)$$
$$= -108.57; \tag{35.33}$$

and for $k_2 = 2$:

$$z_2^{(2)} = -80 + (0.8)(0) + (0.2)(-428.57)$$
$$= -165.71, \tag{35.34}$$

whence

$$\max(z_2^{(1)}, z_2^{(2)}) = z_2^{(1)} = -108.57, \tag{35.35}$$

and we take $k_2^{(2)} = 1$.

Since we find

$$\{k^{(2)}\} = \{k^{(1)}\} = \begin{Bmatrix} 2 \\ 1 \end{Bmatrix},$$
(35.36)

the strategy $\begin{Bmatrix} 2 \\ 1 \end{Bmatrix}$ is optimal.

We discovered in Section 34 that this strategy is optimal by the criterion of the total discounted value when the coefficient of discounting exceeds 0.179, and we could have deduced that it is optimal by the criterion of the average value per period.

This optimal average value is given by (35.24),

$$\varphi = \sigma^* = 148.57.$$
(35.37)

36. Optimization of the Average Value per Period in the Special Case of a Certain Future

The method used in Section 35 can be employed for a certain future; indeed, a certain transition can always be treated as a random or incertain transition with a probability of one.

Using the notation of Chapters 1 and 2, let us consider a stationary dynamic program defined by a correspondence Γx and a present value $v(x, x')$. If we assume the existence of a finite set $\mathbf{X}$ such that $x_0 \in \mathbf{X}$ and $\Gamma \mathbf{X} \subset \mathbf{X}$ (in other words the set of possible states is finite), we can then, by a suitable change of variables, define the state variable x in such a way that

$$\mathbf{X} = \{1, 2, ..., i, ..., M\}.$$
(36.1)

A permanent policy can be represented, in the same way as a permanent strategy in Section 28, by a vector

$$\{k\} = \begin{Bmatrix} k_1 \\ k_2 \\ \vdots \\ k_M \end{Bmatrix}.$$
(36.2)

This signifies that if the state variable at time n is equal to i, the decision taken will have the effect of giving the state variable the value k_i at time $n + 1$.

We can also show a permanent policy $\{k\}$ by a transition matrix $[\mathscr{T}^{(k)}]$, the elements of which are defined by

$$p_{ij}^{(k)} = 1 \quad \text{if} \quad j = k_i ,$$
$$= 0 \quad \text{if} \quad j \neq k_i .$$
(36.3)

Again, we can represent the present value corresponding to this policy, for the different states possible at the beginning of a period, by a vector

$$\{q^{(k)}\} = \begin{Bmatrix} q_1^{(k)} \\ q_2^{(k)} \\ \vdots \\ q_M^{(k)} \end{Bmatrix}, \tag{36.4}$$

such that

$$q_i^{k_i} = v(i, k_i), \qquad i = 1, 2, ..., M. \tag{36.5}$$

Here we again find the notation of Section 28 and can now make direct use of the results obtained in the present chapter, particularly in Section 35.

Example.   We are concerned with the operation of machinery which can, at the beginning of each period, either be replaced or maintained in service. The operating costs consist of: (a) the cost of maintenance known as a function of the age of the machinery; (b) in the case of replacement, the cost either of a new or reconditioned piece of machinery. On the credit side, a replaced machine will be sold.

The numerical data are shown in Table 36.1.

Equipment which is five years old at the beginning of a period is subject to obligatory replacement. We shall take as the state variable the age of a machine immediately before its eventual replacement,

TABLE 36.1

	(1)	(2)	(3)	(4)
	Age	Purchase price	Selling price	Maintenance cost for a period
	0	100	95	2
	1	75	70	5
	2	55	50	8
	3	40	35	14
	4	25	20	20
	5	0	0	—

so that this variable can only have values from 1 to 5. If the machinery is not replaced at the beginning of period n, the cost during this period will be that shown in column 4 of the table. If a machine of age i is replaced by one of age j ($j \neq i$), the total cost is equal to the purchase price for age j, plus the cost of maintenance for a period at age j, less the sale price for a machine of age i. In this way we obtain Table 36.2, which shows the cost for any period n as a function of the state variable at time $(n - 1)$, that is, of the age of the equipment immediately before its eventual replacement and of the state variable at time n. In the case of replacement, this state variable at time n will be $j + 1$, using the notation given above.

TABLE 36.2

n / $n-1$	1	2	3	4	5
1	32	5	−7	−16	−25
2	52	30	8	−4	−5
3	67	45	28	14	10
4	82	60	43	34	20
5	102	80	63	54	45

We shall look for a policy which minimizes the average cost per period,[25] using the algorithm given in Section 35.

First iteration

(1) We shall take for our initial policy the one of not replacing the machinery until it reaches the age of 5, that is,

$$\{k^{(0)}\} = \begin{Bmatrix} 2 \\ 3 \\ 4 \\ 5 \\ 1 \end{Bmatrix}. \tag{36.6}$$

[25] It should be noted, however, that in this type of problem it is often preferable to discount the costs. The case we are considering here is one where the periods are short enough to make discounting unnecessary.

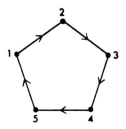

FIG. 36.1

The graph of the transitions is shown in Fig. 36.1. In accordance with the terminology of Markovian chains, which we are perfectly entitled to use even if the evolution of the system is deterministic, we have an irreducible and periodic chain, with a period of 5. We shall calculate the average value per period and a vector of relative values by means of (33.42). We must first calculate the matrix $[\mathscr{L}^{(0)}]$ corresponding to the policy chosen. In accordance with (36.3), the transition matrix is

$$[\mathscr{T}^{(0)}] = \begin{bmatrix} 0 & 1 & 0 & 0 & 0 \\ 0 & 0 & 1 & 0 & 0 \\ 0 & 0 & 0 & 1 & 0 \\ 0 & 0 & 0 & 0 & 1 \\ 1 & 0 & 0 & 0 & 0 \end{bmatrix}. \tag{36.7}$$

The dynamic matrix is

$$[3^{(0)}] = [\mathscr{T}^{(0)}] - [\mathscr{E}_5] = \begin{bmatrix} -1 & 1 & 0 & 0 & 0 \\ 0 & -1 & 1 & 0 & 0 \\ 0 & 0 & -1 & 1 & 0 \\ 0 & 0 & 0 & -1 & 1 \\ 1 & 0 & 0 & 0 & -1 \end{bmatrix}. \tag{36.8}$$

Finally, matrix $[\mathscr{L}^{(0)}]$ is defined by (36.36) and (36.37):

$$[\mathscr{L}^{(0)}] = \begin{bmatrix} 1 & -1 & 0 & 0 & 0 \\ 1 & 1 & -1 & 0 & 0 \\ 1 & 0 & 1 & -1 & 0 \\ 1 & 0 & 0 & 1 & -1 \\ 1 & 0 & 0 & 0 & 1 \end{bmatrix}. \tag{36.9}$$

Then again, the vector of present values defined by (36.5) is

$$\{q^{(0)}\} = \begin{Bmatrix} 5 \\ 8 \\ 14 \\ 20 \\ 102 \end{Bmatrix}. \tag{36.10}$$

Equation (33.41) now becomes

$$[\mathscr{L}^{(0)}]\{\tilde{\delta}^{(0)}\} = \{q^{(0)}\}, \tag{36.11}$$

that is,

$$\begin{bmatrix} 1 & -1 & 0 & 0 & 0 \\ 1 & 1 & -1 & 0 & 0 \\ 1 & 0 & 1 & -1 & 0 \\ 1 & 0 & 0 & 1 & -1 \\ 1 & 0 & 0 & 0 & 1 \end{bmatrix} \begin{Bmatrix} \sigma^{(0)} \\ \delta_2'^{(0)} \\ \delta_3'^{(0)} \\ \delta_4'^{(0)} \\ \delta_5'^{(0)} \end{Bmatrix} = \begin{Bmatrix} 5 \\ 8 \\ 14 \\ 20 \\ 102 \end{Bmatrix}, \tag{36.12}$$

with $\delta'^{(0)} = 0$. By solving the system of Eqs. (36.12), we find

$$\sigma^{(0)} = 29.8 \tag{36.13}$$

and

$$\{\delta'^{(0)}\} = \begin{Bmatrix} \delta_1'^{(0)} \\ \delta_2'^{(0)} \\ \delta_3'^{(0)} \\ \delta_4'^{(0)} \\ \delta_5'^{(0)} \end{Bmatrix} = \begin{Bmatrix} 0 \\ 24.8 \\ 46.6 \\ 62.4 \\ 72.2 \end{Bmatrix}. \tag{36.14}$$

(2) Since matrix $[\mathscr{T}^{(0)}]$ is unireducible, we shall seek a new policy, using (35.4) only. Besides, we can see that line i of the vector

$$\{q^{(k)}\} + [\mathscr{T}^{(k)}]\{\delta^{(n)}\}$$

is equal to $q_i^{(k_i)} + \delta_{k_i}^{(n)}$. Optimization is carried out line by line, and Table 36.3 gives the values of $q_i^{(k_i)} + \delta_{k_i}^{(n)}$ for every value of i and of k_i. The position of the minimum, in each line, gives the new policy obtained.

$$\{k^{(1)}\} = \begin{Bmatrix} 2 \\ 1 \\ 1 \\ 1 \\ 1 \end{Bmatrix}. \tag{36.15}$$

TABLE 36.3

k_i $\diagdown$ i	1	2	3	4	5
1	32	29.8	39.6	46.4	47.2
2	52	54.8	54.6	58.4	67.2
3	67	69.8	74.6	76.4	82.2
4	82	84.8	89.8	96.4	92.2
5	102	104.8	109.6	116.4	117.2

Second iteration

(1) The graph of the transitions corresponding to the policy $\{k^{(1)}\}$ is shown in Fig. 36.2. The Markovian chain obtained is unireducible, and the closed subchain formed by states 1 and 2 is periodic.

The calculations proceed as in the first iteration, and we shall not repeat the explanations.

$$[\mathscr{T}^{(1)}] = \begin{bmatrix} 0 & 1 & 0 & 0 & 0 \\ 1 & 0 & 0 & 0 & 0 \\ 1 & 0 & 0 & 0 & 0 \\ 1 & 0 & 0 & 0 & 0 \\ 1 & 0 & 0 & 0 & 0 \end{bmatrix}, \tag{36.16}$$

$$[\mathscr{L}^{(1)}] = \begin{bmatrix} 1 & -1 & 0 & 0 & 0 \\ 1 & 1 & 0 & 0 & 0 \\ 1 & 0 & 1 & 0 & 0 \\ 1 & 0 & 0 & 1 & 0 \\ 1 & 0 & 0 & 0 & 1 \end{bmatrix}; \tag{36.17}$$

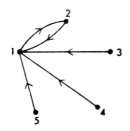

FIG. 36.2

$$\{q^{(1)}\} = \begin{Bmatrix} 5 \\ 52 \\ 67 \\ 82 \\ 102 \end{Bmatrix}. \tag{36.18}$$

$$\begin{bmatrix} 1 & -1 & 0 & 0 & 0 \\ 1 & 1 & 0 & 0 & 0 \\ 1 & 0 & 1 & 0 & 0 \\ 1 & 0 & 0 & 1 & 0 \\ 1 & 0 & 0 & 0 & 1 \end{bmatrix} \begin{Bmatrix} \sigma^{(1)} \\ \delta_2'^{(1)} \\ \delta_3'^{(1)} \\ \delta_4'^{(1)} \\ \delta_5'^{(1)} \end{Bmatrix} = \begin{Bmatrix} 5 \\ 52 \\ 67 \\ 82 \\ 102 \end{Bmatrix}, \tag{36.19}$$

whence

$$\sigma^{(1)} = 28.5, \tag{36.20}$$

$$\{\delta'^{(1)}\} = \begin{Bmatrix} 0 \\ 23.5 \\ 38.5 \\ 53.5 \\ 73.5 \end{Bmatrix}. \tag{36.21}$$

(2) We obtain Table 36.4, and the new policy is defined by the vector

$$\{k^{(2)}\} = \begin{Bmatrix} 2 \\ 3 \\ 3 \\ 3 \\ 3 \end{Bmatrix}. \tag{36.22}$$

TABLE 36.4

k_i / i	1	2	3	4	5
1	32	28.5	31.5	37.5	48.5
2	52	53.5	46.5	49.5	68.5
3	67	68.5	66.5	67.5	83.5
4	82	83.5	81.5	87.5	93.5
5	102	103.5	101.5	107.5	118.5

Third iteration

(1) The graph of the transitions corresponding to the policy $\{k^{(2)}\}$ is shown in Fig. 36.3. The Markovian chain obtained is unireducible, and the closed subchain is formed by state 3. We have successively:

$$[\mathcal{T}^{(2)}] = \begin{bmatrix} 0 & 1 & 0 & 0 & 0 \\ 0 & 0 & 1 & 0 & 0 \\ 0 & 0 & 1 & 0 & 0 \\ 0 & 0 & 1 & 0 & 0 \\ 0 & 0 & 1 & 0 & 0 \end{bmatrix}, \tag{36.23}$$

$$[\mathcal{L}^{(2)}] = \begin{bmatrix} 1 & -1 & 0 & 0 & 0 \\ 1 & 1 & -1 & 0 & 0 \\ 1 & 0 & 0 & 0 & 0 \\ 1 & 0 & -1 & 1 & 0 \\ 1 & 0 & -1 & 0 & 1 \end{bmatrix}; \tag{36.24}$$

$$\{q^{(2)}\} = \left\{ \begin{matrix} 5 \\ 8 \\ 28 \\ 43 \\ 63 \end{matrix} \right\}. \tag{36.25}$$

$$\begin{bmatrix} 1 & -1 & 0 & 0 & 0 \\ 1 & 1 & -1 & 0 & 0 \\ 1 & 0 & 0 & 0 & 0 \\ 1 & 0 & -1 & 1 & 0 \\ 1 & 0 & -1 & 0 & 1 \end{bmatrix} \left\{ \begin{matrix} \sigma^{(2)} \\ \delta_2'^{(2)} \\ \delta_3'^{(2)} \\ \delta_4'^{(2)} \\ \delta_5'^{(2)} \end{matrix} \right\} = \left\{ \begin{matrix} 5 \\ 8 \\ 28 \\ 43 \\ 63 \end{matrix} \right\}, \tag{36.26}$$

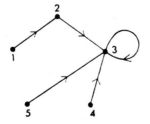

FIG. 36.3

whence

$$\sigma^{(2)} = 28, \tag{36.27}$$

$$\{\delta'^{(2)}\} = \begin{pmatrix} 0 \\ 23 \\ 43 \\ 58 \\ 78 \end{pmatrix}. \tag{36.28}$$

(2) We obtain Table 36.5, and the new policy is defined by the vector

$$\{k^{(3)}\} = \begin{pmatrix} 2 \\ 3 \\ 1 \\ 1 \\ 1 \end{pmatrix}. \tag{36.29}$$

TABLE 36.5

k_i / i	1	2	3	4	5
1	32	_28_	36	42	53
2	52	53	_51_	54	73
3	_67_	68	71	72	88
4	_82_	83	86	92	98
5	_102_	103	106	112	123

Fourth iteration

Figure 36.4 shows the graph of the transitions for $k^{(3)}$. The Markovian chain is unireducible and the closed subchain formed by states 1, 2, and 3 has a period of 3.

$$[\mathcal{T}^{(3)}] = \begin{bmatrix} 0 & 1 & 0 & 0 & 0 \\ 0 & 0 & 1 & 0 & 0 \\ 1 & 0 & 0 & 0 & 0 \\ 1 & 0 & 0 & 0 & 0 \\ 1 & 0 & 0 & 0 & 0 \end{bmatrix}, \tag{36.30}$$

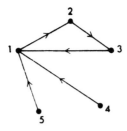

FIG. 36.4

$$[\mathscr{L}^{(3)}] = \begin{bmatrix} 1 & -1 & 0 & 0 & 0 \\ 1 & 1 & -1 & 0 & 0 \\ 1 & 0 & 1 & 0 & 0 \\ 1 & 0 & 0 & 1 & 0 \\ 1 & 0 & 0 & 0 & 1 \end{bmatrix}; \tag{36.31}$$

$$\{q^{(3)}\} = \begin{Bmatrix} 5 \\ 8 \\ 67 \\ 82 \\ 102 \end{Bmatrix}. \tag{36.32}$$

$$\begin{bmatrix} 1 & -1 & 0 & 0 & 0 \\ 1 & 1 & -1 & 0 & 0 \\ 1 & 0 & 1 & 0 & 0 \\ 1 & 0 & 0 & 1 & 0 \\ 1 & 0 & 0 & 0 & 1 \end{bmatrix} \begin{Bmatrix} \sigma^{(3)} \\ \delta_2'^{(3)} \\ \delta_3'^{(3)} \\ \delta_4'^{(3)} \\ \delta_5'^{(3)} \end{Bmatrix} = \begin{Bmatrix} 5 \\ 8 \\ 67 \\ 82 \\ 102 \end{Bmatrix}. \tag{36.33}$$

Whence

$$\sigma^{(3)} = 26.67, \tag{36.34}$$

$$\{\delta'^{(3)}\} = \begin{Bmatrix} 0 \\ 21.67 \\ 40.33 \\ 55.33 \\ 75.33 \end{Bmatrix}. \tag{36.35}$$

(2) We obtain Table 36.6, and the new policy is defined by the vector

$$\{k^{(4)}\} = \begin{Bmatrix} 2 \\ 3 \\ 2 \\ 2 \\ 2 \end{Bmatrix}. \tag{36.36}$$

TABLE 36.6

k_i $\diagdown$ i	1	2	3	4	5
1	32	26.67	33.33	39.33	50.33
2	52	51.67	48.33	51.33	70.33
3	67	66.67	68.33	69.33	85.33
4	82	81.67	83.33	89.33	95.33
5	102	101.67	103.33	109.33	120.33

Fifth iteration

(1) The transition graph for $\{K^{(4)}\}$ is shown in Fig. 36.5. The Markovian chain is unireducible, and the closed subchain formed by states 2 and 3 has a period of 2.

$$[\mathscr{T}^{(4)}] = \begin{bmatrix} 0 & 1 & 0 & 0 & 0 \\ 0 & 0 & 1 & 0 & 0 \\ 0 & 1 & 0 & 0 & 0 \\ 0 & 1 & 0 & 0 & 0 \\ 0 & 1 & 0 & 0 & 0 \end{bmatrix}, \tag{36.37}$$

$$[\mathscr{L}^{(4)}] = \begin{bmatrix} 1 & -1 & 0 & 0 & 0 \\ 1 & 1 & -1 & 0 & 0 \\ 1 & -1 & 1 & 0 & 0 \\ 1 & -1 & 0 & 1 & 0 \\ 1 & -1 & 0 & 0 & 1 \end{bmatrix}; \tag{36.38}$$

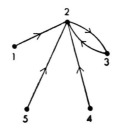

FIG. 36.5

$$\{q^{(4)}\} = \begin{Bmatrix} 5 \\ 8 \\ 45 \\ 60 \\ 80 \end{Bmatrix}. \tag{36.39}$$

$$\begin{bmatrix} 1 & -1 & 0 & 0 & 0 \\ 1 & 1 & -1 & 0 & 0 \\ 1 & -1 & 1 & 0 & 0 \\ 1 & -1 & 0 & 1 & 0 \\ 1 & -1 & 0 & 0 & 1 \end{bmatrix} \begin{Bmatrix} \sigma^{(4)} \\ \delta_2'^{(4)} \\ \delta_3'^{(4)} \\ \delta_4'^{(4)} \\ \delta_5'^{(4)} \end{Bmatrix} = \begin{Bmatrix} 5 \\ 8 \\ 45 \\ 60 \\ 80 \end{Bmatrix}, \tag{36.40}$$

whence

$$\sigma^{(4)} = 26.5, \tag{36.41}$$

$$\{\delta'^{(4)}\} = \begin{Bmatrix} 0 \\ 21.5 \\ 40 \\ 55 \\ 75 \end{Bmatrix}. \tag{36.42}$$

TABLE 36.7

i \ k_i	1	2	3	4	5
1	32	_26.5_	33	39	50
2	52	51.5	_48_	51	70
3	67	_66.5_	68	69	85
4	82	_81.5_	83	89	95
5	102	_101.5_	103	109	120

(2) We obtain Table 36.7, and the policy obtained is

$$\{k^{(5)}\} = \begin{pmatrix} 2 \\ 3 \\ 2 \\ 2 \\ 2 \end{pmatrix}. \tag{36.43}$$

We have obtained (36.36) again; hence this is the optimal policy. The average optimal value for the corresponding periods is given by (36.41).

37. Decomposed Form

In this section our attention will be concerned mainly with the model in the decomposed D.H. form. The models in the decomposed H.D. form or in the general decomposed form have few differences, as we saw in Section 18, and the reader should easily be able to extend the following results to them. We shall, however, consider the H.D. programs in connection with the optimization of the average value per period.

We shall presume that the assumptions of both (17.45) and (17.46) and (28.1) and (28.2) are satisfied, which means, using the notation of Section 18, that:

(a) The probability of transition from state i to state j (with $i, j \in \mathbf{X}$), when the decision $K \in \Delta i$, does not depend on i. We shall assume

$$p_{ij}^{(k)} = h_{kj}, \tag{37.1}$$

and we shall use the term *matrix of hazard* for the matrix with elements h_{kj},

$$[\mathscr{H}] = [h_{kj}]. \tag{37.2}$$

In general, $[\mathscr{H}]$ will be a rectangular matrix of order $m \times M$, where $m = |\mathbf{Y}|$ is the dimension of the set $\mathbf{Y}$ of possible decisions,[26] and $M = |\mathbf{X}|$ is the number of possible states.

(b) The present value is the sum of two terms corresponding respectively to each of the two stages of the period considered,

$$r_{ij}^{(k)} = a_{ik} + b_{kj}. \tag{37.3}$$

[26] Let us recall that we have: $\mathbf{Y} = \bigcup_{i \in \mathbf{X}} \Delta i$.

To a permanent strategy

$$\{k\} = \begin{Bmatrix} k_1 \\ k_2 \\ \vdots \\ k_i \\ \vdots \\ k_M \end{Bmatrix}, \qquad (37.4)$$

there will correspond a matrix of order $M \times m$, called the "decision matrix," defined by

$$[\mathscr{D}] = [d_{ik}], \qquad (37.5)$$

where[27]

$$
\begin{aligned}
d_{ik} &= 1 \quad \text{if} \quad k = k_i \in \varDelta i, \\
&= 0 \quad \text{if} \quad k \neq k_i .
\end{aligned} \qquad (37.6)
$$

The transition matrix of the Markovian chain representing the evolution of the system under the effect of the strategy $\{K\}$, when the unit of time is the period, is then

$$[\mathscr{T}] = [\mathscr{D}][\mathscr{H}]. \qquad (37.7)$$

The element (i, j) of this square matrix of order M is, in fact,

$$p_{ij}^{(k_i)} = h_{k_i, j} . \qquad (37.8)$$

So, we have again obtained (37.1).

LIMITED HORIZON

With a number of finite periods, we use the recurring equation (17.49), which is now expressed,

$$f_n(i) = \underset{k \in \varDelta i}{\mathrm{OPT}} \left\{ a_{ik} + \sum_{j=1}^{M} h_{kj}[b_{kj} + f_{n-1}(j)] \right\}, \qquad (37.9)$$

---

[27] In this book we have confined ourselves to pure strategies (some authors speak of "tactics") in the sense of the theory of games of strategy. More often we could consider mixed strategies which would be represented here by a matrix such that d_{ik} need not be equal to 0 or 1, but only that $d_{ik} \geqslant 0, \sum_k d_{ik} = 1$. Indeed, it is clear from intuition that this probability of the decisions does not enable us to improve the solution, and a proof of this fact was given us by R. Companys Pascual. On this subject the reader should consult [25] and [22]. By contrast, the great value of the concept of a mixed strategy is well known for problems arising from the theory of games.

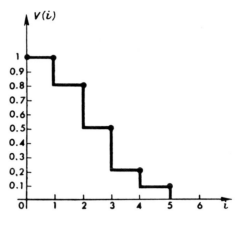

FIG. 37.1

or again,

$$g_n(k) = \sum_{j=1}^{M} h_{kj}[b_{kj} + f_{n-1}(j)],$$ (37.10)

$$f_n(i) = \operatorname*{OPT}_{k \in \Delta i}[a_{ik} + g_n(k)],$$ (37.11)

where $g_n(K)$ is the expected optimal value for $n - 1$ periods plus a stage H.

As an example, let us consider a problem where machinery has to be operated over a five year period. At the beginning of each period the machinery can either be replaced by new machines or maintained in service. If it is replaced, there is an expenditure equal to the difference between the cost of the new machinery and the price obtained for the old. If it is not replaced, there is an expenditure on maintenance proportional to the age of the machinery.

The numerical data are given in Table 37.2. Also, the machinery may suffer a severe breakdown which is beyond repair; its value then becomes null and it must obligatorily be replaced at the beginning of the following year. The survival curve of the machinery is shown in Fig. 37.1 and the rate for breakdown $p_c(i)$, or conditional probability of breakdown between the age of i and $i + 1$ is given in Table 37.1). At the end of the fifth year the machinery is sold in its existing condition.

Figure 37.2 shows the possible evolutions of the system, as well as the expenditure a_{ik} corresponding to each decision ($b_{kj} = 0$), and the probability corresponding to each random transition. There is no

TABLE 37.1

i	$V(v)$	$p_e(n) = \dfrac{V(n-1) - V(n)}{V(n-1)}$
0	1	0
1	1	0
2	0.8	$\frac{1}{5}$
3	0.5	$\frac{3}{8}$
4	0.2	$\frac{3}{5}$
5	0.1	$\frac{1}{2}$
$\geqslant 6$	0	1

point, in this very simple problem, of giving Eqs. (37.10) and (37.11) each time they are used, and we shall merely place the results beside the corresponding vertices of the graph shown in Fig. 37.2.

Figure 37.3 shows the optimal strategy obtained.

TABLE 37.2

i	Cost of maintenance	Value at age i
0	0	100
1	4	60
2	10	40
3	17	30
4	26	20
5	38	10
$\geqslant 6$	—	0

UNLIMITED HORIZON

The methods described in Sections 33–35 obviously apply to the special case of dynamic programs with a decomposed form. Nevertheless, it will be useful to consider the optimization of the average value per period by Howard's method. In the above sections, we obtained equations corresponding to this method by using the intermediary of the total discounted value, and by making the coefficient of discounting approach 1. On this occasion we shall use the direct method employed by Howard,[28]

[28] See our reference [36].

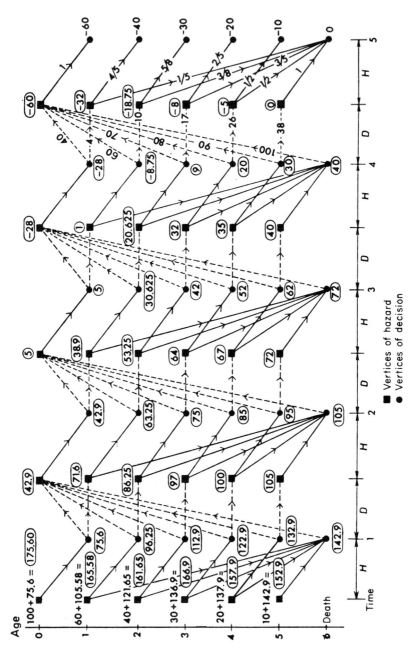

Fig. 37.2

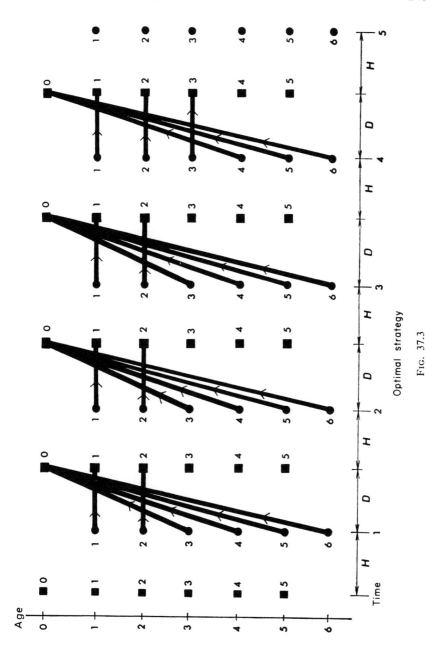

Optimal strategy

FIG. 37.3

who has shown that as n approaches infinity the total value for n periods of any permanent strategy has the form[29]

$$s_n(i) = n\sigma_i + \delta_i ,\tag{37.12}$$

if we neglect the terms which tend toward zero.

In the same way, we could easily show that the total value for $(n-1)$ periods and a stage H is of the form

$$t_n(k) = n\tau_k + \epsilon_k ,\tag{37.13}$$

where τ_k is the average value per period in an H.D. program (an H.D. period is defined as a stage H followed by a stage D), and ϵ_k is the relative value of the possible initial states (in the strategies' space).

By substituting (37.12) and (37.13) in the recurring equations corresponding to (37.10) and (37.11), we obtain

$$n\tau_k + \epsilon_k = \sum_{j=1}^{M} h_{k,j}[b_{k,j} + (n-1)\sigma_j + \delta_j],\tag{37.14}$$

$$n\sigma_i + \delta_i = a_{i,k_i} + n\tau_{k_i} + \epsilon_{k_i} ,\tag{37.15}$$

where K_i is the decision taken in a stage D at the beginning of which the state is i, in other words, the column number of the nonzero element on line i of $[\mathscr{D}]$ (see 37.6).

In their matricial form, these equations become

$$n\{\tau\} + \{\epsilon\} = \{\bar{b}\} + (n-1)[\mathscr{H}]\{\sigma\} + [\mathscr{H}]\{\delta\},\tag{37.16}$$

$$n\{\sigma\} + \{\delta\} = \{a_\mathscr{D}\} + n[\mathscr{D}]\{\tau\} + [\mathscr{D}]\{\epsilon\},\tag{37.17}$$

where $\{\bar{b}\}$ is the vector of probable present values for a stage H, with components

$$\bar{b}_k = \sum_{j=1}^{M} h_{k,j} b_{k,j} ,\tag{37.18}$$

---

[29] This result can be found beginning with (33.3), where we make $r = 1$, and where we substitute the expression (33.19) of $[\mathscr{T}^*(z)]$, taking account of (33.10), (33.27), and (33.28).

and $\{a_{\mathscr{D}}\}$ the vector of present values for a stage D, with components

$$a_{i,k_i} = \sum_{k=1}^{M} a_{i,k}\, d_{i,k}\,. \qquad (37.19)$$

If we consider the terms which $\to\infty$ in (37.16) and (37.17), we see that

$$\{\tau\} = [\mathscr{H}]\{\sigma\} \qquad (37.20)$$

and

$$\{\sigma\} = [\mathscr{D}]\{\tau\}, \qquad (37.21)$$

whence

$$\{\sigma\} = [\mathscr{D}][\mathscr{H}]\{\sigma\} = [\mathscr{T}_{\mathscr{D}}]\{\sigma\}, \qquad (37.22)$$

$$\{\tau\} = [\mathscr{H}][\mathscr{D}]\{\tau\} = [\mathscr{U}_{\mathscr{D}}]\{\tau\}. \qquad (37.23)$$

Here again, we have Eq. (33.12) or (33.44), and at the same time we obtain the corresponding equation for an H.D. dynamic program. By taking $[\mathscr{U}_{\mathscr{D}}]$ for the transition matrix of the Markovian chain in this program, and by premultiplying (37.16) by $[\mathscr{D}]$ and adding (37.17), it follows:

$$\{\sigma\} + \{\delta\} = \{a_{\mathscr{D}}\} + [\mathscr{D}]\{\bar{b}\} + [\mathscr{D}][\mathscr{H}]\{\delta\}; \qquad (37.24)$$

in other words,

$$\{\sigma\} + \{\delta\} = \{q^{(k)}\} + [\mathscr{T}^{(k)}]\{\delta\}, \qquad (37.25)$$

where $[\mathscr{T}^{(k)}]$ is the transition matrix of the D.H. chain. Thus we have again found (33.29), and in the same way, by premultiplying (37.17) by $[\mathscr{H}]$ and by adding (37.16), we obtain the corresponding relation for H.D. programs:

$$\{\tau\} + \{\epsilon\} = \{\bar{b}\} + [\mathscr{H}]\{a_{\mathscr{D}}\} + [\mathscr{H}][\mathscr{D}]\{\epsilon\}. \qquad (37.26)$$

Before turning to the optimization of the average value per period, let us notice certain relations between the D.H. and H.D. types of program. In the first place, relations (37.20) and (37.21) show that if, for the strategy considered, the D.H. chain is unireducible, that is to say, if all the components of $\{\sigma\}$ are equal to the same quantity σ, the same holds true for the H.D. chain, and reciprocally. We then have

$$\sigma = \tau. \qquad (37.27)$$

Further, in every case, if we take (37.20) and (37.21) into account, (37.16) and (37.17) give

$$\{\tau\} + \{\epsilon\} = \{\bar{b}\} + [\mathcal{H}]\{\delta\}, \tag{37.28}$$

$$\{\delta\} = \{a_{\mathcal{D}}\} + [\mathcal{D}]\{\epsilon\}. \tag{37.29}$$

By substituting (37.29) in (37.28), we again have (37.26).

If we treat the dynamic program as a D.H. program the optimization procedure explained in Section 35 can be used unaltered. At the same time, the calculations are rather easier; indeed, each time we seek a new strategy by means of (35.4), or (35.2) if the chain is not unireducible, we can use one calculation to find all the vectors:

$$[\mathcal{H}]\{\sigma^{(l)}\} = \{\tau^{(l)}\} \tag{37.30}$$

and

$$[\mathcal{H}]\{\delta^{(l)}\} = \{\tau^{(l)}\} + \{\epsilon^{(l)}\} - \{\bar{b}\}, \tag{37.31}$$

which do not depend on the new strategy $[\mathcal{D}^{(l+1)}]$ which will be chosen. Equations (35.2) and (35.4) are then expressed as

$$[\mathcal{D}^{(l+1)}]\{\tau^{(l)}\} = \underset{\mathcal{D}}{\mathrm{OPT}}[\mathcal{D}]\{\tau^{(l)}\} \tag{37.32}$$

and[30]

$$\{a^{(l+1)}\} + [\mathcal{D}^{(l+1)}](\{\tau^{(l)}\} + \{\epsilon^{(l)}\}) = \underset{\mathcal{D}}{\mathrm{OPT}}[\{a_{\mathcal{D}}\} + [\mathcal{D}](\{\tau^{(l)}\} + \{\epsilon^{(l)}\})]. \tag{37.33}$$

Let us again use the example given above. The matrix of hazard is

$$[\mathcal{H}] = \begin{array}{c} \\ (0) \\ (1) \\ (2) \\ (3) \\ (4) \\ (5) \end{array} \begin{array}{cccccc} (1) & (2) & (3) & (4) & (5) & (6) \\ \begin{bmatrix} 1 & 0 & 0 & 0 & 0 & 0 \\ 0 & \frac{4}{5} & 0 & 0 & 0 & \frac{1}{5} \\ 0 & 0 & \frac{5}{8} & 0 & 0 & \frac{3}{8} \\ 0 & 0 & 0 & \frac{2}{5} & 0 & \frac{3}{5} \\ 0 & 0 & 0 & 0 & \frac{1}{2} & \frac{1}{2} \\ 0 & 0 & 0 & 0 & 0 & 1 \end{bmatrix} \end{array}. \tag{37.34}$$

[30] It will be observed that as $\{\epsilon\}$ is a vector of relative values, we can make an arbitrary choice from it for each set of closed states, with the result that $\{\tau\} + \{\epsilon\}$ is equally a vector of relative values (for the H. D. chain).

The decision matrix has the form

$$
[\mathscr{D}] =
\begin{array}{c}
 \\
(1) \\
(2) \\
(3) \\
(4) \\
(5) \\
(6)
\end{array}
\begin{array}{cccccc}
(0) & (1) & (2) & (3) & (4) & (5) \\
\left[\begin{array}{cccccc}
* & * & 0 & 0 & 0 & 0 \\
* & 0 & * & 0 & 0 & 0 \\
* & 0 & 0 & * & 0 & 0 \\
* & 0 & 0 & 0 & * & 0 \\
* & 0 & 0 & 0 & 0 & * \\
* & 0 & 0 & 0 & 0 & 0
\end{array}\right]
\end{array},
\tag{37.35}
$$

where, in each line, one of the asterisks represents a 1, and the other a 0. The matrix of present values for a stage D is

$$
[\mathscr{A}] =
\begin{array}{c}
 \\
(1) \\
(2) \\
(3) \\
(4) \\
(5) \\
(6)
\end{array}
\begin{array}{cccccc}
(0) & (1) & (2) & (3) & (4) & (5) \\
\left[\begin{array}{cccccc}
40 & 4 & - & - & - & - \\
60 & - & 10 & - & - & - \\
70 & - & - & 17 & - & - \\
80 & - & - & - & 26 & - \\
90 & - & - & - & - & 38 \\
100 & - & - & - & - & -
\end{array}\right]
\end{array}.
\tag{37.36}
$$

The values are zero in stage H.

We shall use as an initial strategy the optimal strategy for a period (taking the resale into account) shown on the right of Fig. 37.3:

$$
[\mathscr{D}^{(0)}] =
\begin{array}{c}
 \\
(1) \\
(2) \\
(3) \\
(4) \\
(5) \\
(6)
\end{array}
\begin{array}{cccccc}
(0) & (1) & (2) & (3) & (4) & (5) \\
\left[\begin{array}{cccccc}
0 & 1 & 0 & 0 & 0 & 0 \\
0 & 0 & 1 & 0 & 0 & 0 \\
0 & 0 & 0 & 1 & 0 & 0 \\
1 & 0 & 0 & 0 & 0 & 0 \\
1 & 0 & 0 & 0 & 0 & 0 \\
1 & 0 & 0 & 0 & 0 & 0
\end{array}\right]
\end{array}.
\tag{37.37}
$$

The corresponding transition matrix is

$$
[\mathscr{T}^{(0)}] =
\begin{array}{c}
 \\
(1) \\
(2) \\
(3) \\
(4) \\
(5) \\
(6)
\end{array}
\begin{array}{cccccc}
(1) & (2) & (3) & (4) & (5) & (6) \\
\left[\begin{array}{cccccc}
0 & \frac{4}{5} & 0 & 0 & 0 & \frac{1}{5} \\
0 & 0 & \frac{5}{8} & 0 & 0 & \frac{3}{8} \\
0 & 0 & 0 & \frac{2}{5} & 0 & \frac{3}{5} \\
1 & 0 & 0 & 0 & 0 & 0 \\
1 & 0 & 0 & 0 & 0 & 0 \\
1 & 0 & 0 & 0 & 0 & 0
\end{array}\right]
\end{array}.
\tag{37.38}
$$

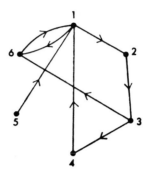

FIG. 37.4

Figure 37.4 shows the graphs of the transitions. We find that the chain is unireducible and that state 5 is transitory.

First iteration

(1) Let us use (37.24) to find $\sigma^{(0)}$ and $\{\delta^{(0)}\}$:

$$\{\sigma^{(0)}\} + \{\delta^{(0)}\} = \begin{Bmatrix} 4 \\ 10 \\ 17 \\ 80 \\ 90 \\ 100 \end{Bmatrix} + \begin{Bmatrix} \frac{4}{5}\delta_2 + \frac{1}{5}\delta_6 \\ \frac{5}{8}\delta_3 + \frac{3}{8}\delta_6 \\ \frac{2}{5}\delta_4 + \frac{3}{5}\delta_6 \\ \delta_1 \\ \delta_1 \\ \delta_1 \end{Bmatrix}, \tag{37.39}$$

whence, by arbitrarily taking $\delta_1 = 0$,

$$\sigma^{(0)} = 35.3; \qquad \delta_1^{(0)} = 0; \qquad \delta_2^{(0)} = 22.9; \qquad \delta_3^{(0)} = 38.4;$$

$$\delta_4^{(0)} = 44.7; \qquad \delta_5^{(0)} = 54.7; \qquad \delta_6^{(0)} = 64.7. \tag{37.40}$$

From (37.31) it follows:

$$\{\tau^{(0)}\} + \{\epsilon^{(0)}\} = [\mathscr{H}]\{\delta^{(0)}\} + \{\bar{b}\} = \begin{matrix} (0) \\ (1) \\ (2) \\ (3) \\ (4) \\ (5) \end{matrix} \begin{Bmatrix} 0 \\ 31.3 \\ 48.3 \\ 56.7 \\ 59.7 \\ 64.7 \end{Bmatrix}. \tag{37.41}$$

(2) We now find a new strategy by using (37.33), that is to say, by minimizing each component of the vector

$$\{a_{\mathscr{D}}\} + [\mathscr{D}][\{\tau^{(0)}\} + \{\epsilon^{(0)}\}] = \{a_{i,k} + \tau_k^{(0)} + \epsilon_k^{(0)}\}. \qquad (37.42)$$

1st line:	$k_1 = 0$	$40 + 0$	$= 40$
	$k_1 = 1$	$4 + 31.3$	$= 35.3 \leftarrow$
2nd line:	$k_2 = 0$	$60 + 0$	$= 60$
	$k_2 = 2$	$10 + 48.3$	$= 58.3 \leftarrow$
3rd line:	$k_3 = 0$	$70 + 0$	$= 70 \leftarrow$
	$k_3 = 3$	$17 + 56.7$	$= 73.7$
4th line:	$k_4 = 0$	$80 + 0$	$= 80 \leftarrow$
	$k_4 = 4$	$26 + 59.7$	$= 85.7$
5th line:	$k_5 = 0$	$90 + 0$	$= 90 \leftarrow$
	$k_5 = 5$	$38 + 64.7$	$= 102.7$
6th line:	$k_6 = 0$	$100 + 0$	$= 100 \leftarrow$

The new matrix of decision is therefore

$$[\mathscr{D}^{(1)}] = \begin{array}{c} \\ (1) \\ (2) \\ (3) \\ (4) \\ (5) \\ (6) \end{array} \begin{array}{cccccc} (0) & (1) & (2) & (3) & (4) & (5) \\ \begin{bmatrix} 0 & 1 & 0 & 0 & 0 & 0 \\ 0 & 0 & 1 & 0 & 0 & 0 \\ 1 & 0 & 0 & 0 & 0 & 0 \\ 1 & 0 & 0 & 0 & 0 & 0 \\ 1 & 0 & 0 & 0 & 0 & 0 \\ 1 & 0 & 0 & 0 & 0 & 0 \end{bmatrix} \end{array}. \qquad (37.43)$$

Second iteration

(1) The transition matrix for the new strategy is

$$[\mathscr{T}^{(1)}] = \begin{array}{c} \\ (1) \\ (2) \\ (3) \\ (4) \\ (5) \\ (6) \end{array} \begin{array}{cccccc} (1) & (2) & (3) & (4) & (5) & (6) \\ \begin{bmatrix} 0 & \frac{4}{5} & 0 & 0 & 0 & \frac{1}{5} \\ 0 & 0 & \frac{5}{8} & 0 & 0 & \frac{3}{8} \\ 1 & 0 & 0 & 0 & 0 & 0 \\ 1 & 0 & 0 & 0 & 0 & 0 \\ 1 & 0 & 0 & 0 & 0 & 0 \\ 1 & 0 & 0 & 0 & 0 & 0 \end{bmatrix} \end{array}. \qquad (37.44)$$

Figure 37.5 shows the graph of the transitions. The chain is uniredu-cible, and states 4 and 5 are transitory.

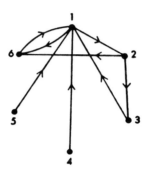

FIG. 37.5

Let us use (37.24) to find $\sigma^{(1)}$ and $\delta^{(1)}$:

$$\{\sigma^{(1)}\} + \{\delta^{(1)}\} = \begin{Bmatrix} 4 \\ 10 \\ 70 \\ 80 \\ 90 \\ 100 \end{Bmatrix} + \begin{Bmatrix} \frac{4}{5}\delta_2 + \frac{1}{5}\delta_6 \\ \frac{5}{8}\delta_3 + \frac{3}{8}\delta_6 \\ \delta_1 \\ \delta_1 \\ \delta_1 \\ \delta_1 \end{Bmatrix}, \qquad (37.45)$$

whence, arbitrarily taking $\delta_1 = 0$,

$$\sigma^{(1)} = 34.6; \qquad \delta_1^{(1)} = 0; \qquad \delta_2^{(1)} = 21.96; \qquad \delta_3^{(1)} = 35.34;$$
$$\delta_4^{(1)} = 45.4; \qquad \delta_5^{(1)} = 55.4; \qquad \delta_6^{(1)} = 65.4. \qquad (37.46)$$

From the use of (37.31) it follows:

$$\{\tau^{(1)}\} + \{\epsilon^{(1)}\} = [\mathcal{H}]\{\delta^{(1)}\} + \{\bar{b}\} = \begin{matrix} (0) \\ (1) \\ (2) \\ (3) \\ (4) \\ (5) \end{matrix} \begin{pmatrix} 0 \\ 30.7 \\ 46.5 \\ 57.4 \\ 60.4 \\ 65.4 \end{pmatrix}. \qquad (37.47)$$

(2) We now seek a new strategy by using (37.33), in other words, by minimizing each of the components of the vector

$$\{a_{\mathcal{D}}\} + [\mathcal{D}][\{\tau^{(1)}\} + \{\epsilon^{(1)}\}] = \{a_{i,k} + \tau_k^{(1)} + \epsilon_k^{(1)}\}. \qquad (37.48)$$

1st line: $k_1 = 0$ $40 + 0 \ = \ 40$
                   $k_1 = 1$ $4 + 30.7 = \ 34.7 \leftarrow$

2nd line: $k_2 = 0$ $60 + 0 \ = \ 60$
                   $k_2 = 2$ $10 + 46.5 = \ 56.5 \leftarrow$

3rd line: $k_3 = 0$ $70 + 0 = 70$ ←
                 $k_3 = 3$ $17 + 57.4 = 74.4$

4th line: $k_4 = 0$ $80 + 0 = 80$ ←
                 $k_4 = 4$ $26 + 60.4 = 86.4$

5th line: $k_5 = 0$ $90 + 0 = 90$ ←
                 $k_5 = 5$ $38 + 65.4 = 103.4$

6th line: $k_6 = 0$ $100 + 0 = 100$ ←

We again obtain the same strategy as before, which shows that this strategy, given by (37.43), is optimal. We had also obtained it in the case of a limited horizon, when there is at least one remaining period after the current one (see Fig. 37.3).

A slightly different method of optimization is to consider the dynamic program as an H.D. program. In that case we use (37.28) and (37.29), and eventually (37.23) if the chain is not unireducible, to calculate the average value per H.D. period and a vector of relative values (arbitrarily choosing a ϵ_k in each set of closed states). We seek a new strategy by using Eqs. (37.32) and (37.33), the latter in the simpler form

$$\{a^{(l+1)}\} + [\mathscr{D}^{(l+1)}]\{\epsilon^{(l)}\} = \underset{\mathscr{D}}{\mathrm{OPT}}[\{a_{\mathscr{D}}\} + [\mathscr{D}]\{\epsilon^{(l)}\}]. \tag{37.49}$$

If we again use the above example, the calculations will proceed as follows:

First iteration

(1) We find $\tau^{(0)}$ and $\{\epsilon^{(0)}\}$ from (37.28) and (37.29):

$$\{\delta^{(0)}\} = \begin{Bmatrix} 4 + \epsilon_1 \\ 10 + \epsilon_2 \\ 17 + \epsilon_3 \\ 80 + \epsilon_0 \\ 90 + \epsilon_0 \\ 100 + \epsilon_0 \end{Bmatrix}, \tag{37.50}$$

$$\begin{Bmatrix} \tau \\ \tau \\ \tau \\ \tau \\ \tau \\ \tau \end{Bmatrix} + \begin{Bmatrix} \epsilon_0 \\ \epsilon_1 \\ \epsilon_2 \\ \epsilon_3 \\ \epsilon_4 \\ \epsilon_5 \end{Bmatrix} = \begin{Bmatrix} \delta_1 \\ \frac{4}{5}\delta_2 + \frac{1}{5}\delta_6 \\ \frac{5}{8}\delta_3 + \frac{3}{8}\delta_6 \\ \frac{2}{5}\delta_4 + \frac{3}{5}\delta_6 \\ \frac{1}{2}\delta_5 + \frac{1}{2}\delta_6 \\ \delta_6 \end{Bmatrix} = \begin{Bmatrix} 4 + \epsilon_1 \\ 28 + \frac{4}{5}\epsilon_2 + \frac{1}{5}\epsilon_0 \\ \frac{1}{8}(385 + 5\epsilon_3 + 3\epsilon_0) \\ 92 + \epsilon_0 \\ 95 + \epsilon_0 \\ 100 + \epsilon_0 \end{Bmatrix} \tag{37.51}$$

whence, arbitrarily taking $\epsilon_0 = 0$,

$$\tau^{(0)} = 35.3; \quad \epsilon_0^{(0)} = 0; \quad \epsilon_1^{(0)} = 31.3; \quad \epsilon_2^{(0)} = 48.3;$$
$$\epsilon_3^{(0)} = 56.7; \quad \epsilon_4^{(0)} = 59.7; \quad \epsilon_5^{(0)} = 64.7. \tag{37.52}$$

(2) We use (37.33) to find a new strategy. The calculations were shown above, and the result is given by (37.43).

Second iteration

(1) We calculate $\tau^{(1)}$ and $\epsilon^{(1)}$ by the use of (37.28) and (37.29):

$$\{\delta^{(1)}\} = \begin{Bmatrix} 4 + \epsilon_1 \\ 10 + \epsilon_2 \\ 70 + \epsilon_0 \\ 80 + \epsilon_0 \\ 90 + \epsilon_0 \\ 100 + \epsilon_0 \end{Bmatrix}, \tag{37.53}$$

$$\begin{Bmatrix} \tau \\ \tau \\ \tau \\ \tau \\ \tau \\ \tau \end{Bmatrix} + \begin{Bmatrix} \epsilon_0 \\ \epsilon_1 \\ \epsilon_2 \\ \epsilon_3 \\ \epsilon_4 \\ \epsilon_5 \end{Bmatrix} = \begin{Bmatrix} 4 + \epsilon_1 \\ 28 + \frac{4}{5}\epsilon_2 \\ 81.25 \\ 92 \\ 95 \\ 100 \end{Bmatrix}, \tag{37.54}$$

with $\epsilon_0 = 0$, whence

$$\tau^{(1)} = 34.6; \quad \epsilon_0^{(1)} = 0; \quad \epsilon_1^{(1)} = 30.7; \quad \epsilon_2^{(1)} = 46.5;$$
$$\epsilon_3^{(1)} = 57.4; \quad \epsilon_4^{(1)} = 60.4; \quad \epsilon_5^{(1)} = 65.4. \tag{37.55}$$

(2) We use (37.33) to find a new strategy and obtain the same one as previously.

It can be seen that the only difference between the two methods is the interpretation given to the quantities obtained; the calculations are the same in both methods.

CHAPTER 6

VARIOUS GENERALIZATIONS

38. Introduction

In the preceding chapters we have presented a number of models of dynamic programming. As a conclusion to the present volume we shall now describe various other fields in which dynamic programming can be applied, and will explain both the structure of the particular process and the nature of the function of value attached to the policies or strategies.

As we mentioned in the preface, the second volume* of this work will be devoted to further important extensions of the method, such as the sensitiveness of the results (distribution of the probability for the value of a strategy, search for the k-optimal policies or strategies), continuous dynamic programs and variation calculus, the use of Lagrange's multipliers, process with adaptation and the approach to cybernetics, and sequential games.

39. Nonsequential Structures

THE CASE OF CERTAINTY

In Section 4 we explained the meaning of a sequential graph, using the concept of the ordinal function, which makes it possible to discover whether a graph is sequential or not. Usually, a dynamic program with a certain or random future, such as it has been defined in this book, and always in the case where the number of states is denumerable, has a sequential graph associated with it.

It may be asked whether the principle of dynamic programming can only be applied to processes with a sequential structure, but as a few examples will show, this is far from being the case.

In order to simplify the question we will begin by considering a problem with a certain future, and will assume that the graph $G = (\mathbf{X}, \Gamma)$, which represents the changes of state in the system, has an ordinal function (see Section 4) such as that of Fig. 39.1. Starting from

* To be published by Dunod, Paris.

255

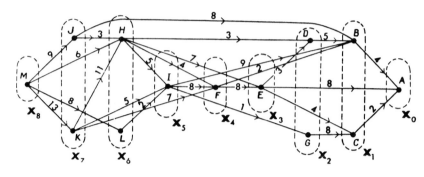

FIG. 39.1

vertex A,[1] the ordinal function shown here has been calculated by the method explained in Section 4, and is as follows:

$$O(A) = 0; \quad O(B) = O(C) = 1; \quad O(D) = O(G) = 2;$$

$$O(E) = 3; \quad O(F) = 4; \quad O(I) = 5; \quad O(H) = O(L) = 6; \quad (39.1)$$

$$O(J) = O(K) = 7; \quad O(M) = 8.$$

To each arc of the graph a value is attached, and the problem is to find a route of minimal value from M to A. To do so, let us decide to start from A and examine in turn all the vertices of the graph in the order of increasing values of the ordinal function, those with the same value being considered in an arbitrary order. Each vertex $x_i \in \mathbf{X}$ will be given a potential equal to the minimal value of a route x_i to A, obtained by considering all the arcs which leave x_i and by taking the minimum of the sum of the value of the arc and of the potential of the vertex at which it ends. This is the method used to obtain the results given in Fig. 39.2, where the optimal route, which in this case is the only one, is shown by heavy lines.

The process we have just described is the same as that used in Section 4 for sequential graphs. As in the latter, the potential given to a vertex is never modified during the subsequent calculations. Hence, as long as the graph possesses an ordinal function the technique of dynamic programming can be employed.

Before we justify the use of the method of dynamic programming for finite graphs with an ordinal function, which enables us to solve problems of a more general nature than those treated so far, we shall

---

[1] This amounts to adopting the definition of the ordinal function given on p. 35, Section 4, or of changing the direction of all the arcs.

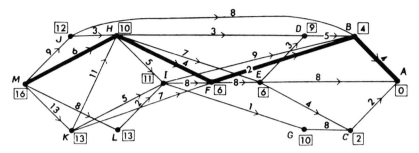

FIG. 39.2

make certain important observations as to the way in which the ordinal
function can be chosen, and on the method of optimization.

In the present example the graph is a transport network without
a circuit, and in the terminology of Chapter 1 both the initial and final
states are unique. In the dynamic programs studied in that chapter,
optimization can equally be carried out in the direction (past → future)
or that of (future → past), and the same is true in the more general case
considered here.

Again, it must be observed that the ordinal function is not necessarily
unique; for example, if it is calculated by the method of Section 4 without
changing the direction of the arcs, we obtain the result shown in Fig.
39.3, and the new one is as follows:

$$O'(A) = 8; \qquad O'(B) = 7; \qquad O'(C) = O'(D) = 6;$$

$$O'(E) = 5; \qquad O'(F) = O'(G) = 4; \qquad O'(I) = 3; \qquad (39.2)$$

$$O'(H) = 2; \qquad O'(J) = O'(K) = O'(L) = 1; \qquad O'(M) = 0.$$

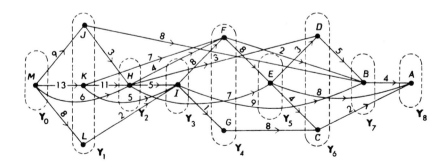

FIG. 39.3

We conclude that there is not a simple inversion of the order of values of the ordinal function, but a modification of the subsets. However, there are graphs in which the same subsets are obtained.

We can check from Fig. 39.4 that optimization gives the same result as before. In this figure we started the optimization from A, but the direction is now the opposite to that used to define the ordinal function. The same result would once more be obtained if optimization were carried out from M toward A.

In the same way we could generalize what was stated in Section 9, for the case in which either the initial or final state is not prescribed.

The method of optimization used above can be justified as follows: First, Theorem 1 of optimality given in Section 3 is valid for a non-sequential graph,[2] and the proof in this case also remains the same. Second, if we consider any route $(x_{\alpha 1}, x_{\alpha 2}, ..., x_{\alpha k})$, and if the graph has an ordinal function $O(x_i)$, we must have

$$O(X_{\alpha 1}) < O(X_{\alpha 2}) < \cdots < O(X_{\alpha k}), \tag{39.3}$$

in accordance with the definition of the ordinal function given in Section 4 (if we have changed the direction of the arcs to find it, inequalities (39.3) must also be inverted). As a result, when a potential is given to a vertex x_i by the method explained above, all the vertices which are the terminal extremity of an arc leaving x_i (or the initial extremity of one going to x_i depending on the direction of optimization) are already marked.

Moreover, we can always transform a nonsequential graph with an ordinal function into a sequential one. To do so, we need only add "artificial" vertices in the following way: For every arc (x_i, x_j) such that

$$O(X_j) - O(X_i) = r, \qquad r > 1,$$

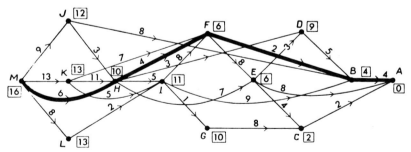

FIG. 39.4

[2] In fact, it is valid for any graph with or without an ordinal function.

we add $(r-1)$ vertices $X_{j,1}, X_{j,2}, ..., X_{j,r-1}$, by replacing the arc (x_i, x_j) by r arcs $(X_i, X_{j,1}), (X_{j,1}, X_{j,2}), ..., (X_{j,r-1}, X_j)$; we then have

$$O(X_{j,1}) = O(X_i) + 1;$$

$$O(X_{j,2}) = O(X_i) + 2; \cdots; O(X_{j,r-1}) = r - 1. \qquad (39.4)$$

On the other hand, we give to the arc $(x_i, x_{j,1})$ the value previously attached to the arc (x_i, x_j) and to the arcs $(X_{j,1}, X_{j,2}), ..., (X_{j,r-1}, X_j)$ the value 0.

In this way we obtain a dynamic program in the sense given to it in Chapter 1, and it can easily be seen that this transform will have no influence on the solution of the problem. Figure 39.5 shows the sequential graph obtained after the transform of the graph of Fig. 39.1. Let us observe that another equivalent sequential graph could be obtained from Fig. 39.3. We can, moreover, conceive of other transform processes leading in certain cases to fewer artificial vertices. We see from Fig. 39.5 that there can be a considerable number of vertices, and as a rule it is preferable to optimize on the nonsequential graph, except, in certain cases, for calculations on a computer.

RANDOM CASE

Fundamentally a random case is not different from one of certainty, and the possible changes of state can always be represented by a graph, which we assume to be without a circuit. Here, however, we must distinguish two types of vertex, depending on whether the choice

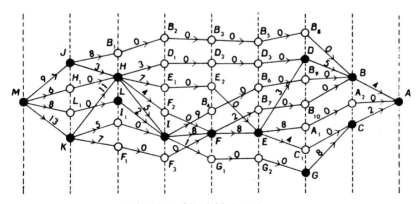

● Vertices of the initial graph
○ Artificial vertices

FIG. 39.5

between the different arcs leaving the vertex is one of decision or of hazard. At the same time, a vertex from which no arc, or only one, leaves may be considered as belonging to either type.

An example is given in Fig. 39.6 where the two types are clearly distinguished, and as in the case of certainty, optimization can either be carried out on the given graph, after finding an ordinal function, or on a sequential one after the use of a suitable transform.

Let us take for an example the graph of Fig. 39.6, an ordinal function of which is shown in Fig. 39.7, and assume that the values and proba-

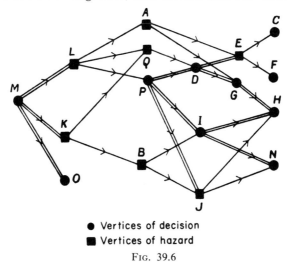

● Vertices of decision
■ Vertices of hazard

FIG. 39.6

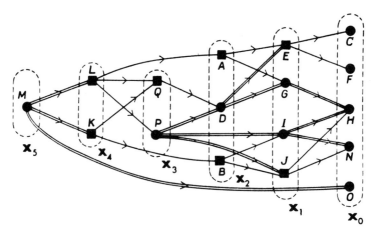

FIG. 39.7

bilities are those given on Fig. 39.8, and that we seek to maximize the expected value. We have given values to the terminal vertices, but we might equally have added them to the values carried by the arcs which end at the terminal vertices.

The optimization process will be analogous to the one for a case of certainty. But, on the one hand, we must obligatorily proceed from the future toward the past, as we discovered in Chapter 3, and on the other, the potential given to each vertex of hazard will be calculated by replacing the operative "maximum of" by "expected value of." Figure 39.9 gives the optimal strategy, calculated as shown on Fig. 39.8.

Let us now consider the second method of procedure by showing that we can always arrive at a dynamic program with a decomposed form. The method that we shall outline gives a dynamic program in which

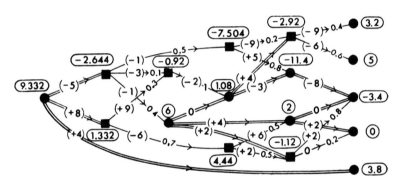

FIG. 39.8

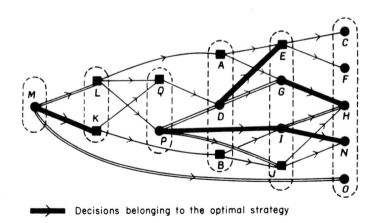

━━▶ Decisions belonging to the optimal strategy

FIG. 39.9

stages D and H alternate, but in certain cases it may prove advantageous to form consecutive D stages and/or consecutive H stages, so as to reduce the number of artificial vertices.

We shall first calculate a function, which we shall call the "biordinal function," and which is defined as follows.

Let us consider a graph $G = (\mathbf{X} \cup \mathbf{Y}, \Gamma)$ which is finite and without a circuit and where, in the present problem, $\mathbf{X}$ will be the set of vertices of decision and $\mathbf{Y}$ the set of the vertices of hazard, the intersection $\mathbf{X} \cap \mathbf{Y}$ representing the set of vertices from which not more than one arc leaves. Let us define the set of vertices $\mathbf{X}_0$, $\mathbf{Y}_0$, $\mathbf{X}_1$, $\mathbf{Y}_1$,..., $\mathbf{X}_N$, $\mathbf{Y}_N$ such that[3]:

$$\mathbf{X}_0 = \{X_r \mid X_r \in \mathbf{X}, \Gamma^{-1}X_r = \varnothing\},$$
$$\mathbf{Y}_0 = \{Y_s \mid Y_s \in \mathbf{Y}, \Gamma^{-1}Y_s \subset \mathbf{X}_0\},$$
$$\mathbf{X}_1 = \{X_r \mid X_r \in \mathbf{X}, \Gamma^{-1}X_r \subset (\mathbf{X}_0 \cup \mathbf{Y}_0)\}.$$
$$\mathbf{Y}_1 = \{Y_s \mid Y_s \in \mathbf{Y}, \Gamma^{-1}Y_s \subset (\mathbf{X}_0 \cup \mathbf{Y}_0 \cup \mathbf{X}_1)\},$$

$$\vdots \qquad\qquad \vdots$$

$$\mathbf{X}_N = \left\{ X_r \mid X_r \in \mathbf{X}, \Gamma^{-1}X_r \subset \left[\left(\bigcup_{n=0}^{N-1} \mathbf{X}_n \right) \cup \left(\bigcup_{n=0}^{N-1} \mathbf{Y}_n \right) \right] \right\}, \tag{39.5}$$

$$\mathbf{Y}_N = \left\{ Y_s \mid Y_s \in \mathbf{Y}, \Gamma^{-1}Y_s \subset \left[\left(\bigcup_{n=0}^{N} \mathbf{X}_n \right) \cup \left(\bigcup_{n=0}^{N-1} \mathbf{Y}_n \right) \right] \right\},$$

where N is the smallest integer such that

$$\bigcup_{n=0}^{N} \mathbf{X}_n = \mathbf{X} \tag{39.6}$$

and

$$\bigcup_{n=0}^{N} \mathbf{Y}_n = \mathbf{Y}. \tag{39.7}$$

We can easily show that the subsets $\mathbf{X}_n$, $\mathbf{Y}_n$, $n = 0, 1, 2,..., N$, are disjoint.[4]

---

[3] Arbitrarily, we define this biordinal function by leaving from vertices of $\mathbf{X}$, but we could equally define another where we leave from those of $\mathbf{Y}$. We could also replace Γ^{-1} by Γ.

[4] It is no longer, as in the case of the ordinal function, a partition of the set of vertices since certain subsets may be empty.

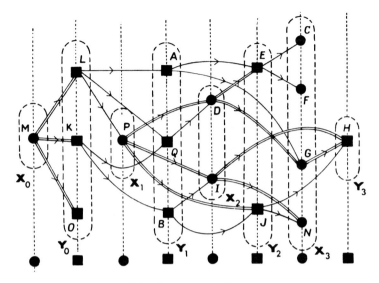

● Vertices of decision
■ Vertices of hazard

FIG. 39.10

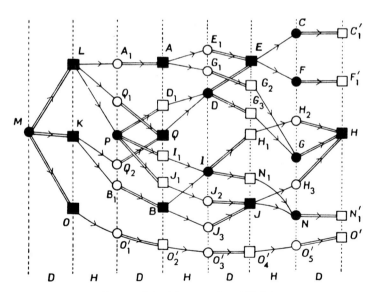

● ○ Vertex of decision: real, artificial;
■ □ Vertex of hazard: real, artificial.

FIG. 39.11

These subsets are totally and strictly ordered by the relation of order $\prec$ defined by

$$
\begin{aligned}
\mathbf{X}_n &\prec \mathbf{X}_{n'} &&\text{if and only if} && n < n', \\
\mathbf{Y}_n &\prec \mathbf{Y}_{n'} &&\text{if and only if} && n < n', \\
\mathbf{X}_n &\prec \mathbf{Y}_{n'} &&\text{if and only if} && n \leqslant n', \\
\mathbf{Y}_n &\prec \mathbf{X}_{n'} &&\text{if and only if} && n < n'.
\end{aligned}
\tag{39.8}
$$

The function $O_2(Z_t)$, defined by

$$
Z_t \in \mathbf{X}_n \cup \mathbf{Y}_n \quad \Rightarrow \quad O_2(Z_t) = n,
\tag{39.9}
$$

will be called the "biordinal function" of the graph in relation to the subsets $\mathbf{X}$ and $\mathbf{Y}$.

TABLE 39.1

	A B C D E F G H I J K L M N O P Q	V_0	V_1	V_2	V_3	V_4	V_5	V_6	V_7	V_8
■ A	. . . . 1	1	1	0	0	×	×	×	×	×
■ B	. . . . 1	1	1	0	0	×	×	×	×	×
C	. . 1	1	1	1	1	1	1	0	×	×
● D	. . . . 1 1	2	2	2	1	0	×	×	×	×
■ E	1 . . 1	2	2	2	2	1	0	×	×	×
F	. . 1	1	1	1	1	1	1	0	×	×
● G	1 . . . 1	2	2	2	2	1	0	0	×	×
H	. . . . 1 . . 1 1	3	3	3	3	3	2	1	0	×
● I	. 1 . . . . 1 . .	2	2	2	1	0	×	×	×	×
■ J	. 1 . . . . 1 . .	2	2	2	1	0	0	×	×	×
■ K	. . . . 1	1	0	×	×	×	×	×	×	×
■ L	. . . . 1	1	0	×	×	×	×	×	×	×
● M	. . . .	0	×	×	×	×	×	×	×	×
N	. . . . 1 1	2	2	2	2	2	1	0	×	×
O	. . . . 1	1	0	×	×	×	×	×	×	×
● P	. . . . 1	1	1	0	×	×	×	×	×	×
■ Q	. . . . 1 1	2	2	0	0	×	×	×	×	×

	V_0	V_1	V_2	V_3	V_4	V_5	V_6	V_7	V_8
	M	K L O	P	A B Q	D I	E J	C F G N	H	

● ■ ● ■ ● ■ ● ■ ●

We can calculate this function by a suitable modification of the method given in Section 4 for finding an ordinal function.

As in Section 4, we shall write the boolean transposed matrix of the graph (Table 39.1), marking each line and column with a circle or square according to whether the corresponding vertex belongs to **X** or to **Y**; those belonging to **X** ∩ **Y** are not marked. We next apply the algorithm given in Section 4, but each time we calculate a new vector V_i we only retain among the new zeros those corresponding to a line marked with a circle if i is even, or those corresponding to a line marked with a square if i is uneven. To calculate the following vector we subtract only the columns corresponding to the vertices thus retained. It is in this manner that Table 39.1 and Fig. 39.10 were obtained.

Once the biordinal function has been found, we need only add artificial vertices in the same way as in the case of certainty; in addition, we prolong the terminal vertices which are not in $\mathbf{Y}_N$, as shown for $(M, 0)$ in Fig. 39.11.

40. Nonadditive Values

Let us return to the models studied in the previous chapters, and consider a dynamic program with a certain future and a limited horizon, in which state x_0 is prescribed and the final state x_N has to be chosen. We discovered in Sections 8 and 9 that we can then use the recurring equations of type IV:

$$0 \leqslant n < N - 1,$$

$$f_{n,N}(x_n , \cdot) = \underset{x_{n+1} \in \Gamma_{n+1} x_n}{\text{OPT}} [v_{n+1}(x_n , x_{n+1}) + f_{n+1,N}(x_{n+1} , \cdot)] \quad (40.1)$$

and

$$f_{N-1,N}(x_{N-1} , \cdot) = \underset{x_N \in \Gamma_N x_{N-1}}{\text{OPT}} v_N(x_{N-1} , x_N). \quad (40.2)$$

These equations relate to the case where the value of a policy is the sum of the present values of N periods:

$$s(\varpi) = v_1(x_0 , x_1) + v_2(x_1 , x_2) + \cdots + v_N(x_{N-1} , x_N), \quad (40.3)$$

where

$$\varpi = (x_0 , x_1 ,..., x_N). \quad (40.4)$$

We may inquire whether the principle of dynamic programming can be extended to the case where the operation "addition" is replaced in (40.3) by another operation, and if so, what conditions the latter must satisfy.

Let us consider a law of internal composition $\perp$ on a set $\mathbf{V} \subset \mathbf{R}$, where $\mathbf{R}$ is the set of real numbers, in other words, a law which ensures that there is a correspondence between every oriented pair (v_1, v_2), such that $v_1, v_2 \in \mathbf{V}$, and an element $v \in \mathbf{V}$:

$$v_1, v_2 \in \mathbf{V} \quad \Rightarrow \quad v_1 \perp v_2 = v \in \mathbf{V} \tag{40.5}$$

The set $\mathbf{V}$ may be the set of real numbers or a part of this set. For simplification, we shall assume that the law $\perp$ is *associative*, in other words, that we have

$$(v_1 \perp v_2) \perp v_3 = v_1 \perp (v_2 \perp v_3). \tag{40 6}$$

Let us define the value of a policy ϖ (given by (40.4)) by the formula

$$s(\varpi) = v_1(x_0, x_1) \perp v_2(x_1, x_2) \perp \cdots \perp v_N(x_{N-1}, x_N). \tag{40.7}$$

An optimal policy ϖ^* is then such that

$$s(\varpi^*) = f_{0,N}(x_0, \cdot)$$

$$= \underset{(x_1,\ldots,x_N)\in\mathbf{D}_1(x_0)}{\mathrm{OPT}} [v_1(x_0, x_1) \perp v_2(x_1, x_2) \perp \cdots \perp v_N(x_{N-1}, x_N)], \tag{40.8}$$

where $\mathbf{D}_1(x_0)$ is the domain defined by the constraints Γ_n, successively applied, beginning with x_0:

$$(x_1,\ldots, x_N) \in \mathbf{D}_1(x_0) \Leftrightarrow x_1 \in \Gamma_1 x_0, \qquad x_2 \in \Gamma_2 x_1,\ldots, x_N \in \Gamma_N x_{N-1}. \tag{40.9}$$

To obtain recurring equations similar to (40.1) we must be able to state

$$f_{0,N}(x_0, \cdot)$$

$$= \underset{x_1\in\Gamma_1 x_0}{\mathrm{OPT}} \{v_1(x_0, x_1) \perp \underset{(x_2,\ldots,x_N)\in\mathbf{D}_2(x_1)}{\mathrm{OPT}} [v_2(x_1, x_2) \perp \cdots \perp v_N(x_{N-1}, x_N)]\}, \tag{40.10}$$

where $\mathbf{D}_2(x_1)$ is defined in a similar way to $\mathbf{D}_1(x_0)$. For that, it is sufficient if the relation $\perp$ is compatible with the relation of order of real numbers, that is to say, that we have

$$\forall v, v', v'' \in \mathbf{V}: \quad v' > v'' \Leftrightarrow (v \perp v') > (v \perp v''). \tag{40.11}$$

Indeed, let us consider two policies from x_0 to $n = N$:

$$\varpi = (x_0, x_1, x_2, ..., x_N), \qquad (40.12)$$

$$\varpi' = (x_0, x_1, x_2', ..., x_N'), \qquad (40.13)$$

and let us assume that

$$v_2(x_1, x_2) \perp \cdots \perp v_N(x_{N-1}, x_N) > v_2(x_1, x_2') \perp \cdots \perp v_N(x_{N-1}', x_N'). \quad (40.14)$$

In accordance with (40.11) we then have

$$v_1(x_0, x_1) \perp v_2(x_1, x_2) \perp \cdots \perp v_N(x_{N-1}, x_N)$$
$$> v_1(x_0, x_1) \perp v_2(x_1, x_2') \perp \cdots \perp v_N(x_{N-1}', x_N'),$$

that is to say,

$$s(\varpi) > s(\varpi'). \qquad (40.15)$$

If OPT = MAX, the policy ϖ' is not optimal; if OPT = MIN, the policy ϖ is not optimal. In every case, a policy from x_0 to $n = N$ can only be optimal if the subpolicy from x_1 to $n = N$, which it contains, is optimal. We have thus proved the theorem of optimality 3.1 with these new assumptions. In consequence, optimal policies can be found by solving the equations which follow and are similar to (40.1) and (40.2):

$$0 \leqslant n < N - 1,$$

$$f_{n,N}(x_n, \cdot) = \underset{x_{n+1} \in \Gamma_{n+1} x_n}{\text{OPT}} [v_{n+1}(x_n, x_{n+1}) \perp f_{n+1,N}(x_{n+1}, \cdot)] \quad (40.16)$$

and

$$f_{N-1,N}(x_{N-1}, \cdot) = \underset{x_N \in \Gamma_N x_{N-1}}{\text{OPT}} v_N(x_{N-1}, x_N). \qquad (40.17)$$

In the same way we could show that generalizations can be obtained for all the models described in this book by replacing the operation of addition by a law of internal composition over a subset **V** of real numbers, provided this law is associative and compatible with the relation of order of these numbers.

The only concrete problems known to us in which the value of a policy is defined by an operation other than addition are those where the value of a policy is the product of the present values.[5] For example, if a probability is given to each arc of a graph (all the vertices being vertices of hazard in the sense of Section 39), the search for the most

---

[5] See references [16] and [139].

probable route from a given vertex can be carried out by dynamic programming; the value of a route is then the product of the probabilities of the arcs forming it. Since all the values of the arcs are between 0 and 1, the set **V** is here the set of real numbers in the closed interval (0, 1), and the law of internal composition for this set is multiplication, an associative law which can easily be verified as compatible with the relation of order of the real numbers, though it would not be the case if **V** were the set of real numbers, since multiplication by a negative number inverts the order. Besides, in this set we can obtain additive values by taking the logarithm of the probabilities.

BIBLIOGRAPHY

I. Theory

[1] Hachiro Akama, Un aspect de la programmation dynamique: Problème des mines d'or, *Cahiers du Bureau Universitaire de Recherche Opérationnelle*, Institut de Stat. de l'Univ. de Paris, No. 2, 27–36 (1957).

[2] S. Azen, R. Bellman, and S. Dreyfus, *Some Applications of Polynomial Approximation of Dynamic Programming*, RAND Corp. RM-3728-PR, Aug. 1963, 59 pp.

[3] R. Beckwith, "Analytic and Computational Aspects of Dynamic Programming Processes of High Dimension," Ph. D. thesis, Purdue Univ., 1959.

[4] C. S. Beightler, L. G. Mitton, and G. L. Nemhauser, A short-table of z-transforms and generating functions, *Oper. Res.* 9, No. 4, 574–78 (1961).

[5] R. Bellman, *On a General Class of Problems Involving Sequential Analysis*. RAND Corp. RM-647, July 1951.

[6] R. Bellman, On the theory of dynamic programming, *Proc. Nat. Acad. Sci. U.S.A.* 38, No. 8, 716–19 (Aug. 1952).

[7] R. Bellman, The theory of dynamic programming, *Bull. Amer. Math. Soc.* 60, 503–16 (1954).

[8] R. Bellman, Some problems in the theory of dynamic programming, *Econometrica* 22, No. 1, 37–48 (Jan. 1954).

[9] R. Bellman, A Markovian decision process, *J. Math. Mech.* 6, 679 (1957).

[10] R. Bellman, *Dynamic Programming*. Princeton Univ. Press, Princeton, N. J., 1957, 342 pp.

[11] R. Bellman, *Some Directions of Research in Dynamic Programming*. RAND Corp. RM-3661, April 1963, 5 pp.

[12] R. Bellman (ed.), *Mathematical Optimization Techniques*. Univ. Calif. Press, Berkeley, 1963, 346 pp.

[13] R. Bellman and S. Dreyfus, On the computational solution of dynamic programming processes. I: On a tactical air warfare model of Mengel, *Oper. Res.* 6, 65–78 (1958).

[14] R. Bellman and S. Dreyfus, *Applied Dynamic Programming*. Princeton Univ. Press Princeton, N. J., 1962, 363 pp.

[15] R. Bellman and R. Kalaba, On the principle of invariant imbedding and propagation through inhomogeneous media, *Proc. Nat. Acad. Sci. U.S.A.* (1956).

[16] R. Bellman and R. Kalaba, On kth best policies; *J. Soc. Indust. Appl. Math.* 8, No. 4, 582–88 (Dec. 1960).

[17] R. Bellman and R. Kalaba, *An Inverse Problem in Dynamic Programming and Automatic Control*. RAND Corp. RM-3592-PR, April 1963, 14 pp.

[18] R. Bellman, R. Kalaba, and B. Kotkin, Polynomial approximation. A new computational technique in dynamic programming: Allocation processes, *Math. Comp.* 17, No. 82, 155–61 (April 1963).

[19] R. Bellman, R. Kalaba, and J. Lockett, *Dynamic Programming and Ill-Conditioned Systems.* RAND Corp. RM-3815-PR, Dec. 1963, 33 pp.

[20] R. Bellman and R. Karush, *Dynamic Programming: A Bibliography of Theory and Application.* RAND Corp. RM-3951-PR, Feb. 1964, 146 pp.

[21] R. Bellman and W. Karush, Functional equations in the theory of dynamic programming. XII: An application of the maximum transform, *J. Math. Anal. Appl.* **6**, No. 1, 155–57 (Feb. 1963).

[22] D. Blackwell, On the functional equation of dynamic programming, *J. Math. Anal. Appl.* **2**, No. 2, 273 (1961).

[23] P. J. M. Van den Bogaard, A. Monreal Luque, and C. van de Panne, Étude sur les implications des horizons alternatifs dans la programmation quadratique dynamique, *Rev. Franç. Rech. Oper.* **23**, 163–83 (2nd quart. 1962).

[24] D. C. Carton, Une application de l'algorithme de Howard pour des phénomènes saisonniers, *Communications à la 3ᵉ Conf. Internat. de R. O.*, Dunod, 1964.

[24'] R. Companys Pascual, Private communication.

[25] C. Derman, On sequential decisions and Markov chains, *Management Sci.* **9**, No. 1, 16–24 (1962).

[26] S. E. Dreyfus, Computational aspects of dynamic programming, *Oper. Res.* **5**, No. 3, 409–15 (1957).

[27] S. E. Dreyfus, *Dynamic Programming Solution of Allocation Problems*, RAND Corp. P-1083, 1957.

[28] S. E. Dreyfus, Dynamic programming, in: *Progress in Operations Research* (R. L. Ackoff, ed.), Vol. 1, Chap. 5. Wiley, 1961.

[29] F. d'Epenoux, Sur un problème de production et de stockage dans l'aléatoire, *Rev. Franç. Rech. Oper.* **14**, 3–15 (1960).

[30] F. Ferschl, Grundzüge des dynamic Programming, *Unternehmensforschung* **3**, No. 2, 70–80 (1959).

[31] R. Fortet, Théorèmes de point fixe dans les programmes dynamiques, *Cahiers du Centre d'Études de R. O.* (Brussels) **4**, No. 1, 5-19 (1962).

[32] R. Fortet, Propriétés des applications de transition des programmations dynamiques, *METRA* **2**, No. 1, 79–96 (1963).

[33] G. de Ghellinck, Les problèmes de décisions séquentielles, *Cahiers du Centre d'Études de R. O.* (Brussels), **2**, No. 2 (1960).

[34] J. J. Gignabodet, Majoration des erreurs de quantification dans les calculs de programmation dynamique, *C. R. Acad. Sci. Paris* **255**, No. 5, 828–30 (1962).

[35] G. Th. Guilbaud, Programmes dynamiques et programmes linéaires. Note sur un modèle de R. Bellman, *Cahiers du Bureau Universitaire de R. O.*, Inst. de Stat. de l'Univ. de Paris, No. 2 (1957).

[36] R. Howard, *Dynamic Programming and Markov Processes.* Technology Press of M.I.T., Wiley, 1960, 136 pp.

[37] R. Kalaba, *Some Aspects of Nonlinear Allocation Processes.* RAND Corp. P-2715, March 1963, 30 pp. To appear in *Military Operations Research*, Publications in O. R., ORSA.

[38] S. Karlin, *Duality in Dynamic Programming.* RAND Corp. RM-971, Oct. 1952, 9 pp.

[39] S. Karlin, The structure of dynamic programming models, *Naval Res. Log. Quart.* **2**, No. 4, 285–94 (Dec. 1955).

[40] S. Karlin and H. N. Shapiro, *Decision Processes and Functional Equations.* RAND Corp. RM-933, Sept. 1952, 10 pp.

[41] S. Karlin and H. N. Shapiro, *Some Simple Nonlinear Models.* RAND Corp. RM-949, Sept. 1952, 7 pp.

[42] A. Kaufmann, *Méthodes et modèles de la recherche opérationnelle*, Vol. II. Dunod, 1963. English language edition: "Graphs, Dynamic Programming, and Finite Games." Academic Press, New York, 1967.

[43] P. Lemonon, Un problème de décision séquentielle: Calcul d'une série économique, *Cahiers du Bureau Universitaire de R. O.*, Inst. de Stat. de l'Univ. de Paris, No. 3 (April, 1961).

[44] G. de Leve, Stochastic ∞-staps beslissingsproblemen (Stochastic decision problems with an infinite horizon), *Statistica Neerlandica* 16, No. 4, 433–48 (1962).

[45] A. Manne, Linear programming and sequential decisions, *Management Sci.* 6, No. 3 (1960).

[46] P. Massé, *Les réserves et la régulation de l'avenir dans la vie économique*. Vol. I: *Avenir déterminé*; Vol. II: *Avenir aléatoire*. Herman, 1956.

[47] P. Rosenstiehl and A. Ghouila Houri, *Les choix économiques. Décisions séquentielles et simulation*. Dunod, 1960.

[48] Y. H. Rutenberg, *Sequential decisions models*. Case Inst. of Technology, U. S. Govt. Res. Rep., AD 256-217, April 1961, 116 pp.

[49] K. D. Tocher, The role of models in operational research, *Royal Stat. Soc. Ser. A*, 124, Part 2, 121–42 (1961).

[50] S. Vajda, *Mathematical Programming*. Addison-Wesley, 1961, 310 pp.

[51] R. Vichnevetsky and J. P. Waha, Dynamic programming and hybrid computation, *Ann. Assoc. Internat. Calcul Anal.*, J, No. 2, 80–87 (April 1963).

II. Practice*

1. MANAGEMENT OF PRODUCTION AND STOCKS. ALLIED PROBLEMS

[101] M. Barbut, Méthodes récurrentes dans les problèmes de renouvellement de stock, *Cahiers du Bureau Universitaire de Recherche Opérationnelle*, Institut de Stat. de l'Univ. de Paris, No. 2, 11–26 (1957).

[102] M. Barbut, La programmation dynamique dans les problèmes de renouvellement de stock en avenir aléatoire, *Rev. Franç. Rech. Op.* 1, No. 5, 209–16 (4th trim. 1957).

[103] M. J. Beckmann, Production smoothing and inventory control, *Oper. Res.* 9, No. 4, 456–67 (July–Aug. 1961).

[104] B. Bernholtz and W. Shelson, Dynamic programming in production scheduling of generating stations, *Proc. 1st Annual Conf. Can. O. R. Soc. Univ. Toronto*, 13–16 (May 7–8, 1959).

[105] A. Bhatia and A. Garg, Application of dynamic programming to a class of problems in inventory control, *J. Indust. Eng.* 11, No. 6, 509–12 (Nov.–Dec. 1960).

[106] F. d'Epenoux, A probabilistic production and inventory problem, *Management Sci.* 10, No. 1, 98–108 (1963).

[107] T. Fabian, J. L. Fisher, M. W. Sasieni, and A. Yardeni, Purchasing raw material on a fluctuating market, *Oper. Res.* 7, No. 1, 107–22 (1959).

[108] H. P. Galliher, Production scheduling, in: *Notes on Operations Research*, pp. 211–30. Operations Research Center, M.I.T., 1959.

[109] G. de Ghellinck, Application de la théorie des graphes: matrices de Markov et programmes dynamiques, *Cahiers du Centre d'Études de R. O.* (Brussels) 3, No. 1, 5–35 (1961).

* Section II arbitrarily assigned numbers [101]–[173] to permit insertion of new references in Section I.

[110] G. Hadley and M. Whitin, A family of dynamic inventory models, *Management Sci.* **8**, No. 4, 458–69 (July 1962).

[111] D. L. Iglehart, *Dynamic programming and stationary analyses of inventory problems.* Applied Math. and Stat. Labs, Stanford Univ., Calif. U. S. Govt. Res. Rep. AD-260 925. Technical Report No. 27, July 1961, 50 pp.

[112] P. Lemonon, Un problème de décision séquentielle: Calcul d'une série économique, *Cahiers du Bureau Univ. de R. O.*, Inst. de Stat. de l'Univ. de Paris, No. 3 (April 1961).

[113] T. Matsuda, Case study: Some computational experiences in dynamic programming. Production and inventory planning under a quadratic cost function, *Oper. Res. as a Management Sci.* (Japan) **1**, No. 2, 35–37 (1956).

[114] C. van de Panne and G. J. Aeyelsts Averink, Imperfect management decisions and predictions and their financial implications in dynamic quadratic cost minimization, *Statistica Neerlandica* **15**, No. 3, 293–318 (1961).

[115] E. S. Phelps, *Optimal Decision Rules for the Procurement, Repair or Disposal of Spare Parts.* RAND Corp. RM-2920-PR, U. S. Govt. Res. Rep. AD-275 526, May 1962, 49 pp.

[116] H. A. Simon, C. C. Holt, and F. Modigliani, *Some Techniques for the Solution of Dynamic Programming Problems in Production Scheduling*, O. N. R. Res. Memo. No. 29, Graduate School Indust. Admin., Carnegie Inst. Tech., 1955.

[117] E. Ventura, Application of dynamic programming to maximum stock capacity, *Proc. 2nd Internat. Conf. on O. R.*, English Universities Press, 1961.

[118] E. Ventura, Application of dynamic programming to the control of stock and to the calculation of a maximum stock capacity, *Operational Res. Quart.* **12**, 66–78 (May 1961).

[119] D. E. Wagner and C. M. Shetty, Solution to a production scheduling problem with fixed costs, *Operational Res. Quart.* **13**, No. 1, 87–94 (March 1962).
D. E. Wagner and C. M. Shetty, *See also* [14], pp. 125–42 and [29].

REGULATION OF PRODUCTION

[120] A. B. Bishop and T. H. Rockwell, A dynamic programming computational procedure for optimal manpower loading in a large aircraft company, *Oper. Res.* **6**, No. 6, 835–48 (1958).
A. B. Bishop and T. H. Rockwell, *See also* [14], pp. 103–13 and 285–89.

PRODUCTION OF ELECTRICITY

[121] T. Fukao and R. Hiruma, Applications of dynamic programming (I), *J. Inform. Proc. Soc. Japan*, **2**, No. 3, 138–45 (May 1961).

[122] S. H. Hovanessian and E. J. Smith, *Dynamic Programming Formulation of Load Allocation in Power Plants.* TRW Computers Co., Tanoga Park, Calif., 1963.

[123] E. V. Tvetkov, A digital computer algorithm for the solution of three power problems of optimization in time (in Russian), *Izv. Akad. Nauk SSSR Otd. Tehn. Nauk Energet. Avtomat.* **1**, 54–62 (1962).

SEQUENCING AND BALANCING A PRODUCTION LINE

[124] M. Held and R. M. Karp, A dynamic programming approach to sequencing problems, *J. Soc. Indust. Appl. Math.* **10**, 196–210 (1962).

[125] M. Held, R. M. Karp, and R. Shareshian, Assembly-line balancing. Dynamic programming with precedence constraints, *Oper. Res.* **11**, No. 3, 442–59 (1963).

[126] J. R. Jackson, A computing procedure for a line balancing problem, *Management Sci.* **2**, 261–71 (1956).

[127] D. W. Jorgenson and J. J. McCall, Optimal replacement policies for a ballistic missile, *Management Sci.* **9**, No. 3, 358–79 (April 1963).

2. REPLACEMENT OF MACHINERY AND PREVENTIVE MAINTENANCE

[128] T. Mitsuhashi, Dynamic programming approach to maintenance intervals, *Management Sci. Japan* **4**, No. 4, 199–207 (March 1961).

[129] I. Nabeshima, The order of *n* items processed on *m* machines, *J. Oper. Res. Soc. Japan*, **3**, No. 4, 170–75 (March 1961); **4**, No. 1, 1–8 (Sept. 1961).

[130] R. Radner and D. W. Jorgenson, Opportunistic replacement of a single part in the presence of severed monitored parts, *Management Sci.* **10**, No. 1, 70–97 (1963).

[131] D. J. White, Optimal revision periods, *Internat. J. Production Res.* (G.B.), **1**, No. 1, 44–47 (1961).

D. J. White, *See also* [14], pp. 114–24 and 308–19.

[132] S. Zacks, *On a Pseudo-Solution to a Scheduling Problem.* Tech. Rep. No. 84, Applied Math. and Stat. Labs., Stanford Univ., Calif., Dec. 1962, 15 pp.

S. Zacks, *See also* [14], pp. 142–45.

3. DISTRIBUTION OF RESOURCES. INVESTMENTS

[133] O. Gross, *Minimal Weight Design for a Built-in Beam.* RAND Corp. RM-3371-PR, Dec. 1962.

[134] O. Gross and W. Prager, *Minimum-Weight Design for Moving Loads.* RAND Corp. RM-2887-PR, Jan. 1962.

[135] W. A. Hall and N. Buras, The dynamic programming approach to water resources development, *J. Geophys. Res.* **66**, 517–20 (1961).

[136] W. Karush, A general algorithm for the optimal distribution of effort, *Management Sci.* **9**, No. 1, 50–72 (Oct. 1962).

[137] R. Shear and W. Sacco, *The Optimum Allocation of Weapons to Targets: A Dynamic Programming Approach.* Ballistic Res. Labs., Aberdeen Proving Ground, Md., Rep. No. 1175, Sept. 1962, 25 pp.

R. Shear and W. Sacco, *U. S. Gov. Res. Rep.* AD-290 670.

[138] H. Shulman, The pole spotting problem, *SIAM Rev.* **4**, No. 1, 12–15 (Jan. 1962).

H. Shulman, *See also* [14], pp. 27–31 and 42–47; [146] and [168].

RELIABILITY

[139] R. Bellman and S. Dreyfus, Dynamic programming and the reliability of multicomponent devices, *Oper. Res.* **6**, No. 2, 200–206 (1958).

[140] J. D. Kettelle, Jr., Least-cost allocations of reliability investment, *Oper. Res.* **10**, No. 2, 249–65 (1962).

J. D. Kettelle, Jr., *See also* [14], pp. 31–35 and 65–70.

INVESTMENTS

[141] J. L. Fisher, *A Class of Stochastic Investment Problems.* Case Inst. of Tech., June 1959, 102 pp.

J. L. Fisher, *Oper. Res.* **9**, No. 1, 53–65 (1961).

[142] W. Hess, A dynamic programming approach to R. and D. budgeting and project selection, *IEEE Trans. Eng. Man.* (U.S.A.), *EM*-**9**, No. 4, 170–79 (Dec. 1962).

[143] A. J. Truelove, *A Multistage Stochastic Investment Process.* RAND Corp. RM-4025-PR, March 1964, 39 pp.
[144] D. J. White, Comments on a paper by McDowell, *Oper. Res.* **9**, No. 4, 580–84 July–Aug. 1961.

4. TRANSPORT PROBLEMS

[145] R. Bellman, Notes on the theory of dynamic programming: transportation models, *Management Sci.* **4**, No. 2, 191–95 (1958).
[146] R. Bellman, Combinatorial processes and dynamic programming, in: *Proc. Symposia Applied Math.*, Vol. X: *Combinatorial Analysis*, pp. 217–50. Amer. Math. Soc., 1960.
R. Bellman, *See also* [14], pp. 70–78 and 88–96.

5. CHEMICAL INDUSTRY

[147] R. Aris, *The Optimal Design of Chemical Reactors.* Academic Press, New York, 1961, 191 pp.
[148] R. Aris, R. Bellman, and R. Kalaba, Some optimization problems in chemical engineering, *Chem. Eng. Progress Symp. Series* **56**, 95–102 (1960).
[149] J. S. Dranoff, L. G. Mitten, W. F. Stevens, and L. A. Wanninger, Jr., Application of dynamic programming to countercurrent flow processes, *Oper. Res.* **10**, No. 3, 410–11 (May–June 1962).
[150] B. Messikommer, Die Optimierung eines halbkontinuierlichen chemischen Reaktors mittels dynamischer Programmierung, *Proc. Internat. Seminar on Analogue Computation Applied to the Study of Chemical Processes.* Presses Académiques Européennes, Bruxelles, 1961.
[151] S. Roberts, *Dynamic Programming in Chemical Engineering and Process Control.* 1964, 470 pp.

6. AGRICULTURE

[152] P. Badier, G. Nahon, and B. Roy, Stockage et exportation des céréales françaises (Exemple d'application de la programmation dynamique), *METRA* **2**, No. 1, 49–78 (1963).
[153] L. O. Loftsgard and E. O. Heady, Application of dynamic programming models for optimum farm and home plans, *J. Farm. Economics* **41**, No. 1, 51–62 (1959).

7. THEORY OF COMMUNICATION. DETECTION

[154] R. Bellman, *Dynamic Programming and Linear Prediction Theory.* RAND Corp. P-2308, May 1961.
[155] R. Bellman and R. Kalaba, On the role of dynamic programming in statistical communication theory, *IRE Trans. Information Theory* **3**, No. 3, 197–203 (Sept. 1957).
[156] R. Bellman, R. Kalaba, and D. Middleton, Dynamic programming, sequential estimation, and sequential detection processes, *Proc. Nat. Acad. Sci.* (U.S.A.) **47**, No. 3, 338–41 (March 1961).

8. DECISION THEORY. QUALITY CONTROL

[157] R. Kalaba, Optimum preventative sampling via dynamic programming, *Oper. Res.* **6**, No. 3, 439–40 (1958).

BIBLIOGRAPHY 275

BIBLIOGRAPHY 275

[158] D. V. Lindley, Dynamic programming and decision theory, *Appl. Statist.* (G.B.) *X*, No. 1, 39–51 (March 1961).

[159] M. Sakaguchi, Programmation dynamique de certains plans de prélèvement séquentiels (in Japanese), *Keiei-Kagaku* **4**, No. 3, 170–82 (Feb. 1961).

9. LINEAR APPROXIMATION OF CURVES OR SURFACES

[160] R. Bellman, On the approximation of curves by line segments using dynamic programming, *Comm. Assoc. Computing Machinery* **4**, No. 4, 284 (April 1961).

[161] R. Bellman and B. Kotkin, *On the Approximation of Curves by Line Segments Using Dynamic Programming*, II. RAND Corp. RM-2978-PR, Feb. 1962, 9 pp.

[162] B. Gluss, Least squares fitting of planes to surfaces using dynamic programming, *Comm. Assoc. Computing Machinery* **6**, No. 4, 172–75 (March 1963).

[163] B. H. Mayoh, On the approximation of curves by line segments using dynamic programming, *Comm. Assoc. Computing Machinery* **4**, No. 6, 284 (June 1961).

10. PROBLEM OF THE TRAVELING SALESMAN

[164] R. Bellman, Dynamic programming treatment of the traveling salesman problem, *J. Assoc. Computing Machinery* **9**, No. 1, 61–63 (Jan. 1962).

[165] R. H. Gonzalez Zubieta, *Solution of the Traveling Salesman Problem by Dynamic Programming on the Hypercube*. Interim. Techn. Rep. No. 18, M.I.T., Project Fundamental Investigations in Methods of Operations Research, 1962.

11. VARIOUS

[166] R. Bellman, *Dynamic Programming, Intelligent Machines, and Self-Organizing Systems*. RAND Corp. RM-3173-PR, June 1962, 15 pp.

[167] R. Bellman, J. Holland, and R. Kalaba, On an application of dynamic programming to the synthesis of logical systems, *J. Assoc. Computing Machinery* **6**, No. 4, 486–94 (Oct. 1959).

[168] O. R. Burt and C. C. Harris, Jr., Apportionment of the U. S. House of Representatives: A minimum range, integer solution, allocation problem, *Oper. Res.* **11**, No. 4, 648–52 (1963).

[169] J. N. Franklin, The range of a fleet of aircraft, *J. Soc. Indust. Appl. Math.* **8**, No. 3, 541–48 (Sept. 1960).

[170] A. J. Goldman, On the range of a fleet of aircraft, *J. Res. Nat. Bur. Standards Sect. B*, **65**, No. 4, 237–38 (Oct.–Dec. 1961).

[171] W. Hall, Aqueduct capacity under an optimum benefit policy, *Proc. Amer. Soc. Civil Engineers* IR-3, 1–11 (1961).

[172] W. Sacco, *A Dynamic Programming Solution for a Combinatorial Problem Involving the Selection of a Set of Optimum Weapon Yields*. Ballistic Research Labs, Aberdeen Proving Ground, Md., Memo. Rep. No. 1436, Oct. 1962, 23 pp. W. Sacco *U. S. Govt. Res. Rep.*, AD-291 753.

[173] XXX, *Celestial Mechanics and Optimum Methods. Part I: Optimum Methods and Dynamic Programming* Sci. and Tech. Sect. Air Information Div., Washington D.C. Background Report for 1959–60, AID Report No. 61–103, July 1961, 35 pp. XXX, *U. S. Govt. Res. Rep.* AD-261 455.

SUBJECT INDEX